D1612944

BRITISH MILITARY HELICOPTERS

Above: A TOW missile en route to its target. Making maximum use of natural cover to reduce its vulnerability, the Lynx usually fires its missiles from the hover. (British Aerospace)

BRITISH MILITARY HELICOPTERS

John Everett-Heath

ARMS AND ARMOUR PRESS
LONDON NEW YORK SYDNEY

Dedication: To Judith

First published in Great Britain
in 1986 by Arms and Armour Press Limited,
2-6 Hampstead High Street, London NW3 1QQ.

Distributed in the USA by Sterling Publishing Co. Inc., 2 Park Avenue,
New York, N.Y. 10016.

Distributed in Australia by
Capricorn Link (Australia) Pty. Ltd., P.O. Box 665, Lane Cove,
New South Wales 2066, Australia.

© John Everett-Heath, 1986
© Arms and Armour Press Limited, 1986
All rights reserved. No part of this book may be reproduced or
transmitted in any form or by any means, electronic or mechanical,
including photocopying, recording or any information storage and
retrieval system, without permission in writing from the Publisher.

British Library Cataloguing in Publication Data:
Everett-Heath, E. J.
British military helicopters.
1. Military helicopters—Great Britain—History
I. Title 623.74'6047 UG1235.G7
ISBN 0-85368-805-2

Designed by David Gibbons; layout by Anthony A. Evans; edited by
Michael Boxall; typeset by Typesetters (Birmingham) Limited;
printed and bound by R. J. Acford, Chichester, England.

Jacket illustrations. Front, a Lynx fire team armed with TOW anti-tank
missiles. Back, top: Little space left! The cockpit of an RAF Sea King Mk
3; below: a Lynx Mk 1 cockpit modified so that it is compatible with
aircrew night vision goggles. (All courtesy of Westland Helicopters)

HOW A HELICOPTER FLIES

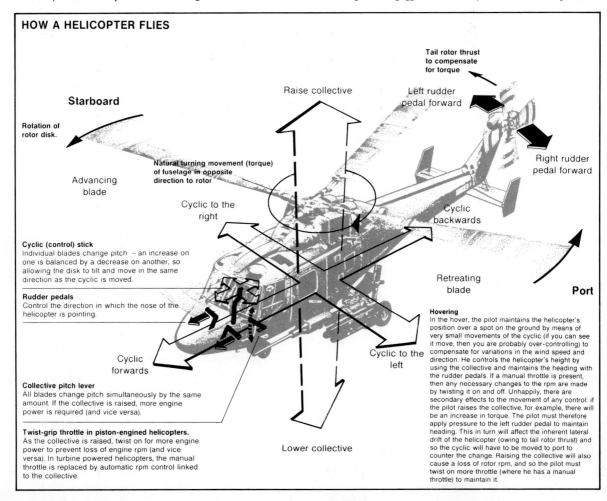

Tail rotor thrust to compensate for torque

Raise collective

Left rudder pedal forward

Starboard

Rotation of rotor disk.

Right rudder pedal forward

Natural turning movement (torque) of fuselage in opposite direction to rotor

Advancing blade

Cyclic backwards

Cyclic to the right

Cyclic (control) stick
Individual blades change pitch – an increase on
one is balanced by a decrease on another, so
allowing the disk to tilt and move in the same
direction as the cyclic is moved.

Retreating blade

Port

Rudder pedals
Control the direction in which the nose of the
helicopter is pointing.

Hovering
In the hover, the pilot maintains the helicopter's
position over a spot on the ground by means of
very small movements of the cyclic (if you can see
it move, then you are probably over-controlling) to
compensate for variations in the wind speed and
direction. He controls the helicopter's height by
using the collective and maintains the heading with
the rudder pedals. If a manual throttle is present,
then any necessary changes to the rpm are made
by twisting it on and off. Unhappily, there are
secondary effects to the movement of any control: if
the pilot raises the collective, for example, there will
be an increase in torque. The pilot must therefore
apply pressure to the left rudder pedal to maintain
heading. This in turn will affect the inherent lateral
drift of the helicopter (owing to tail rotor thrust) and
so the cyclic will have to be moved to port to
counter the change. Raising the collective will also
cause a loss of rotor rpm, and so the pilot must
twist on more throttle (where he has a manual
throttle) to maintain it.

Cyclic to the left

Cyclic forwards

Collective pitch lever
All blades change pitch simultaneously by the same
amount. If the collective is raised, more engine
power is required (and vice versa).

Twist-grip throttle in piston-engined helicopters.
As the collective is raised, twist on for more engine
power to prevent loss of engine rpm (and vice
versa). In turbine powered helicopters, the manual
throttle is replaced by automatic rpm control linked
to the collective.

Lower collective

Contents

Preface

Even before the initial tethered flights of the first British helicopter in 1909, Sir George Cayley and others had been puzzling over the problems of rotary-wing flight. Some solutions had been fanciful, others more practical. This book, while concentrating on the period since the Second World War, aims to trace the historical development of British helicopters from the beginning. It could not do so without giving due credit to the enormous influence of the autogiro before the Second World War. The book includes, towards the end, a brief look into the technological future. The use of technical terms is inevitable, but I have attempted to reduce them to a minimum and a glossary is included.

While technical developments are of interest to the enthusiast, the world-wide operation of these helicopters is of equal interest and importance. I have therefore introduced the human element by including accounts of helicopters in action, both in search and rescue and during military operations. Many remarkable and courageous feats have been achieved by helicopter aircrew, and this book would not be complete without a small sample. The final chapter of the book is devoted to the military employment of British helicopters in Europe.

It would have been impossible to write this book without the generous help of many people who have given me their time, knowledge, documents and photographs. I must first express my gratitude to Colonel Mike Badger, David Balmford, Colonel Bob Begbie, Wing Commander Reginald Brie, Wing Commander John Dowling, Ken Fry, Lieutenant-Commander Jim Milne (himself the author of *Flashing Blades over the Sea*) and Lieutenant-Commander Brian Prendergast, all of whom reviewed parts of the manuscript describing developments and events in which they actually participated or with which they are familiar.

I am very grateful to Michael Hooks, Eric Myall and Elfan ap Rees (Editor of *Helicopter International*), all of whom have written on the subject of rotary-wing aircraft and who possess between them a huge reservoir of knowledge and documentation of which they have given freely besides providing the answers to many questions.

I am in great debt to Colonel John Moss who, in addition to giving advice, made my various visits to the Westland plant at Yeovil so pleasant and worthwhile. I am pleased to acknowledge the assistance I received from the staff of the Fleet Air Arm Museum at Yeovilton, notably Messrs Mottram and Lovell, and from Commander Paul Madge at RNAS Yeovilton; also David Russell at the Royal Air Force Museum at Hendon, who was kind enough to unearth some interesting old photographs for me. Sergeant Richard Tring at the Museum of Army Flying at Middle Wallop has been a tower of strength throughout and he must be very relieved that this book has now been completed!

Without the generous supply of photographs from Westland Plc and Rolls-Royce Ltd in particular, this book would be significantly less well illustrated. I have to thank Michael Haywood and Peter Squire respectively for their painstaking work in this respect. The advice and help received from my publishers has, of course, been indispensable. I should like to offer my great thanks to David Gibbons, the editorial director, Michael Boxall, the editor, and to Anthony Evans who so skilfully produced the three-view line drawings.

It would be remiss of me if I were not to mention the encouragement and tolerance that I have received from my wife and children and the help given in a number of ways by my son Tom.

E.J.E-H.

Introduction

Since 1950, when the Dragonfly arrived in Malaya, British helicopters have brought a hitherto unimagined degree of flexibility to a variety of military operations and commercial enterprises world-wide. There is little doubt, however, that it was the Falklands War that demonstrated in the most compelling manner to a wide audience the versatility of the helicopter both on land and at sea. More than 150 helicopters of seven different types, six of which were built by Westland, were employed in a great diversity of roles. Despite their success in that conflict, in many other previous trouble spots round the world, and in peacetime for search and rescue and other tasks, the priority accorded by the Government to improving existing helicopters and buying new ones historically has been low. The complaint that there were never enough helicopters available has been heard after every military campaign since 1950.

The British did not turn their attention seriously to the development of helicopters until just before the Second World War when, in 1938, their first, and the world's second, truly successful helicopter was built. After the war, and a decade later, Britain could claim the distinction of having designed and built both the fastest and heaviest helicopters in the world. Tragically both crashed while still at the prototype stage and the health and vitality of the helicopter industry were seriously affected. It is clear, in retrospect, that during the 1950s, while the industry was struggling to overcome these disasters and make good, it was hampered by official apathy and misconception. The Colonial Office, for example, stated that twin-engined helicopters only would be suitable for work in the colonies because single-engined helicopters were unsafe. The fact that the American single-engined Bell 47 had been operating perfectly safely for a number of years appears to have been studiously ignored. The Air Ministry was little better, exhibiting at the higher levels, an astonishing degree of ignorance and lack of curiosity about the helicopter and what it could do. It was thought to be somewhat esoteric and, in the words of Wing Commander John Dowling, was 'generally regarded with attitudes varying from amused tolerance to superstitious horror by those not personally involved'. Beset by lack of encouragement and funds from official circles, and frustration and misunderstanding on all sides, it is little wonder that the initial pace of British

helicopter development was hesitant and cautious. The inevitable result was the predominance of American helicopters and the conclusion of various licence agreements.

There is another side to the coin, however. Expectations of the helicopter's capabilities were perhaps raised too high by a small band of enthusiasts who tended simultaneously to disregard or suppress its shortcomings. In July 1954 the Chief Executive of BEA was quoted in the *Sunday Times* as saying that by 1958 30-passenger twin-engined helicopters could be expected to be operating between London, Paris, Amsterdam, Brussels, Birmingham and Manchester. When this prediction proved to be outrageously optimistic he felt obliged to express himself in a more realistic way: 'available helicopters resemble a pretty girl – they are small, nice to look at and be seen about with, exciting, pleasant to take out, apt to be noisy; and the more you have to do with them the more expensive they get and the more problems they bring around your neck'.

After the industry had been concentrated under the Westland flag in the 1960s following various mergers, a period of strong growth was experienced in the 1970s. Contrary to predictions, however, this growth was not continued into the 1980s. There are many reasons why this was so, but perhaps the most important were the international recession and very keen industrial competition. Recent market predictions by the major helicopter manufacturers differ, but the world helicopter industry appears now to be on the upturn and sales of more than 10,000 new helicopters over the next ten years are confidently forecast. The split between civil and military is expected to be roughly equal. In Europe the civil market is expanding while the military market is going through a somewhat stagnant phase before production of new designs starts towards the end of the decade.

In a capital-hungry industry, Westland, as a small and private Company, has always found it difficult to compete with the other major foreign helicopter manufacturers, which are either state-owned or part of huge conglomerates. Its position is made no easier by having always been unhealthily dependent on the Ministry of Defence for orders. Success in the civil market has been elusive. By early 1985 it had become evident that only a few more orders from the MoD could be expected until the end of the decade. The imminent cash crisis appeared alarming. The first would-be saviour was the Bristow Rotorcraft consortium, which began a take-over bid in mid-year only to withdraw shortly afterwards. The crisis widened and deepened when two new offers of help came in quick succession: Sikorsky (part of the United Technologies Corporation) and Fiat together proposed a financial reconstruction package giving them a 29.9% stake in Westland. Hard on their heels came a European consortium of British Aerospace, GEC, Aérospatiale, Agusta and Messerschmitt-Bölkow-Blohm (MBB) with marginally better terms. There were undoubted advantages and disadvantages to both offers; the reconstituted Westland board with its new chairman faced a complex situation, further clouded by improved offers, claims and counter-claims by both sides, the activities of major shareholders and Government involvement.

In 1978 the Governments of France, West Germany, Italy and the UK had signed a Declaration of Priniciples whereby each country agreed to make every effort to meet its needs for helicopters by machines developed jointly in Europe. Aérospatiale, Agusta, MBB and Westland have since then edged away from past dependence on American technology. Much collaboration has been set in motion to strengthen the European industry and compete on equal terms with US companies world-wide. Aérospatiale and MBB are working together on the Eurocopter combat helicopter for the 1990s. In April 1985, Westland and Agusta signed a Memorandum of Understanding to collaborate in the design, production and marketing of different helicopter types. This followed work already begun on the EH-101 naval helicopter and the A.129 combat helicopter. All four Companies, together with Fokker, have agreed jointly to study the feasibility of a new transport helicopter, the NH 90. In preference to this European connection the Westland board strongly recommended to its shareholders the reforging of the time-honoured links with Sikorsky which had proved so beneficial to Westland in the past.

Timeline 1907–1946

1907 — At Douai in France the Breguet-Richet Gyroplane No. 1 takes off but is restrained by four people.

Paul Cornu makes the first free flight in a helicopter at Lisieux in France.

1912 — First free flight of a helicopter in Britain.

1918 — The Royal Air Force is established.

1924 — Maiden flight of an autogiro: Cierva's C-4 gets airborne near Madrid.

Pescara's helicopter No. 3 sets a world distance record of 736m (2,415ft).

1925 — A Dutchman, von Baumhauer, builds and flies the first single rotor helicopter.

Maiden flight at Hamble of the first autogiro built in Britain: the Cierva C-6C.

Maiden flight by an autogiro, a Cierva C-8L Mk 4, in the USA.

Cierva becomes the first passenger ever to fly in an autogiro.

1928 — A Cierva C-8L Mk 2 flies from Croydon to Le Bourget, the first flight over the English Channel by a rotary-wing aircraft.

1930 — The Italian d'Ascanio helicopter sets a world altitude record of 18m (59ft) and an endurance record of 8 minutes 45.2 seconds.

The Cierva C-19 Mk 5 is the first autogiro to dispense with aeroplane-type control surfaces.

Maiden flight by a Soviet rotary-wing aircraft: the KaSkr-1 autogiro.

Raoul Hafner begins construction of his first helicopter, the R-1, in Vienna.

Maiden flight of the Soviet Union's first helicopter, the TsAGI 1-EA.

1934 — Cierva announces the successful development of a direct take-off autogiro.

Maiden flight of the German Focke-Wulf 61, usually described as the first practical helicopter.

The Breguet-Dorand Gyroplane Laboratoire sets a world altitude record of 158m (518ft).

While flying a record distance of 44km (27.34 miles) the Gyroplane Laboratoire remains airborne for one hour, 2 minutes and 5 seconds.

Cierva is killed in an air crash at Croydon.

1934 — The RAF takes delivery at Old Sarum, near Salisbury, of its first rotary-wing aircraft, the Avro Rota Mk 1 autogiro.

1937 — The Fw-61 sets a new world altitude record of 3,427m (11,243ft).

The Fw-61 sets four world records: Speed in a closed circuit: 122.553kph (76.151mph) Altitude: 2,439m (8,002ft) Endurance: 1 hour, 20 minutes, 49 seconds Distance in a closed circuit: 80.604km (50.08 miles)

The first tethered lift-off of the Sikorsky VS-300. Unlike European helicopters it has a main rotor and an anti-torque rotor at the tail.

1938 — Maiden flight of the first successful British helicopter, the Weir 5.

Thirty prototypes and 15 production Flettner 282 Kolibris are ordered by the German Navy.

Lt Harman of the US Army Air Force makes the first recorded rescue of soldiers behind enemy lines (the Japanese); in Burma, flying a YR-4B.

Maiden flight of the Cierva W.9.

The Sikorsky R-4B is the first helicopter in the world to be mass produced. Some arrive in Britain for service with the RN.

Maiden flight of the Bell 47, the first helicopter in the world to be awarded, in March 1946, a Type Approval Certificate for commercial operations. As the Sioux it entered service with the British Army in April 1964.

Maiden flight of Bell Model 30, forerunner of the Bell Model 47.

1944 — The Kamov design bureau is established in the USSR.

The first helicopter squadron in the world is commissioned in the US Navy; it is equipped with the Sikorsky R-6.

The RAF receives seven Sikorsky YR-4Bs, a development of the VS-300 and designated Hoverfly Mk 1 in service.

OPERATIONAL BRITISH ROTARY-WING AIRCRAFT IN SQUADRON SERVICE WITH THE ARMED FORCES

Helicopter	Royal Navy	Army*	Royal Air Force
Rota 1			1934-45
Rota 2	1939-45		
Sycamore		1951-7	1952-72
Skeeter		1958-68	
Dragonfly	1950-67		1950-62
Whirlwind	1954-75		1954-81
Wessex	1961-		1964-
Belvedere			1961-9
Scout		1963-	
Wasp	1964-		
Sioux		1964-78	
Sea King	1970-		1978-
Gazelle		1974-	1973-
Lynx	1977-	1978-	

Note: This appendix does not include those aircraft only used for training. For example, the RAF had a few Skeeters and Sioux, and the Royal Navy have some Gazelles for this purpose.

*Including Royal Marines.

At the close of 1985 vital questions still remained to be answered: did the UK really want the capability to design and build its own helicopters? If it did, was this capability better assured by Westland turning towards the Europeans or towards the Americans? The Byzantine saga, immortalized now as the Westland Affair and attracting massive media attention and causing unforeseen political repercussions, rumbled on into 1986.

It may come as a surprise to learn that the British Army operates more helicopters than either the Royal Navy or the RAF although it was the last of the three Services to possess its own aircraft (if one ignores the Royal Flying Corps). Until the Army Air Corps was established on 1 September 1957, a small number of Army pilots had flown as members of RAF units supporting the Army. Since then most military campaigns have been supported by helicopters of all three Services and sometimes the Commando Brigade Air Squadron of the Royal Marines, all working in close and friendly co-operation.

Everybody connected with aviation worships at the altar of flight safety. In a book of this kind, it would be wrong not to mention the record of the Services in this respect. In 1984 only five helicopters were lost or damaged. Accident rates are usually measured per 10,000 flying hours and for 1984 the rate was 0.207 or one helicopter lost or seriously damaged every 48,309 flying hours. Given the roles of Service helicopters and the conditions in which they have to operate, these figures are remarkable.

Although there was some British input to the design of the Puma and those procured for the RAF were assembled in the UK, it is primarily a French helicopter and therefore merits no more than a brief reference in the appropriate chapter. Two hundred and ninety-four Anglo-French Gazelles were built by Westland and so this helicopter is included; since it was a joint venture, however, details of export sales have been excluded. If export sales are indicated elsewhere, these refer only to initial deliveries from the manufacturer.

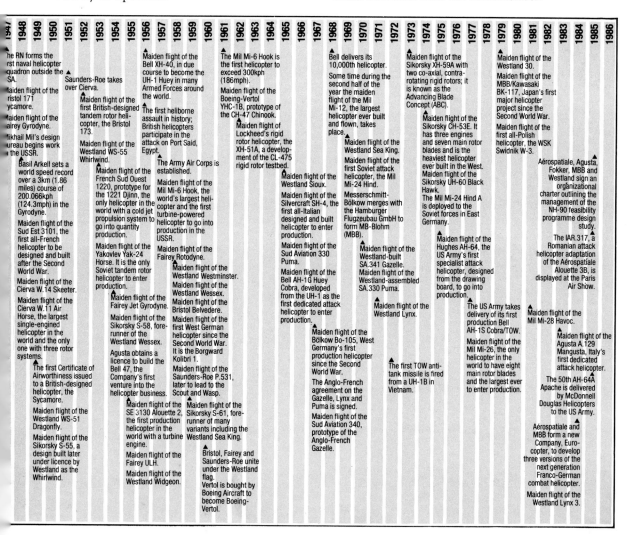

Prelude

The Nineteenth Century

Sir George Cayley, revered as the 'Father of British Aeronautics', was born on 27 December 1773. He could rightly claim to be the first man to annunciate the problems associated with flight and to appreciate how they might be overcome. In doing so he laid down the first principles of heavier-than-air flight from which all aviation has subsequently evolved. He went to the heart of the matter in 1808 when he wrote: 'The problem is confined within these limits, viz. to make a surface support a given weight by the application of power to the resistance of air.' Having identified the central issue he then applied himself to its solution, made no easier by the lack of a suitable engine with a manageable power-to-weight ratio.

In 1796 he built a 'Chinese top' consisting of a two-bladed rotor mounted at each end of a shaft with motive power coming from the tension of a bow to the ends of which was attached a string which was twisted around the shaft. He then turned his attention to fixed and flapping wing designs and between 1799 and 1809/10, when he published a paper 'On Aerial Navigation', he founded the new science of aerodynamics. In this paper he gave details of his model which, some would claim, was the original prototype of the helicopter and of which Cayley said 'for the purposes of ascent this is perhaps the best apparatus'.

In another paper, published in April 1843, Cayley described a convertiplane which he called an 'aerial carriage' and he went on to extol the benefits of vertical flight: 'Aerial navigation by mechanical means must depend upon surfaces moving with considerable velocity through the air, but these vehicles will ever be inconvenient, not to say absolutely inefficient . . . for, to be of ordinary use, they must be capable of landing at any place where there is space to receive them, and of ascending again from that point. They should likewise be capable of remaining stationary, or nearly so, in the air, when required.' He was well aware of the need for plenty of power because he mentioned that 'very great power, in proportion to the weight of the engine, is necessary'. What was lacking, however, was just this engine power in a usable form: a situation that remained until well after Cayley's death in December 1857.

It was probably due to Cayley that Horatio Phillips was inspired to design a 20kg (44lb) steam-powered model helicopter which actually flew in 1842. This was an historic event for it was the first time that a model aircraft – and a helicopter at that – had flown under the

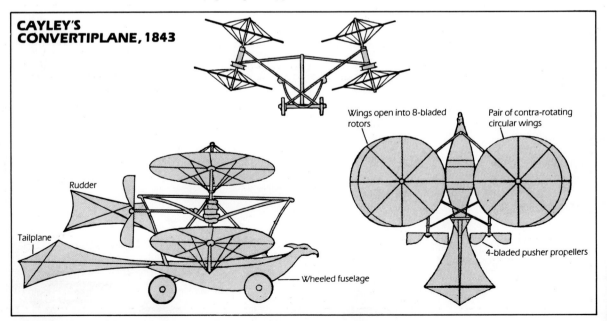

CAYLEY'S CONVERTIPLANE, 1843

Wings open into 8-bladed rotors

Pair of contra-rotating circular wings

Rudder

Tailplane

4-bladed pusher propellers

Wheeled fuselage

power of an engine rather than springs or other devices. Steam from a tiny boiler passed along the hollow rotor shaft and out to rearward-facing holes at the tips of two blades. This jet propulsion was achieved by the combustion of a mixture of charcoal, nitre and gypsum.

In 1876 a German engineer, N. A. Otto, invented the 4-stroke cycle petrol engine, the first internal combustion engine to use liquid fuel and an advance in technology of the most vital significance to aviation. Nine years later the first practicable petrol engine appeared. Usable power-to-weight ratios had at last been achieved and man-carrying flight was now inevitable.

The Denny Helicopter
On 13 November 1907, Paul Cornu, a Frenchman, made the first free flight in a helicopter at Lisieux. He coaxed the 260kg (573lb) machine up to a height of 0.3m (1ft), remaining airborne for twenty seconds. The twin rotors each had a diameter of 6m (19ft 8in). A couple of years before this historic flight, however, experiments into the use of propellers as a primary lifting device had begun at the Leven Shipyard of William Denny Brothers at Dumbarton in Scotland.

These were to lead eventually to the flight of the first British helicopter. On each side of a tubular frame were mounted three two-bladed 7.6m (25ft) diameter rotors. The major problem, not surprisingly in early 1906, was the engine and it was not until September 1911 that one which could produce between 37 and 41hp became available.

The first tethered flights were made in 1909, not with the petrol-driven engine but with power from an electric motor. Late in 1914 the first free flight – or extended hop – was made when the helicopter was manoeuvred onto the nearby water and covered about 100m (328ft) at a height of 3m (10ft) at a speed of about 28kph (17mph). Unfortunately the machine was destroyed in a gale that same night. By this time the First World War had started, the shipyard had returned exclusively to ship construction and the Denny helicopter was not rebuilt.

Brennan's Helicopter
Having given some thought to vertical flight in the 1880s, Louis Brennan, previously Superintendent of the Government Torpedo Factory, approached the War Office in 1915 with his plans for a helicopter. Although the idea was accepted, little practical progress was

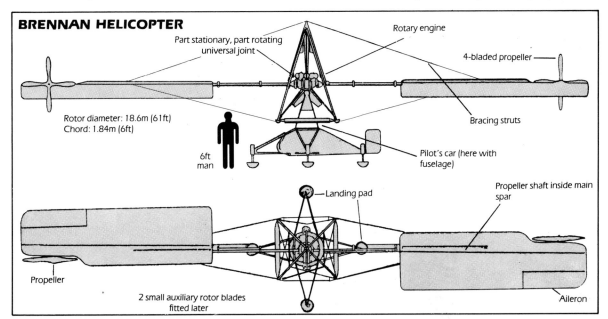

made during the War and it was not until June 1919 that the Air Ministry assumed responsibility for the project, enabling Brennan to begin serious work in the Balloon Shed at the Royal Aircraft Establishment (RAE) at Farnborough.

The diameter of the two-bladed main rotor was 18.2m (60ft) and blade chord an astonishing 1.8m (6ft). To solve the problem of torque each main blade was driven by a large four-bladed wooden propeller mounted at the wing tip. Both propellers were powered by a single 230hp Bentley BR-2 engine. The pilot's car, as it was called, was situated directly below the rotating upper structure, which contained the engine, and was suspended from a universal joint.

After nearly two years of design, development and construction, engine runs began on 3 November 1921. Problems arose that necessitated major modifications, but on 14 March 1922 the pilot and four men together with an hour's supply of fuel were easily lifted to 6m (20ft). This was the maximum height available since at

Above: Louis Brennan stands in front of his helicopter, suspended in its test rig, in the shed at Farnborough. The rotor was driven by propellers at the tips and powered by a centrally-positioned rotary engine. The pilot's car was suspended from a universal joint on the rotating structure. (RAE Farnborough)

this stage all flying was confined to within the Balloon Shed. Brennan slowly continued development until at last, on 16 May 1924, there was enough confidence in the helicopter to move it outside. Hovering capability was tested but stability remained a problem throughout. While the Air Ministry considered the cost-effectiveness of a major re-design, the helicopter crashed during a demonstration on 2 October 1925.

It was not rebuilt. It had undertaken some 200 flights each of two or three minutes' duration. Despite this measure of success the techniques of control had not been satisfactorily mastered, the pilot never being sure that he could direct the machine where he wanted and then keep it there. Brennan had fallen into the trap of thinking that his major concern would be to get

Right: Brennan's helicopter in a low hover at Farnborough in 1925. (Westland Helicopters)

sufficient lift whereas in reality this had proved to be easier than achieving anything like the desired stability and control. The crash caused the Air Ministry to call for advice on helicopters in general and on Brennan's in particular from the Aeronautical Research Committee. This committee reported that there was no point in proceeding with helicopters of the Brennan type, that is with driven rotors, but that the future for rotary-wing aircraft probably lay with Cierva-type autogiros.

The Age of the Autogiro

The name of the Spaniard, Juan de la Cierva, will forever be remembered as the inventor of the autogiro, the machine that was to make so big a contribution to the development of rotary-wing flight during the next fifteen years. The difference between a helicopter and an autogiro is that in the latter the rotor blades freewheel as a result of air, generated by forward flight, flowing through the rotor disc; they are not driven by an engine. This method of deriving lift from an unpowered rotor is known as autorotation. In deciding not to make use of a powered rotor but to separate the functions of lift and propulsion, Cierva deliberately sacrificed a hover capability and initially vertical take-off. The advantages offered by the autogiro, however, were that it was safe at low speed or when the engine failed and, with no mechanical drive to the rotor, it was very much less complex than a helicopter.

Cierva's first three autogiros were failures largely because of the fact that the rotor blades were rigidly attached to the hub. A truly brilliant technological innovation, however, characterized the fourth. Incorporating a hinge at each blade root, the advancing

Above: The Cierva C-6C was the first autogiro to be built in Britain, making its maiden flight in June 1926. (RAF Museum)

blade was able to flap up as it reached the front of the disc, reducing its angle of attack and losing some lift; the retreating blade, on the other hand, flapped down, deriving more lift and thus equalizing lift overall and damping any tendency to roll.

The C-4, featuring the new rotor system with flapping hinges, made a successful maiden flight in Spain on 9 January 1923. These first autogiros looked much like an aeroplane with a conventional engine and propeller, tail unit and control surfaces. The normal biplane wings were removed and replaced by a stub wing or outriggers, in place of the lower wing, with ailerons to provide lateral control. Atop the fuselage were mounted the rotor mast and blades.

In early October 1925 Cierva brought his C-6A, based on an Avro 504K, to England at the invitation of the Air Ministry which agreed to sponsor and pay for the subsequent tests. After the first of these the Secretary of State for Air announced on 9 November that he had decided to have several different types of autogiro built in England for further trials by the RAF. In January 1926 the first order was placed with A. V. Roe Ltd (Avro) for two aircraft for test and evaluation. The first autogiro ever to be built in Britain was the C-6C which flew for the first time at Hamble on 19 June. It was a single-seater whereas the C-6D was a two-seater.

After Cierva had decided to dispose of the world rights to his invention, the Cierva Autogiro Company Ltd was established in the UK on 24 March 1926, not to manufacture any machines but to carry out research

Above: *The Cierva C-19 Mk 4 introduced mechanical rotor starting. (RAF Museum)*

Opposite page, top: *The Duke of Aosta, Chief of the Italian Air Force, poses in front of a C-19. From left to right: Test pilot Alan Marsh, Cierva, the Duke, two accompanying Italians, test pilot Reginald Brie. (RAF Museum)*

Opposite page, bottom: *A Rota Mk I, the RAF version of the C-30, on floats. Only one was so fitted for experimental purposes and the normally fixed fin was hinged to facilitate directional control when water-borne. (M. J. Hooks)*

and development and issue licences. A succession of designs followed, some successful, some not. The C-8L-II, for example, made the first crossing of the English Channel by a rotary-wing aircraft on 18 September 1928 and the C-12 was given floats and flown from Southampton Water as a hydrogiro.

The C-19 broke new ground in two respects. It was the first autogiro to be designed by the Cierva Company from a clean sheet of paper rather than being based on an existing fixed-wing aircraft. It dispensed with the cumbersome method of rotor starting which involved men pulling on a rope wound round the rotor shaft. The C-19's design included a completely new fuselage, and a tailplane with elevators which could be tilted upwards at an extreme angle to deflect the slipstream from the propeller up into the rotor blades to get them moving. This simple arrangement considerably shortened the start-up time and the take-off run which was reduced to about 30m (100ft).

After building three distinctive versions, Cierva still considered that the method of starting the rotor was rather crude and in 1931 the prototype C-19 Mk 4 appeared with a much better mechanical system whereby the rotor was connected to the engine drive through a light clutch. This was the same year that the Mk 5 first flew. An experimental prototype, it was used as a testbed for a new 'direct', rather than fixed, control head; by means of a control stick suspended from the rotor pylon the pilot could fly the aircraft by tilting the rotor head, mounted on a sort of universal joint, in any

direction he wanted. The main reason for this innovation was the poor aileron control of the earlier autogiros at low speed which sometimes resulted in a landing on one wheel and a ground strike by a wing or blade tips. Until this modification was embodied autogiros had relied upon aeroplane-type control surfaces which naturally depended upon the airflow from forward flight. This was fine for the rudder and elevators but the ailerons were outside the slipstream and therefore much less effective at low speed. The new system worked independently of forward flight and thus there was no further need of ailerons, or indeed stub wings. The Mk 5 therefore had none and, since they were also unnecessary, dispensed with rudder and elevators. Most of the signs of the autogiro's fixed-wing ancestry had now disappeared.

Satisfied with the tests of the Mk 5, Cierva decided to employ his tilting rotor head to a new design, the C-30. The trials of this machine were so successful that the Air Ministry ordered twelve of the production version, the C-30A, for the RAF in February 1934. Avro undertook production and the first Rota Mk 1, as the

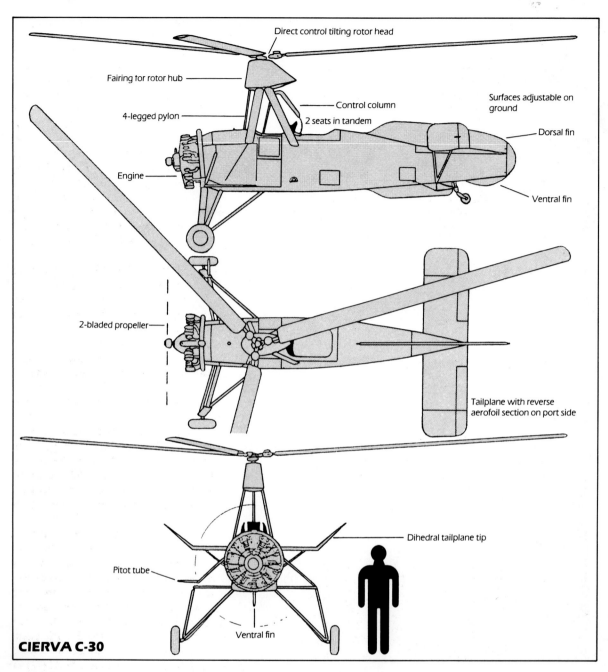

Direct control tilting rotor head

Fairing for rotor hub

Control column

4-legged pylon

2 seats in tandem

Surfaces adjustable on ground

Dorsal fin

Engine

Ventral fin

2-bladed propeller

Tailplane with reverse aerofoil section on port side

Dihedral tailplane tip

Pitot tube

Ventral fin

CIERVA C-30

autogiro was designated in RAF service, was delivered in December 1934 to the RAF School of Army Co-operation at Old Sarum in Wiltshire. The Rota had a three-bladed direct control rotor head which came with a mechanically driven starting gear. More orders followed from civil customers both in the UK and abroad and from foreign military services. In all, close to 100 were built in the UK and others under licence abroad.

Although Squadron Leader Reginald Brie had made some spectacular landings and take-offs from an Italian cruiser in 1935 in support of a potential sale to the Italian Navy, the Fleet Air Arm was slow to take advantage of the new technology. Nevertheless the Admiralty asked for further sea trials and two C-30 carried these out on board HMS Furious in the English Channel.

The War Office had barely given the autogiro a thought. But a young captain in the Royal Artillery, H. J. Parham, reasoned that it could operate from bases much further forward than the RAF's conventional artillery spotting aircraft, because of its ability to fly low

artillery officer on board the aircraft with two-way radio communications. He pointed out that the autogiro could be used for carrying commanders and staff officers on visits, for traffic control and for route reconnaissance besides, of course, its primary role of directing the fire of the guns. Such tasks, Parham was suggesting, were a function of the land battle and properly the business of the Army, not the RAF. Like a staff car, the autogiro could undertake its jobs without fighting, but if attacked by fighters it had a fair chance of escaping because of its small size and agility. Parham recommended that the autogiro be accepted as a new form of Army transport and advocated trials both in peacetime and during any expeditions or skirmishes that might crop up on Imperial frontiers. Behind this seemingly innocuous proposal lay the germ of all subsequent flying in the Army.

In the summer of 1935 the Air Ministry agreed to hold trials in which artillery officers, flying as passengers, were to engage targets using the normal gunnery procedures. The passengers found it hard to tell where the shells landed because, more often than not, the autogiro was facing in the wrong direction at the critical moment. It was therefore suggested that the pilot should control the shoots himself and that he should be an artillery officer. In due course this came to pass – but not in autogiros, light fixed-wing aircraft being the chosen vehicle.

Early in 1940 as many civil C-30 as possible were requisitioned and 1448 Rota Calibration Flight RAF was formed on 1 May with Squadron Leader Brie as commander. In June 1943 it became 529 Autogiro Squadron, the only RAF squadron to have autogiros, and with Squadron Leader Alan Marsh, another experienced autogiro pilot, now in command. The Rotas were not employed in any fighting but were deployed singly to RAF airfields close to coastal radar stations for the vital task of calibration (checking the accuracy of the radar returns) which, until then, had been undertaken, somewhat ponderously, by balloons. The Rotas were ideal as targets, able to fly very slowly and on different headings and heights as directed. This work sounds unspectacular but, close to the French coast, the Rotas were always susceptible to attack by German fighters. Indeed, in July 1943, one was attacked by a pair of Focke-Wulf 190, but by putting the aircraft's manoeuvrability to good effect the pilot was able to escape unscathed to Hawkinge airfield.

The war brought to a halt any further development of autogiros in the UK and in mid 1940 the Cierva Company closed down. It came as no surprise, therefore, when the Squadron disbanded in October 1945, the RAF selling off its remaining aircraft.

While tests with the C-19 Mk 5 were proceeding satisfactorily in 1932, the Scottish firm of G & J Weir Ltd of Cathcart, Glasgow acquired a Cierva licence to build

Top: Squadron Leader Brie carries out demonstrations aboard the Italian cruiser *Fiume* off La Spezia in 1935. Note the plane guard! (RAF Museum)

Above: Reginald Brie poses by a C30. (Westland Helicopters)

and slow, to take-off and land almost anywhere and because it was relatively inconspicuous both in the air and on the ground. The existing procedures for requesting an aircraft to direct artillery and then the passage of the appropriate information by Morse and ground signals were laborious and sometimes unsuccessful. What was needed, Parham thought, was an a 'motorcycle of the air', a small single-seat autogiro of about 272kg (600lb). James Weir, besides being a director of his company, was also chairman of the Cierva Autogiro Company. The two-bladed articulated wooden rotor was of the direct control type, had a mechanical starter and a diameter of 8.53m (28ft). Alan Marsh conducted the initial flight trials in May 1933 on the W-1 and its rather more capable successor, the W-2, which flew in March 1934. The single-seat W-3 was a completely new design, embodying a new autodynamic head, on which Cierva had been working for some years with an experimental C-30, and a more powerful engine designed by the Weir engineers. The maiden flight took place on 9 July 1936 at Abbotsinch. The W-4 was similar to the W-3 since it was intended to be the production version. Shortly after its first flight on 6 December 1937 it was destroyed in a taxiing accident.

The accident was not the reason for the rather abrupt cessation of work on autogiros at Weir. At the suggestion of Cyril Pullin, Weir's Chief Engineer, it was decided in late 1937 to concentrate henceforth on the design and construction of helicopters. Two major reasons may be advanced for this decision: the success of the larger C-30A and the consequent lack of orders for the W-4 and, more importantly, the remarkable achievements of the German Focke-Wulf 61 which, by making the first helicopter autorotational landing in May 1937 and setting up a host of new world records a month later, demonstrated that the helicopter could be reliable, safe and practicable.

Westland, Britain's major manufacturer of helicopters today, began to take an interest in rotary-wing aircraft in 1934 when two autogiros, the CL-20 and the C-29, were built. Only the CL-20 flew, making a few flights in 1935. The C-29 was the biggest autogiro of the time, a five-seater with a maximum take-off weight of 2,268kg (5,000lb). Excessive ground resonance, however, precluded flight.

A Scot, David Kay, built two autogiros, the second of which flew for the first time in February 1935. It was an attractive little all-metal single-seater and it flew quite regularly. Its final flight was at Perth in August 1947.

The C-30 had not been the last Cierva autogiro. Back in 1933, using the first prototype of the C-30, Cierva had discreetly started work on vertical take-off with Dr James Bennett who was an aerodynamicist at Weir. Such an ability would overcome the major drawback of the autogiro. With Cierva's new system the rotor blades adopted a zero pitch angle when the rotor clutch was engaged. In this condition no lift was generated. While still on the ground the engine then speeded up blade rotation to an rpm higher than that needed for flight. As soon as take-off rpm were reached the pilot de-clutched the rotor and the angle of attack of the blades increased automatically. The result was that the autogiro, using the kinetic energy stored in the rotor,

Opposite page, top: Weir's W-3 with an 'autodynamic' head. It first flew in 1936. (M. J. Hooks)

Opposite page, bottom: The Westland CL-20, designed by the Frenchman Lepère, flew briefly in 1935 but did not enter production mainly because it was under-powered and did not have the direct take-off feature. (Westland Helicopters)

leapt suddenly into the air – this phenomenon being known as a jump, or direct, take-off. Once airborne the pilot applied throttle to accelerate into forward flight. It was, of course, vital to de-clutch the rotor driveshaft before take-off because, with no anti-torque device, the autogiro would have revolved merrily as soon as the wheels left the ground. While still on the ground the weight of the machine prevented any turning.

After many months of secret testing the new system was installed on a C-30 (G-ACWF). On 23 July 1936 Alan Marsh gave the first public display of vertical take-off in this aircraft and the W-3 from a small clearing among some gorse bushes on Hounslow Heath. G-ACWF was, to all intents and purposes, the first experimental prototype of the C-40 'autodynamic' autogiro. In its production form, however, it did not fly until 1938.

In June 1937 the Air Ministry, on behalf of the Royal Navy, ordered five C-40 which were later designated the Rota Mk 2. The first two were delivered before the outbreak of war in 1939. Two other Rota 2, flown by RAF pilots, were sent to France before the end of 1939 for Army observation and communications duties. At the fall of France in June 1940 one C-40 was lost while the other returned to the UK and joined 1448 Flight. Further development of the C-40 was halted because of the war.

Although C-30s and C-40s were to remain in service until the end of the Second World War, the future of the autogiro was already beginning to appear dim to the perceptive by the end of 1937. The success of the Fw-61 was the second nail in the coffin. Proving itself to be the world's first truly successful helicopter, the Fw-61 had set four world records in June 1937; the most extraordinary of these was to raise the altitude record from 158m (518ft) to 2,439m (8,002ft). The first nail had been the untimely death of Cierva on 9 December 1936 at the age of 41. To some the autogiro may have seemed an aeronautical freak, but it was fun to fly, had no vices, provided extremely good lookout when the wingless models were introduced, and had a comparatively wide speed range. But no autogiro that flew ever carried more than one pilot and one passenger and this was a serious drawback when compared to fixed-wing aircraft of the day; its ability to take-off and land in confined spaces, however, helped to redress the balance.

A paradox surrounds the autogiro. In 1923 the Air Council offered a prize of £50,000 for the successful completion of certain performance criteria by a helicopter. Although the autogiro could not hover and

Above: A C-40 in flight over Hanworth in 1938. Note the shape of the rotor hub fairing, tail plane and the fact that the two seats are side-by-side. (RAF Museum)

therefore could not win the prize, its very success promised a bright future for the helicopter, despite Brennan's comparative failure and the absence of anyone to follow him. The Council of the Royal Aeronautical Society was far from ecstatic about the prize and believed 'that it gave a wrong view of the relative values of serious work on well-established lines and such highly speculative experimental constructions as the helicopter'. The prize was quickly withdrawn – but it was the helicopter that was eventually to eclipse the autogiro.

Raoul Hafner

In 1928 Raoul Hafner, an Austrian engineer, designed his first single-seat helicopter which flew in Vienna in 1930. He brought his second one to England in 1932 and soon set up the A.R.III (Hafner Gyroplane) Company at Feltham, near to Cierva. A.R. stood for autorotational.

Hafner had quite quickly realized that the major problem associated with rotorcraft was not in obtaining sufficient lift, which could be achieved without too

much trouble, but effective control of the rotor with the minimum mechanical complexity. In 1934 he proceeded to design his third rotary-wing craft, a single-seat autogiro. In contrast to the tilting hub of Cierva's autogiros, the A.R.III had a fixed hub, the rotor disc being tilted by a three-armed 'spider' actuated by a suspended control column or cyclic stick. The spider also offered independent collective pitch to the blades by means of a collective pitch lever. This allowed the pilot to overspeed the rotor and then use the stored kinetic energy, in the same manner as Cierva, to 'jump take-off'. Where it was an advance on Cierva's system, however, was in the control that the pilot had in selecting the rotor speed at which he wanted to take-off. Hafner also introduced the concept of torsional steel tie-rods for blade suspension; these carried the centrifugal loads between the hub and the blades, which permitted feathering without the usual heavy control forces. This new system improved rotor

efficiency and the light and responsive control system offered admirable manoeuvrability.

The A.R.III Mk 1 flew at Heston for the first time in September 1935. The rotor control system enabled it to take-off vertically and climb quite steeply, giving rise to the term 'towering take-off'; thanks to the collective pitch it could also land vertically, the pilot using the kinetic energy in the rotor by decreasing pitch and increasing rpm. The Mk 1 was damaged in 1936 and from it, with certain modifications, was built the Mk 2 which made its maiden flight in February 1937.

The success of the Mk 2 encouraged Hafner to start work on more powerful and larger versions, but these did not get beyond the design stage. The major weakness in the fledgling rotary-wing industry at this time, and the principal obstacle to quick progress, was recognized in Government circles as being inadequate centralization of research, engineering, manufacturing and financial resources. Attempts had been made to get the Hafner and Cierva Companies to amalgamate but both steadfastly refused; nor would Weir join Hafner. There was no lack of enthusiasm from individuals for

Above: Hafner's A.R.III shows off its paces at Hatfield in 1937. (RAF Museum)

their work, however. In a lecture to the Aeronautical Society in October 1937, Hafner's consuming desire to further the cause of rotorcraft was quite evident. He proclaimed: 'We cannot afford to disregard the clear indications towards progress offered by the rotative wing. We can see the limitations of fixed wings – we must beware of the limitations of fixed ideas; and if we are to avoid flying and thinking in circles we must make the wing rotate.' The war put paid for the time being to all his plans. When France fell, all aliens in Britain, with Hafner among them, were interned. Having applied for British nationality, Hafner was released in September and within a month suggested the development of an ultra-light rotary-wing glider.

The principle behind the Rotachute was that it was a one-man rotary-wing parachute, an unpowered device with two rotor blades which could be folded when inside a specially modified transport aircraft. On ejection from the aircraft the blades would open automatically, spin up during the early part of the descent, and the pilot could then steer himself down, in formation with others, to a chosen point, intended normally to be behind enemy lines. One reason put forward for the advent of the Rotachute was the lack of silk for parachutes, nylon being in the early stage of development at that time.

The Rotachute Mk 1, without its pilot, weighed only 22kg (48lb) and consisted of little more than a tubular steel framework, a two-bladed 4.6m (15ft) diameter wooden rotor and a crude wheeled landing gear. The pilot had no protection, but behind him was a sail-like fairing with a small tail plane to provide stability. This fairing, inflated in flight by ram air, had no framework but was of rubberized fabric because of the need to minimize dimensions to facilitate storage. The pilot controlled the craft by means of a hoop-shaped bar suspended from the rotor hub to tilt it in any direction. A rubber mounting between the rotor and frame precluded the need for drag hinges and dampers and acted as a rotor vibration absorber. The loaded weight was 132kg (291lb) and this allowed for the weight of a fully equipped pilot with a parachute, a Bren gun and 300 rounds of ammunition. The gun was mounted below the pilot's seat and could be detached for use on the ground.

Above: A Rotachute under precarious tow. (Westland Helicopters)

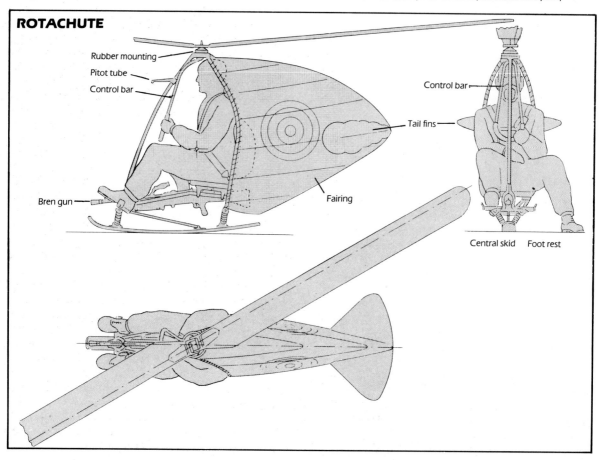

ROTACHUTE

Rubber mounting

Pitot tube

Control bar

Control bar

Tail fins

Bren gun

Fairing

Central skid   Foot rest

Above: The Rotabuggy airborne under tow. (AFEE)

After various tests on models beginning in October 1940 and trials on tow behind a car starting in February 1942, the first free flight from an aircraft, which remained firmly on the ground, occurred on 17 June; then, after a few flights behind a Tiger Moth at low level, the Rotachute, by now the Mk 3, was towed up to about 1,190m (3,900ft) and let free. Further tests were continued after more modifications, but by May 1943 it was obvious that the operational requirement for a Rotachute was fast disappearing and its last flight took place on 18 October 1943. It was never launched from the inside of a transport aircraft.

The experience gained with the Rotachute was not wasted and detailed proposals were formulated for a very large glider to carry a Valentine tank and a smaller one to lift a jeep. To study the feasibility of these proposals work on modifying a jeep began in August 1942. This time a 14.8m (48ft 7in) diameter two-bladed rotor and control system mounted on a pylon attached to the chassis, a tail fairing with tail plane and two fins at the back, and a towing attachment at the front, were superimposed on a simple jeep, the whole contraption being known commonly as the Rotabuggy or Rotajeep. In the new concept a transport aircraft would merely tow the jeep behind it along the runway until both became airborne – just like a glider – and then release it over the landing zone. The rationale behind this scheme was that the Rotabuggy could deliver itself to the battlefield and not require a Horsa glider for the purpose; the towing aircraft could be loaded normally.

One prototype was built, based on a Willys 4×4 ¼-ton truck; gross weight was 1,411kg (3,111lb). It could be no more than this or the arrival on the landing zone would have made the occupants' teeth rattle, if not more, the jeep's normal suspension being retained. But with a comparatively slim payload only two seats could be occupied or, if the vehicle were carrying its normal equipment, only the pilot went aloft. A Bentley was the chosen towing vehicle for the first tests and on 27 November 1943 the Rotabuggy became airborne for the first time. About 60 flights, all at low level were made during the next year. Finally, on 11 September 1944, towed behind a Whitley Mk 5 bomber, the Rotabuggy was taken to 520m (1,700ft). Rotor vibration was excessive and so, on the demand of the pilot, Squadron Leader Ian Little, the Whitley returned to earth, the Rotabuggy landing under tow. Because of doubts about the efficiency of the tail surfaces and the vibration, however, the Rotabuggy never made a free flight. Before it was able to prove its efficacy it was overtaken by new parachuting techniques and the use of troop- and vehicle-carrying gliders, demonstrated during the invasion of Sicily and the attack on Arnhem.

Despite the fact that further technical development and tactical employment were not pursued, the technical feasibility of Hafner's concepts had been proven. The lessons learned undoubtedly contributed to the subsequent development of the helicopter.

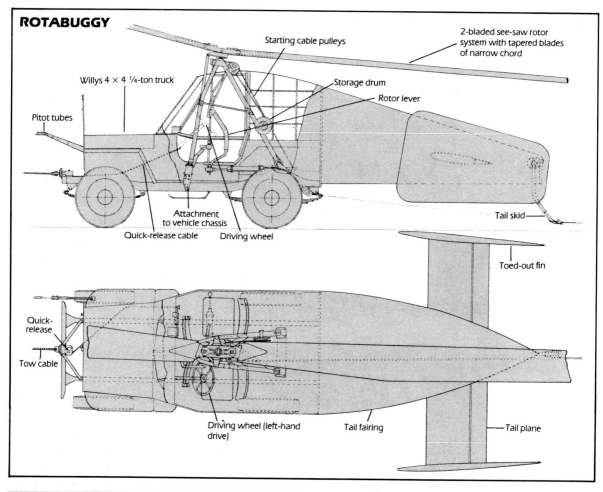

ROTABUGGY

2-bladed see-saw rotor system with tapered blades of narrow chord

Starting cable pulleys

Willys 4 × 4 ¼-ton truck

Storage drum

Rotor lever

Pitot tubes

Tail skid

Attachment to vehicle chassis

Quick-release cable

Driving wheel

Toed-out fin

Quick-release

Tow cable

Driving wheel (left-hand drive)

Tail fairing

Tail plane

Left: Raoul Hafner gives an interview to the BBC, 1955. (Westland Helicopters)

Cierva Helicopters

During the heyday of the autogiro in the 1930s little attention had been paid to the helicopter, and its development had languished since Brennan's crash in 1925. But in 1937 the pendulum began to swing again when Pullin asked James Weir if his Company would build a helicopter that he was designing. Weir readily agreed and in October construction of the prototype began. Weir, however, had no intention of changing his basic philosophy despite the new direction his Company was to take: his prime objective was still to build a simple and safe machine. The ability to take-off vertically and hover was of secondary importance.

The move from the unpowered to the powered rotor had been quite long in coming but was quickened now by the success of the Fw-61. The unpowered rotor, for all the disadvantages associated with it, could have a higher disc loading and required no torque balancing. With the piston engines of the day a helicopter needed practically all the available power just to hover. The main rotor soaked this up but power was still required to counter torque. To reduce the power required in the hover, therefore, disc loading had to be lower for the powered rotor and the downwash velocity would consequently be less. But these practical problems were no doubt open to elegant solutions, it was thought, and the powered rotor offered the enormous advantage of vertical take-off, landing and hovering.

W-5

Originally Pullin had intended converting the W-4 autogiro to a helicopter with two coaxial, contra-rotating rotors. Nevertheless, mainly because of apparently insurmountable problems associated with control and stability, it was not long before he abandoned this idea in favour of two side-by-side contra-rotating rotors on outriggers, a configuration adopted by the record-breaking Fw-61. The diminutive, single-seat W-5 had a welded steel tube fuselage with the framework open at the rear and weighed only 381kg (840lb) fully loaded. For reasons of economy it was powered by a 50hp Weir Pixie engine, air-cooled by a special blower unit, and mounted in the nose. Long transmission shafts ran inside wooden box-like outriggers which had conspicuous dihedral. The constant-chord, two-bladed rotors, with a diameter of 4.57m (15ft), were constructed with compressed

wooden spars to which a synthetic resin-bonded plywood skin was moulded. Fore and aft cyclic provided pitch control while differential fore and aft cyclic gave control in yaw; lateral control was achieved by differential collective, but there was no conventional collective pitch. Vertical movement was achieved by use of the throttle to alter rotor rpm; with this fixed pitch system autorotation was possible only through simple freewheeling. It was clearly inadvisable, therefore, to fly at any great height. A tail plane was fitted above the rudder.

After a couple of months of ground runs, Raymond Pullin, the son of the designer and an experienced autogiro pilot, made the maiden flight on 6 June 1938 at Dalrymple. Prior to this he had also carried out some tethered tests in a hangar which had resulted in some modifications, particularly to the dihedral angle of the outriggers which was changed from 11.5° to 22° and a 1.5m (5ft) increase in the length of the tail boom. The wheel control was replaced by a cyclic stick and rudder pedals. These early tests had revealed that the machine was almost totally devoid of static stability while in the hover and extremely short of dynamic stability as well. The combination of instability and over-sensitivity of the controls, and Pullin's attempts to teach himself to fly a helicopter, was apparently a frightening spectacle for the onlookers, not to mention an ordeal for Pullin himself. None the less, Pullin was the first Englishman to have his pilot's licence endorsed for helicopter flying.

By the outbreak of war, more than 100 flights had been accomplished and some 78 hours logged. Unpleasant incidents were not unknown: on one occasion the rotor lost a blade which sailed over the heads of 100 incredulous RAF recruits. There were others, less serious perhaps, which caused Pullin's adrenalin to flow just a little faster. On another occasion the aircraft entered a dive from 46m (150ft) instead of turning as the pilot had intended. Fortunately ground effect came into play and flattened out the dive. But the machine proved its controllability and manoeuvrability in the hover and at speeds up to 113kph (70mph); estimated rate of climb was 2m/s (400ft/min) at a forward speed of 48kph (30mph).

The W-5 certainly deserved the title of Britain's first, and the world's second, successful helicopter, the Fw-61 being the first. There is no doubt that the W-5,

and indeed the W-6, were far in advance of Sikorsky's VS-300 which did not fly until two years after the W-5. Although the W-5 could not match the achievements of the Fw-61, it was important in that it regenerated interest in helicopters in Britain and, if confirmation were needed after the exploits of the Fw-61, showed that with more development the helicopter had a bright future.

W-6

Even while flight testing of the W-5 was continuing, design of a larger two-seat tandem helicopter – the first in the world – was begun in October 1938 under a Government contract. The layout was similar to that of the W-5, but the three-bladed wooden rotor systems had a diameter of 7.92m (26ft) and turned at 275rpm. The machine was powered by a 205hp de Havilland

Top: The Weir W-5, with its twin side-by-side rotors, was claimed to be the world's second successful helicopter. (M. J. Hooks)

Above: The two-seat W-6 which flew between 1939 and 1941. Note the nose and tail wheels. (M. J. Hooks)

Gipsy Six Series II engine and weighed 1,070kg (2,360lb). Apart from the rotors the W-6 was of all-metal construction with steel and light alloy tubing but no fabric covering.

The first two flights took place over waste ground at the Argus Foundry at Thornliebank on 27 October 1939, there being wartime restrictions on the use of airfields. The very next day two passengers were carried in a single flight in the front cockpit – it is not known why. A number of people later enjoyed the experience of helicopter flight as passengers including Air Chief Marshal Sir Arthur Tedder who had a trip on

25 February 1940; Pullin, the pilot, noted in his log that the weather had been bad but the machine had been smooth. After only eight hours of testing, however, one passenger was unlucky enough to be on board when a blade broke off at the root, as a result of a mechanical defect, when the aircraft was in the hover at 15m (50ft). Fortunately both occupants escaped unhurt, but not so the pride of the designers who until then had considered flight safety to be quite satisfactory.

With the Weir autogiros Pullin had confined himself to the orientable direct control system, but with the W-5 and W-6 he had turned to cyclic pitch. Two methods of control for hovering were tested, but the one favoured achieved lateral control by increasing pitch on one rotor and decreasing it on the other, with longitudinal control coming from harmonic pitch change. In 1940 a new hub, known as the aerodynamically stabilized rotor (ASR), was manufactured and tested. One of the problems associated with the orientable hub had been the suppression of flapping, but the ASR incorporated pitch change together with flapping displacement. It was a marked improvement over the earlier system. In the event of an engine failure, as the rotor speed reduced to a predetermined figure, blade pitch changed automatically to the autorotative range by means of a hydraulic relay. A freewheel assembly was mounted on the final rotating member of the hub. Entry into autorotation was also achieved by closing the throttle. With no collective lever and no engine power available after a failure, there was no way to slow the rate of descent immediately before touchdown so a long-stroke undercarriage was provided to help soften the impact.

The W-6's method of flight control closely resembled that of the Fw-61. Hovering in gusty wind conditions close to the ground was comparatively simple although the machine was a little unstable in these circumstances. It was certainly a good deal less sensitive on the controls than the W-5. Both machines, however, exhibited good stability in the rolling plane but were less stable in pitch.

The W-6 achieved some good performance figures during its 79 hours of flight: a maximum speed of 125kph (78mph) and a rate of climb of 3.3m/s (650ft/min). It is thought that towards the end of its life a little testing was carried out at RAE Farnborough before the machine was broken up in 1941. By mid 1940 the development of the W-6 had reached a watershed: significantly more resources would be needed henceforth, particularly if it were to meet Specification S.22/38 for a three-seat shipborne night observation aircraft, for which Weir eventually proposed a new design, the W-7. But the demands of the war were now forcing concentration on more obvious machines of war and so development ended in July 1940. This was in accord with a Government decision that no helicop-

ter development should be continued to the detriment of more important war work. Skilled labour could not be spared. Nevertheless, this strangulation of the embryo British helicopter industry was a serious setback, all the more unfortunate given the clear success of the W-6. Equally regrettable has been the lack of recognition accorded to Pullin and his team who were on the verge of leading the world in helicopter development.

Before leaving the W-6, which had so much in common with the Fw-61, it is interesting to reflect on what might have happened if the British Government had succeeded in procuring a copy of the German helicopter and the associated engineering drawings. Negotiations had begun in 1938, but the terms offered by Focke-Wulf were 'too fantastic to be seriously entertained'. Even when later toned down they remained unacceptable.

W-9

In 1942 James Weir began to press the Air Ministry to be allowed to re-start work on helicopters, stung into action, no doubt, by the fact that 250 Sikorsky R-5 had been ordered by the Royal Navy. (This order was subsequently reduced to six and later still cancelled). It was Weir's opinion that the prototype R-5, by this time under test by the US Army Air Force, was unstable and, worse, dangerous and he believed that the UK was being left behind in the development of helicopter technology. He recommended his own design, the W-9, in its place. Government experts and the Aeronautical Research Panel disagreed, however, and firmly considered that Hafner had a better appreciation of rotary-wing problems than anyone else in Britain and that Weir's proposals were not worthy of further consideration. Moreover the Panel believed Hafner to be ahead of the USA in his theoretical and design work, but the Americans to have a substantial lead with regard to practical experience. It was clear to the Air Ministry, however, that at least two years would elapse before any British prototype helicopter could fly and considerably longer before such a helicopter could enter service. With the Allied victories of late 1942 and early 1943 it was bravely assumed that the war would be over before Britain could build a satisfactory production helicopter; therefore, the UK should depend on the USA to produce any helicopters required. Thus, when Weir first proposed re-starting helicopter research and development and two new designs, the hearing he received was something less than sympathetic.

In about the middle of 1943 the Government finally agreed that Weir could commence work and so the Cierva Autogiro Company began its resuscitation. A somewhat opaque report on this decision appeared in *The Aeroplane* on 22 October 1943. Little was given away other than the fact that activities would be confined to

Above: The experimental W-9 used jet thrust to compensate for torque. (M. J. Hooks)

helicopter research and development. Under Weir's chairmanship Pullin became managing director and the new endeavour began at Thames Ditton in Surrey. This decision annoyed Hafner whose Company remained closed while he was refused release from his war work.

Pullin was able to capitalize on the design work already undertaken privately at Weir in October 1943 based on the possibility of using jet thrust to counteract torque. The W-9 project was to meet Ministry of Aircraft Production Specification E.16/43 which was probably written using the W-9 details as a basis! Weir considered his design to be an improvement on Sikorsky's in terms of simplicity, safety and smoothness of flight. Weir wanted a rotor system where blade pitch could be controlled automatically by the throttle and in which entry to autorotation was also automatic. As far as simplification was concerned Weir wished to reduce the skill levels required by the pilot. The key to all this was a constant velocity universal joint through which the tilting hub was driven. This was actually more important than the conspicuous attempt to dispense with a tail rotor. Another innovation was the installation of a torque meter, the first helicopter ever to have had such an instrument. By October 1944 the prototype was built, ground tested and ready for flight.

The W-9 had a three-bladed 10.97m (36ft) diameter rotor with the blades having conspicuous taper. There was seating for two. The machine was unique, however, in its anti-torque arrangement: engine cooling air from a fan driven by the engine was ducted along the

inside of the tail boom, joined and heated by the exhaust gases and ejected through a tail pipe on the port side at about 45.7m/s (150ft/sec). Two horizontal shutters at the fan intake controlled the efflux of air to control the reactive thrust. To start with, flying controls were manual but hydraulic servo controls were soon introduced because of the excessive effort required to tilt the rotor physically. This may have been the first time that such controls had been installed in a helicopter. There was no collective pitch and, like the W-5/6, lift was achieved by use of the engine throttle speeding up or slowing rotor rpm. Inevitably, there was a lag in response while the inertia of the rotor was overcome. Thus hovering was not easy. Autorotation was achieved automatically at low rotor speed by means of a link between the blade pitch and flapping angles. If rotor rpm decreased momentarily blade pitch was automatically increased. The fixed pitch fan and shutters were found to be inadequate and they were replaced by a multi-bladed variable pitch fan coupled to the 'rudder' pedals to vary the jet velocity. This succeeded in providing the necessary yaw control. There was no rudder, only a tail fin, and the early flights were undertaken without even this.

This strange-looking, all-metal helicopter with its tapered cylindrical shape (and sometimes referred to as the 'drainpipe') weighed 1,200kg (2,646lb) and was powered by a 6-cylinder 205hp Gipsy Six Series II

Above: The W-9 test hovering in October 1945. Note the absence of the tail fin. (Avia)

engine positioned behind the cockpit. The fuselage covering was removed in 1947.

After its first flights in the last three months of 1944, the W-9 was taken to Henley for Alan Marsh to carry out more flight trials and it was because of the unsatisfactory nature of these that the modifications to the flying controls and anti-torque system were made. Early in 1946 the Cierva Company moved to Eastleigh Airport, near Southampton, having signed an agreement with Cunliffe-Owen Aircraft. Marsh continued the trials. In general he was content but found the 'feel' of the cyclic stick to be 'impersonal' and he experienced some difficulty because of the absence of a combined collective pitch and throttle lever to which he was accustomed in the only other helicopter that he had flown, a Sikorsky R-4B. He also complained about a certain lag in yaw control; this was a surprise to the designers, but the fact that this control arrangement required 25 per cent of the total power was not – and was recognized as a design shortcoming.

The progress of the W-9 had been a well-guarded secret and it was not publicly revealed until 21 months after its first flight when it was displayed at the Air League Air Pageant at Southampton on 22 June 1946.

It was Marsh who brought the life of the W-9 to an abrupt end. With dual controls fitted on the orders of the Ministry, Marsh decided to have a go from the starboard seat. With a central collective lever already fitted this meant that he would have to change hands to fly. This was too much for him and on the first take-off he succeeded only in rolling the aircraft over. It was written off.

Jacob Shapiro, the chief technical officer for the W-9, was in no doubt that 'this research helicopter provided some very valuable lessons'. It became clear that the anti-torque system was not as efficient as a tail rotor and the means of controlling lift by changing the speed of the rotor was no substitute for full collective pitch. By the time Marsh crashed, it was realized that further work on these arrangements would not be cost-effective and no attempt was made to re-build the W-9. It is not known exactly how many hours it flew and its flight performance has never been described as anything but modest. It was perhaps the simultaneous development of the unique W-11 Air Horse that diverted attention away from the W-9 but it certainly served its purpose as an experimental helicopter.

W-11 Air Horse

In late 1944 the Cierva Company began design work on a heavy lift helicopter for a variety of tasks, Shapiro being the new project's Chief Technician. But it was not long before the Company's attention was focused on crop spraying by Pest Control Ltd of Cambridge; the preliminary designs of the new helicopter, designated the W-11, were thus altered to take this new role into account. Confidence in such a role for a helicopter was not lacking because Cierva had already adapted a

Above: The W-11 Air Horse, believed to be the only helicopter ever built with three rotor systems. The tall undercarriage is clearly visible. In the spring of 1949 the fins were increased in area as can be seen in this picture taken during the 1949 SBAC Show. (M. J. Hooks)

Sikorsky Hoverfly I with a spray bar and carried out very successful trials during the summer of 1945. By September 1945 a maximum take-off weight of 6,804kg (15,000lb) and a payload of 2,903kg (6,400lb) were envisaged. The maximum weight, however, was limited to that weight which could be lifted vertically at 1.8m/s (355ft/min) at maximum engine power. Nevertheless, to reduce capital and operating costs it was thought that the larger the helicopter the better; there might also be a spin-off for the military in the lifting of heavy loads. The payload was considered both appropriate and achievable.

It was agreed that Cunliffe-Owen at Southampton would actually build the aircraft and the necessary spares, under the technical and financial control of Cierva. A conscious decision to appeal for support was made at the end of 1945 and both the Ministry of Agriculture and Fisheries and the Agriculture Research Council were approached. Both agreed and the project was enshrined in Civil Aviation Operational Requirement (CAOR) No. 3/46, which was issued in June 1946, and later Ministry of Supply Specification E.19/46; this Ministry signed a development contract for a single prototype in July 1946. A second prototype was ordered in February 1947. The W-11 Air Horse was to be the world's biggest helicopter. The CAOR envisaged the aircraft flying at about 1.2m (4ft) above ground level (AGL) at speeds up to 40kph (25mph) while crop spraying. Carrying a payload of 2,495kg (5,500lb) a still air range of 185km (115 miles) was required; it was thought that the insecticide load could be sprayed in fifteen minutes so no endurance figures were stipulated. Lateral and longitudinal stability were considered to be very important.

The first two major decisions to be made were the choice of power plant and rotor system. The first was relatively simple: during the war the water-cooled Rolls-Royce Merlin had been progressively developed and so a single Mk 24 supercharged engine giving 1,620hp was selected. This was mounted in the fuselage just aft of the nose wheel, together with the distributor gearbox for the three rotor drives, in such a way that a flight engineer could walk round it and minister to it in flight if necessary. One of the problems with a 'submerged' engine is exhaust cooling and an ingenious cross-over manifold surrounded by a jacket through which cooling air was drawn by the action of the exhaust gas was devised.

The rotor system was more difficult, a number of features having to be carefully assessed: disc loading, tip speed and rotor solidity among them. Autorotative characteristics were also taken into account. Without

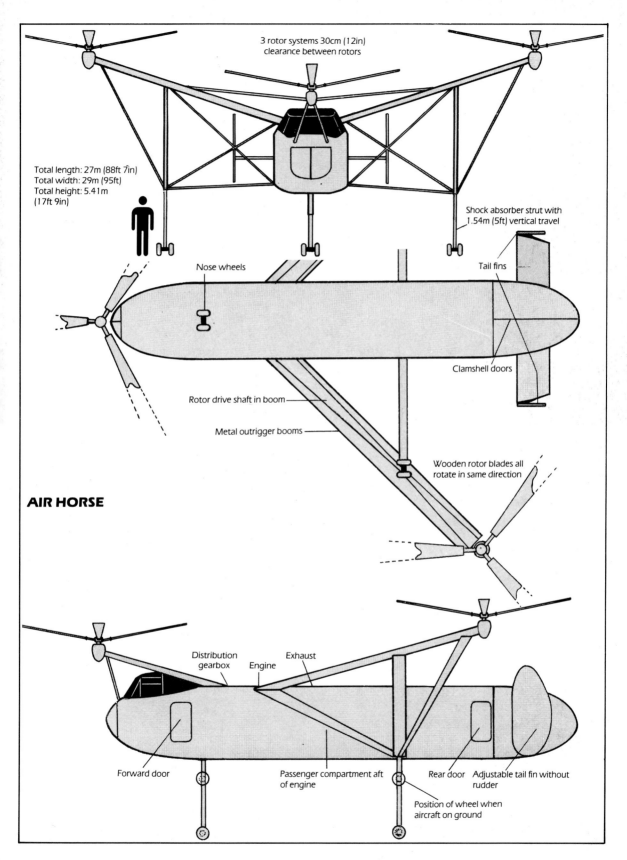

3 rotor systems 30cm (12in)
clearance between rotors

Total length: 27m (88ft 7in)
Total width: 29m (95ft)
Total height: 5.41m
(17ft 9in)

Shock absorber strut with
1.54m (5ft) vertical travel

Nose wheels

Tail fins

Rotor drive shaft in boom

Clamshell doors

Metal outrigger booms

Wooden rotor blades all
rotate in same direction

AIR HORSE

Distribution
gearbox

Engine

Exhaust

Forward door

Passenger compartment aft
of engine

Rear door

Adjustable tail fin without
rudder

Position of wheel when
aircraft on ground

Above: The first prototype W-11 with its rear clamshell doors open. When it began flight trials in 1948 it was the largest helicopter in the world. (M. J. Hooks)

increasing the disc loading to carry the desired payload it was calculated that a single rotor would require a diameter of about 27.5m (90ft) but it was well understood that the larger the diameter the greater the attendant problems. If two rotors were employed each would need a diameter of some 18m (60ft). This was also considered excessive so the decision was taken to adopt a unique three rotor configuration, each rotor having a diameter of 14.32m (47ft). Comfort was derived from the success of the twin-rotor W-5/6 and their excellent roll stability; the less impressive stability in pitch could be improved by installing a third rotor at the rear. The layout chosen was thus triangular with all three three-bladed rotors mounted on outriggers, two side-by-side aft of the fuselage centre and one central but rather placed above the nose. With the centre-to-centre distance between the rear hubs and between each rear hub and the front hub being 14.6m (48ft), tip clearance between any two rotors was only 30cm (12in). Tests of a scale model in a 7.3m (24ft) wind tunnel had revealed earlier that this layout was to be preferred to one where the single rotor was at the rear – for reasons of stability. One great advantage offered by this triangular layout was that movement of the centre of gravity was quite acceptable: fore and aft it could be moved as much as 1.2m (4ft) while laterally there was no real limit given the loading practicalities of the aircraft. Despite some criticism it was argued that this rotor system enjoyed the benefits of both tandem and side-by-side configurations. The rotors all turned anti-clockwise (viewed from above) by means of transmission drives from a single distributor gearbox driven by the engine. All three rotor gearboxes and hubs were identical and interchangeable, thus reducing production costs and easing maintenance.

To control yaw the side-by-side rotors were tilted differentially in the fore and aft sense by application of cyclic pitch through the 'rudder' pedals, thereby setting up horizontal thrust components with a yawing couple between them. To counteract torque a lateral tilt to the rotors with a horizontal thrust component against the direction of torque reaction was built-in. Differential application of collective pitch to the three rotors provided pitch and roll control. There was no separate throttle, the collective lever being mechanically linked to it so that when the lever was raised to increase collective pitch the throttle was opened simultaneously. The reverse was also true. A throttle override for fine tuning power output to match rotor power requirements was provided. The articulated, tapered rotor blades were made of wood and had a moulded plywood covering. They turned at 190rpm.

The cigar-shaped fuselage was a semi-monocoque, all-metal structure to which the metal outriggers were attached. The cockpit, above the nose, offered excellent vision to the two pilots who had dual controls. The tail unit had a fixed tailplane and two endplate fins, adjustable by a few degrees in flight to trim out minor imbalances; there were no rudders. The Lockheed-designed stalk-like fixed tricycle undercarriage had shock-absorber units with a travel of 1.5m (5ft); inside the fuselage opposite the port door was a cylinder some 46cm (18in) in diameter which extended from floor to ceiling: the casing for the forward undercarriage leg. With a stroke of 1.5m (5ft) the actual fully extended length of the telescopic leg from its head to axle centre line was 5m (16ft 5in)! This travel was calculated to be able to absorb the energy of a touchdown at 12.5m/s (2,460ft/min), a rate that very few helicopters can match today. The reason for this feature was that the Air Horse was expected to spend a good deal of its time hover-taxiing at heights up to 12m (40ft) AGL. It was intended that 24 passengers could be carried in a compartment, aft of the engine and separated from it by a fireproof bulkhead. This compartment had a volume of 23.25cu.m (82cu.ft) and was 5.8m (19ft) long, 2.31m (7ft 7in) wide and 1.8m (6ft) high. To facilitate the loading of freight the rear fuselage consisted of two doors which hinged outwards. At the same time that it had been decided to move the single rotor to the front it had been agreed that it was desirable to have a fully enclosed cabin for passenger carrying rather than the skeleton fuselage which was all that was necessary for crop spraying. This was in direct contrast to Pest Control's recommendation that the spray tank at least should not be enclosed because of the chemical fumes which had to be dispersed as quickly as possible. Under the fuselage floor was a 712lit (157Imp gall) fuel tank giving an endurance of more than four hours. The insecticide load was to be contained in a tank aft of the centrally mounted engine bay, it being possible to jettison the total load in five seconds if necessary.

After static exhibition in civil colours at Farnborough at the Society of British Aerospace Companies (SBAC) Show in 1948 and the usual ground running, the first tethered hovering flights took place in October. The first full flight followed on 8 December 1948 under the control of Alan Marsh. Take-off weight was 6,622kg (14,600lb), the heaviest weight until then taken off the ground by a rotary-wing aircraft. As was to be expected modifications were needed but these did not prevent the Air Horse, or Spraying Mantis as it was sometimes irreverently called, being demonstrated at Farnborough in September 1949. On 12 October it completed its maximum weight trials, thus confirming its claim to be the heaviest helicopter in the world at 7,938kg (17,500lb). Testing, including autorotation trials, continued and by the spring of 1950 the initial flight test programme was complete, as were the tie-down tests of the second prototype. Control in autorotation had been good at a rate of descent of 6.4m/s (1,260ft/min) at 65kph (40mph) at a weight of 6,804kg (15,000lb).

But a tragedy occurred on 13 June 1950 when the W-11 crashed, killing all three men on board, including Marsh and 'Jeep' Cable, another experienced rotary-wing pilot. The pilot on this occasion was actually Cable who was carrying out the first flight of an RAF evaluation. The cause of the crash was quickly discovered: fatigue failure of a small component in the pitch control mechanism of the forward rotor which caused an uncontrollable pitch down movement due to the blades going into coarse pitch. The machine was not rebuilt and the second prototype, which had not yet become airborne in free flight, was 'grounded'. The first prototype had achieved some 80 flying hours and

the second some twenty hours of ground running and tethered flight.

The decision to suspend development was taken by the Ministry of Supply who had clearly lost courage and decided that the rush to lift heavy payloads had been inadvisable; discouraging noises were now needed. The icy grip of officialdom had the desired effect and the programme came to a gradual halt. Indeed, all work being undertaken by the Cierva Company under contract to the Ministry of Supply was taken over by Saunders-Roe Ltd and with this move the Cierva Company temporarily ceased its connection with helicopters.

The Air Horse's progress had been monitored by the Air Ministry as a possible vehicle to meet the Army's requirement for a heavy lift helicopter, although it was recognized that the payload was a good deal less than that needed. The Colonial Office also had sufficient interest in the machine to contribute £45,000 towards development costs and the Government of Southern Rhodesia had declared an interest. Ironically, Pest Control Ltd had by this time begun to lose interest because new spraying methods permitted the use of smaller, cheaper helicopters. Despite its tragic end the Air Horse had been an ambitious and challenging project and a technical achievement of some magnitude. However, it was not able to reach the stage where it could demonstrate that it had met the flight performance estimated for it.

W-14 Skeeter

In parallel with the Air Horse went the development of a helicopter at the other end of the size scale. The W-14 Skeeter was to be the last rotary-wing product of the Cierva Autogiro Company; indeed, only the Mks 1 and 2 had flown by the time the Company ceased work. The Skeeter was designed as a light two-seater for training and private use by Pullin and his team at Eastleigh. So that volume sales might be achieved low production and operating costs were the goals: a fly-away cost of £3,000 was intended with running costs roughly equivalent to a 20hp car of the time. Only a helicopter of extreme simplicity could possibly meet such demands.

It was quickly decided to use the single main and tail rotor configuration, by now well-established for all but the bigger helicopters. More important was the choice of engine which fell upon the new British 106hp Jameson 4-cylinder FF-1 piston engine, largely because of its low specific fuel consumption. Thus, in building a new airframe with a new engine, a conscious risk was being taken – a risk which proved arguably to have been unwise. The two rotors were both three-bladed and the main rotor diameter was 8.84m (29ft). The blades were manufactured from cut-down C-30 blade spars with Redux adhesive used to bond 5mm ply-

Above: The first prototype of the W-14 Skeeter, built by Cierva. The shape and angle of the tailboom were changed substantially in succeeding versions. (Museum of Army Flying)

wood to the metal. The spars were cured in a local baker's oven until the Eastleigh Laundry Company came to the rescue by supplying steam passed through the base of the spar. Given the maximum take-off weight of 549kg (1,210lb), the cockpit with two side-by-side seats was quite spacious and certainly offered excellent all-round vision. Behind the cockpit was located the 45lit (10Imp gall) fuel tank. Noticeable in this first prototype was the unusual triangular shape of the tailboom. The undercarriage was of the fixed tricycle type.

Only one prototype, G-AJCJ, of the Skeeter Mk I was built. It flew for the first time at Eastleigh on 8 October 1948, having already been on static display at that year's Farnborough Air Show. Progress towards the first flight was not the smooth experience that had been expected and many hard lessons had to be learned on the way. Alan Marsh undertook the maiden flight and the early trials indicated that the design was fundamentally right although many shortcomings were soon evident. The most important one perhaps was the engine which proved to be unequal to the task demanded of it. Although itself reliable, cooling was quite inadequate with the temperature of the cylinder heads reaching the maximum permitted after only twenty minutes' flying. Equally disconcerting was the yawing oscillation which was tamed by removing the carburettor, positioning it on the airframe and connecting it by a flexible pipe; the induction of air was thus regularized.

There was no doubt that it was worth persevering with the Skeeter and so a single Mk 2, G-ALUF, was built and flown for the first time on 15 October 1949 again with Marsh at the controls. The Jameson engine had been replaced by the well-tried de Havilland Gipsy Major 10 engine of 145hp mounted athwartships – a wise decision given the number of different engines subsequently installed without the need for major modifications to the airframe. Other changes were a circular section and slightly longer tail boom and a larger rotor diameter of 9.75m (32ft). Like its predecessor, the Mk 2 was displayed statically at Farnborough before its first flight. Its major problem was severe ground resonance and, despite strenuous efforts to eliminate this, the Mk 2 eventually succumbed, destroying itself on the ground on 26 June 1950.

Cierva had now been rocked by two disasters in thirteen days with the loss of the Air Horse and Skeeter, heightened by the tragic death of Britain's most experienced helicopter pilot. One should perhaps reflect at this stage how remarkable it was that a Company the size of Cierva with less than 100 people could confidently undertake the simultaneous design and development of two such diverse projects. The fact that they were helicopters, as opposed to fixed-wing aircraft, made it even more astonishing. Nevertheless,

Above: A Skeeter Mk 11 manoeuvres on to the back of a lorry at the Farnborough Show in 1956. (Museum of Army Flying)

the Ministry of Supply ordered two Mk 3 Skeeters to Specification A.13/49 for Service evaluation. These were to have the 145hp Gipsy Major 10 engine.

Development began, but a little while later Saunders-Roe Ltd made a bid for the ailing Company. It was accepted and the transfer was completed on 22 January 1951 with Pullin and Shapiro both going elsewhere. Saunders-Roe were more keen on acquiring the floor space and some of the Cierva personnel than on inheriting Cierva's problems with the Air Horse and Skeeter. However, part of the deal was to complete the Skeeter programme and, to their credit, they (now known as Saunders-Roe [Helicopter Division]) later put their own resources into sustaining it when the Ministry began to lose heart and temporarily suspended the contract in 1953. Ted Ciastula and Maurice Brennan henceforth were responsible for the Skeeter.

The Mk 3 was little different from the Mk 2, but its maximum take-off weight had risen to 907kg (2,000lb). Service trials at the Aeroplane and Armaments Experimental Establishment (A & AEE) at Boscombe Down in Wiltshire and at Gosport by 705 Squadron RN took place in 1951 and 1952. These were considered satisfactory apart from performance in hot and high conditions. In early 1952, therefore, the Gipsy Major engine was removed and in its place was put a 180hp Blackburn Bombardier 702 engine and the aircraft was re-designated the Mk 3B. Maximum weight was now 952kg (2,100lb) and endurance three hours at 138kph

(86mph), a 105lit (23Imp gall) fuel tank having been fitted. In April 1953 WF-112, one of the two Mk 3B, crashed at Eastleigh, Ken Reed, Saunders-Roe's chief test pilot, breaking his back. Not long afterwards the other Mk 3 began to disintegrate while running over the ground at 45kph (28mph).

A single Mk 4 prototype was built to meet a Royal Navy requirement for a light observation helicopter. It had a larger, 123lit (27Imp gall) tank, a steel main rotor shaft and the Bombardier engine. It underwent trials at Boscombe Down in March 1953, but still the ground resonance persisted and so Saunders-Roe set about solving the matter once and for all. Some 230 hours of full-scale 'live' testing of various solutions took place with the resonance induced by internal and external excitation of the airframe.

The Mk 5 prototype was built as a private venture with a modified undercarriage and rotor blade dampers; it was the first Skeeter to exhibit complete freedom from ground resonance. A few other innovations were incorporated, notably the removal of one blade from the tail rotor. Starting as G-AMDC, when it flew in the summer of 1953, it became G-AMTZ and then, when given a camouflaged paint scheme and moved to Boscombe Down in March 1954, it was re-designated XG-303. After trials there it reverted to

G-AMTZ and in 1955 was brought up to Mk 6 standard with a 200hp de Havilland Gipsy 200 engine. This aircraft was also a testbed for a Saunders-Roe idea to give the machine a respectable 'tropical' performance. In the summer of 1956 a Napier rocket motor was added to each blade tip to produce a further 54 torqueless hp. The system could be switched on and off by the pilot whenever he chose. The 27lit (6Imp gall) tank of high test peroxide was installed above the rotor hub. While improving the rate of climb, particularly at high density altitudes, the logistic problem concerned with supplying and storing two separate fuels on the one airframe was considered excessive and the idea was not taken up. This 'boosted' Skeeter was, however, displayed at the Farnborough Air Show in 1957 and flew with four people, two in stretchers mounted externally.

Meanwhile three Mk 6 had been built with a Gipsy Major 200 Mk 30 engine. Compared to the Mk 1 the Mk 6 had almost twice the power and was not far off being twice as heavy with maximum take-off weight of 998kg (2,200lb). The first one flew on 29 August 1954. By this time the Army was making a strong case for a light observation and reconnaissance helicopter and experience could be gained on the Skeeter. Even before the

Skeeter had flown for the first time in October 1948 the Air Ministry had viewed it as a possible contender to meet the Army's air observation post (AOP) requirements. At the end of 1952 a requirement had been issued for a simple and robust light helicopter for AOP and reconnaissance tasks and this had been passed to the Ministry of Supply in July 1953. In-service date was planned for June 1957 and it was Fairey Aviation that won the ensuing competition with its Ultra-Light Helicopter since it was the only Company that was considered likely to meet the target date. However, in the first half of 1956 the contract with Fairey was cancelled on financial grounds and renewed interest was directed at the Skeeter. In the meantime the Sycamore (page 41) continued as the AOP helicopter.

All three Mk 6 Skeeters became military aircraft. One was sent to 1906 Flight at Middle Wallop for two weeks in January 1956 for a short user trial to familiarize a couple of pilots and technicians. By this time the Skeeter had already been demonstrated at the Paris Air Show in June 1955 and been the object of an evaluation by the German Armed Forces. Another Mk 6 was trialled with all-metal rotor blades and was later re-engined with a 215hp Gipsy Major 215 in May 1957 and designated as a result the Mk 7. Four more Mk 6

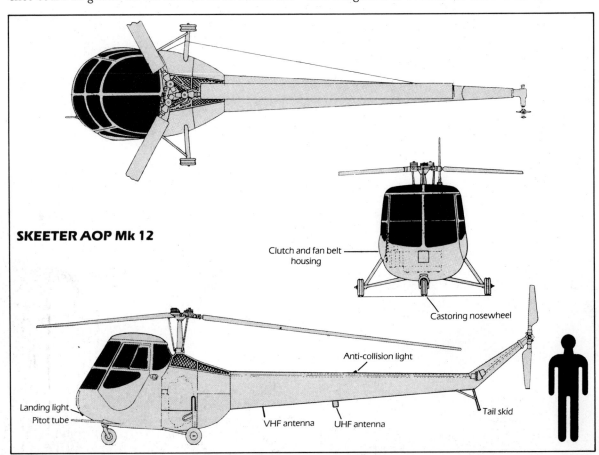

SKEETER AOP Mk 12

Clutch and fan belt housing

Castoring nosewheel

Anti-collision light

Landing light
Pitot tube

VHF antenna   UHF antenna

Tail skid

were ordered for Service evaluation: three with provision for the observer's seat to face rearwards and an HF radio. These were designated the AOP Mk 10 (Skeeter 6A) for the Army; the fourth became a T.Mk 11 (Skeeter 6B) with dual controls for the RAF. Two Mk 10 were delivered to 1906 Flight in January 1957 and trialled in the UK and in Germany under the command of Major Bob Begbie. But it was soon appreciated that 200hp was insufficient for military purposes; both aircraft suffered enough damage in accidents to warrant a return to Eastleigh to be straightened out – which they were amazingly quickly. The third Mk 10 was retained by Saunders-Roe, by now often referred to as Saro, to permit installation of the 215hp Gipsy Major. Even more powerful engines were available but none could have been handled by the Skeeter's transmission; a substantial re-design would have been necessary and this would have involved yet more delay.

With its new engine the new variant became the AOP Mk 12 (Skeeter 7A), the definitive production version of which 64 copies were built for the Army Air Corps (AAC) to Specification H.163/P2. Ordered in three batches in May 1956 (for 27), November 1957 (for 20) and January 1959 (for 17), the manufacture took place at Cowes and Eastleigh. The first production delivery

was made in May 1958, reaching Middle Wallop in August with a limited flight clearance; the last Skeeter was delivered in July 1960 by which time Westland had taken over Saunders-Roe.

In February 1957 Mr Sandys, the Minister of Defence, had directed that the War Office was to assume responsibility for the manning and operation of un-armed aircraft not exceeding a maximum take-off weight of 1,814kg (4,000lb) from 1 September 1957. The AAC was formed on that day. The arbitrary constraints on weight and armaments, imposed at the insistence of the Air Ministry, soon proved to be impracticable and were henceforth ignored.

One Mk 12 was sent to Norway to obtain a low temperature clearance but was unable to find any temperatures low enough. However, that it could manage down to −35°C (−31°F) was proved during the 1959/60 winter in Canada. This was sadly not the case in high temperatures. In the late summer of 1959 a two-part trial was conducted in Aden where the temperature rose to 35°C (95°F); the first part in the

Below: Originally a Skeeter Mk 5, G-AMTZ was converted to a Mk 6 in 1955. A year later it was tested with rotor-tip rocket motors, the high test peroxide fuel being carried in the tank above the rotor head. Here, two external stretchers are also installed. (Westland Helicopters)

Above: *Seven Army AOP Mk 12 in the hover. (Westland Helicopters)*

normally aspirated condition and the second with an exhaust-driven supercharger. In neither condition could the required vertical rate of climb be met.

No specific training version of the Mk 12 was built because all Skeeters had provision for dual controls. Three Mk 12 were therefore used by the RAF to train Army helicopter instructors at the Central Flying School and these were designated the T.Mk 12 and, occasionally for some reason, the T.Mk 13. They were, none the less, part of the order for 64. Army pilots were trained on the AOP Mk 12 at the Army Air Corps Centre (AACC) at Middle Wallop.

Various trial modifications were tested: for example, a skid undercarriage and a 400shp Blackburn Turmo 603 turboshaft engine de-rated to deliver 250shp. This was not for the benefit of the Skeeter but as a testbed for development of the P-531.

One Skeeter Mk 8 was built, three having been laid down. G-APOI was a commercial variant, not much different from the Mk 7, which remained in private hands.

The final two variants were the Mk 50 and Mk 51, export models of the Mk 7/AOP Mk 12 for the West German Army and Navy respectively. Six Mk 50 and four Mk 51 were ordered in 1957. They were delivered in 1958 and used until June 1961 when they were sold to the Portuguese Air Force since when their fate has

become impenetrably obscure. Indeed, it is doubtful whether they ever flew.

The two-seater AOP Mk 12 had a sheet metal cockpit and monocoque tailboom with a tubular steel centre section which contained the engine mounted athwartships. Fuel capacity was 105 litres (23Imp gall). The three-bladed main rotor, which could be folded to the rear, had steel spars, wooden ribs and a wood and fabric skin; the two-bladed tail rotor was pure wood. Unique among British helicopters of the time was the ability to start and run-up the engine without engaging the rotor. Engine starting was by means of a cartridge after priming from the Ki-gas pump. Start-up on a cold or damp morning was often a temperamental affair and on exercises pilots were inclined to take the starter cartridges into their sleeping-bags to preclude any embarrassment the next morning. Flight performance was considered as adequate, if slightly disappointing, with a maximum cruise speed of 163kph (101mph) and a useful endurance of three hours. But it was never good enough to get a tropical clearance and operations were confined to temperate climates, mainly the UK and Germany. This was regrettable because the Skeeter would have been invaluable outside Europe during the many counter-insurgency campaigns which took place while it was in service. However, it simply did not have an adequate power-to-weight ratio and transmission and the engine was not able to produce sufficient power to permit operations at high-density altitudes.

Right: The only Skeeter, a Mk 12, to have skids. XM 528's first flight was on 12 August 1960 and in November 1961 it was handed over to the Army with wheels. (Westland Helicopters)

Furthermore, the Skeeter proved unreliable and serviceability was poor. The major problem in the early years was inadequate engine cooling to the extent that the exhaust quite regularly burned through and then fell off. Stronger fan belts and new cylinders and bolts eventually cured that particular weakness but other engine shortcomings kept cropping up. The Skeeter also lacked the ability to carry more than one passenger and had no cargo space; those who voiced this criticism, however, were ignoring the fact that the Skeeter was never envisaged as anything more than a two-seater. Operationally it was severely hampered by having unsatisfactory radio communications. It was

CHARACTERISTICS: CIERVA TYPES

Designation	W-5	W-6	W-9	W-11	W-14***
Engine	Weir 50hp	de Havilland Gipsy 205hp	de Havilland Gipsy 205hp	Rolls-Royce Merlin 1,620hp	de Havilland Gipsy 215hp
Rotor diameter	2 × 4.57m (15ft)	2 × 7.92m (26ft)	10.97m (36ft)	3 × 14.32m (47ft)	9.76m (32ft)
Fuselage length	4.88m (16ft)	8.53m (28ft)	11.2m (36ft 9in)	15.85m (52ft)	8.1m (26ft 6in)
Height	1.29m (4ft 3in)*	3.2m (10ft 6in)	3.04m (10ft)	5.41m (17ft 9in)	2.29m (7ft 6in)
Empty weight	268kg (590lb)	?	?	5,508kg (12,140lb)	750kg (1,653lb)
Max gross weight	381kg (840lb)	1,070kg (2,360lb)	1,200kg (2,645lb)	7,938kg (17,500lb)	1,043kg (2,300lb)
Maximum speed	113kph (70mph)	125kph (78mph)	185kph (115mph)	225kph (140mph)**	167kph (104mph)
Range	?	?	?	531km (330 miles)**	343km (213 miles)
Service ceiling	?	3,810m (12,500ft)	?	7,100m (23,300ft)**	3,900m (12,800ft)
Manufacturer	Weir	Weir	Cierva	Cierva	Cierva/Saunders-Roe

*To top of fuselage. **Estimated. ***AOP Mk 12.

Above: A Mk 12 about to leave a field location. (Museum of Army Flying)

unarmed, although trials with a 7.62mm fixed forward-firing machine-gun took place in 1961 on the grounds that a reconnaissance helicopter needed a defensive weapon if it was to operate close to the enemy.

The Skeeter was, none the less, small, extremely manoeuvrable, easily handled on the ground and provided excellent vision for the crew. Its major contribution to Army flying was the very fact that it existed: besides giving the AAC valuable experience in the operation of helicopters and the Royal Electrical and Mechanical Engineers (REME) in their maintenance and repair, the Skeeter also introduced the Army at large to the unit light helicopter, its advantages and disadvantages. If the Army had not accepted the Skeeter when it did there might have been quite a gap before another, suitable, helicopter could have entered

service. It was understood, if never formally stated, that foreign procurement was unacceptable and that, for example, a purchase of the American Sioux could not be contemplated. Some years later, and perhaps inevitably, the position changed: from June 1964 the Westland-Agusta-Bell Sioux began to replace the Skeeter although ironically the design of the Sioux was started before that of the Skeeter! The last Skeeter was withdrawn from Army service at the end of 1968. So its time in service was shorter than its prolonged development phase – perhaps a unique achievement given that, in all, 88 Skeeters were built. Ironic, too, that it was conceived as a civilian helicopter yet never received a single order, all being for military versions.

CIERVA AND SAUNDERS-ROE TYPES AND VARIANTS

W-5: Single-seat helicopter with twin rotors on outriggers; 1 built. First flight (FF) 6 June 1938.

W-6: Tandem two-seater with twin rotors on outriggers; 1 built. FF 27 October 1939.

W-9: 2-seater with jet thrust rather than a tail rotor to counteract torque; 1 built. FF October 1944.

W-11 AIR HORSE: 3-rotor, single-engined helicopter for 24 passengers; 2 built. FF 8 December 1948.

W-14 SKEETER: 88 built.

Mk 1: First prototype of two-seat reconnaissance helicopter with 106hp engine and triangular tail boom; 1 built. FF 8 October 1948.

Mk 2: Second prototype with 145hp engine, circular section tail boom and larger main rotor; 1 built. FF 15 October 1949.

Mk 3: Heavier version of Mk 2; 2 built. FF 3 October 1951.

Mk 3B: The Mk 3 modified with a 180hp engine.

Mk 4: Similar to Mk 3B with larger fuel tank; 1 built.

Mk 5: Private venture prototype similar to Mk 4 but with one less tail rotor blade and re-designed undercarriage. Tested with rocket motor at each main rotor blade tip; 1 built. FF summer 1953.

Mk 6: Military prototype with 200hp engine; 3 built. FF 29 August 1954.

Mk 6A: Military designation AOP Mk 10; 3 built for Army.

Mk 6B: Military designation T Mk 11; 1 built for RAF.

Mk 7: Production versionof Mk 6 with 215hp engine.

Mk 7A: Military designation AOP Mk 12; 64 built for Army.

Mk 7B: 3 AOP Mk 12 designated T.Mk 12/13 and used by RAF for training.

Mk 8: Commercial variant of Mk 7; 1 built.

Mk 50: Export model of Mk 7 for West German Army; 6 built. FF March 1958.

Mk 51: Export model of Mk 7 for West German Navy; 4 built. FF July 1958.

Foreign Users: West Germany (10).

Bristol Helicopters

The Horsa and Hamilcar gliders having met the demands of the Normandy invasion in June 1944 and the assault on Arnhem three months later, Hafner's development of rotary-wing gliders was suspended. He and some of his colleagues were thus free to join the Bristol Aeroplane Company when it began to form a Helicopter Division within its Aircraft Division in the autumn of 1944. Bristol took over all the assets, patents and manufacturing rights of the A.R.III (Hafner Gyroplane) Company and offered the post of Chief Designer (Helicopters) to Hafner.

Almost immediately Hafner and a small team began the study of a four-seat single main rotor helicopter. In October the group moved to Weston-super-Mare in Somerset and then in June 1945 to Filton, Bristol. All the while work continued, some time being consumed in an assessment of potential engines. The Alvis Leonides was considered the most suitable but it was not cleared for series production and so the tried and tested 450hp Pratt & Whitney R-985 Wasp Junior was eventually selected for the first two prototype aircraft. These were given the designation Bristol Type 171, later attracting the Service name Sycamore (because of the alleged resemblance to a sycamore leaf) when in production, and were to conform to Ministry of Supply Specification E.20/45. This was to be Bristol's first venture into the discipline of rotating wing aircraft and the first British commercial helicopter.

In 1946 the War Office had informed the Air Ministry that three classes of helicopter would be needed in future in support of the Army: a two-seater AOP helicopter, an eight-to-ten-seater general-purpose helicopter and a much larger one able to lift 10,160kg (22,400lb). Although perhaps slightly larger than necessary the Type 171 appeared as though it might be suited to meeting the first requirement even though it was still in a very early stage of development. Throughout 1947 progress was monitored but at the end of the year the Services withdrew support, such as it was, for financial reasons.

In considering how to tackle the design problem facing him, Hafner decided that evolution, rather than revolution, in configuration would be the approach of least risk. He therefore stayed with the single main and tail rotor design advocated by Sikorsky while adapting the main rotor system and its control that had been so successful in his A.R.III Gyroplane; finally he was keen to put to good use the technical expertise and knowledge of Bristol as regards structures. Three features distinguished the Type 171 from the Sikorsky helicopters. First, the engine throttle was linked to the collective lever so that when the lever was raised the throttle was opened; this was not rotor speed governing as such but it did reduce the amount of throttle adjustment demanded of the pilot. Second, efforts were made to build a high inertia rotor so that in the event of an engine failure considerable kinetic energy was available in the rotor to permit a safe landing. Indeed, an autorotative descent could be reduced to a momentarily stationary hover before completing the landing. The descent, however, was steep and could not be varied much. Thus there was little choice of landing spot. The contemporary Westland-built S-51 Dragonfly (page 72), on the other hand, came down slowly, and distance over the ground could be increased by raising the speed. The choice of landing area was therefore greater. The third difference was the use of Hafner's torsional tie-bar system. It was Hafner's aim to establish a common design standard of control force limits to be achieved before power assistance was applied; he proposed pilot's muscle power as a suitable standard for helicopters up to 9,072kg (20,000lb). This was widely regarded as hopelessly ambitious but in fact the first Type 192 at 8,618kg (19,000lb) was flown with manual controls. In trying to minimize control loads by means of rotor head and blade design, Hafner's tie-bar concept was the first step in replacing conventional hinges by flexible elements. The Sycamore incorporated tie-bars to produce very light control forces; residual and changing forces were balanced by lateral and longitudinal springs operated by the pilot by means of trimmer wheels.

Type 171 Sycamore

The first Type 171 prototype, the Mk I, had a fuselage in three sections: a metal monocoque cabin in the nose, a welded tubular frame with metal skin housing the engine in the centre and a metal monocoque tail boom. A large door on each side gave entry to the cabin. In front were two side-by-side seats with dual controls; behind the crew two or three passengers could sit on a single bench athwartships. This bench was removed, however, so that flight test instrumentation could be installed in its place. The undercarriage

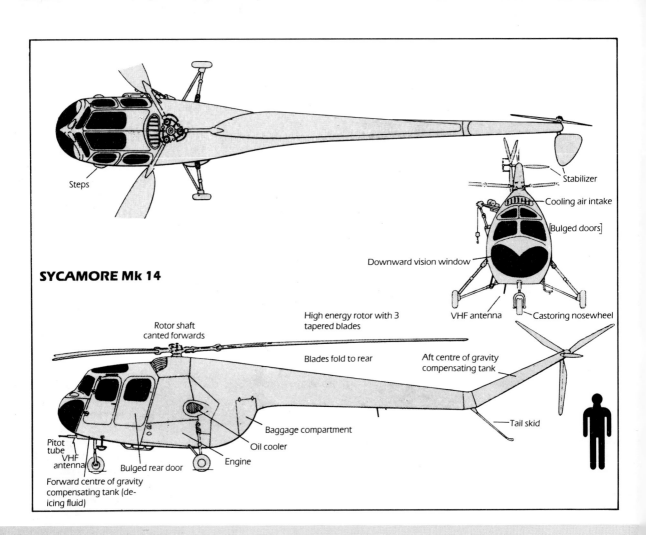

SYCAMORE Mk 14

Steps

Stabilizer

Cooling air intake

[Bulged doors]

Downward vision window

VHF antenna

Castoring nosewheel

High energy rotor with 3
tapered blades

Rotor shaft
canted forwards

Blades fold to rear

Aft centre of gravity
compensating tank

Tail skid

Baggage compartment

Oil cooler

Engine

Pitot
tube

VHF
antenna

Bulged rear door

Forward centre of gravity
compensating tank (de-
icing fluid)

was of the fixed tricycle type with a castoring nose-wheel. The engine's crankshaft lay horizontally with power being transmitted to the rotor's vertical drive shaft by means of the main rotor gearbox. The 14.46m (47ft 5in) diameter main rotor had three tapered wooden blades of varying aerofoil section and thickness as did the tail rotor. Pitch control was achieved from a three-armed spider in much the same manner as with the A.R.III.

The design and component testing of the Type 171 was a protracted affair. The main rotor underwent 70 hours of exhaustive tests atop the first rotor test tower in the world, 15m (50ft) high to eliminate any ground cushion effects. Simultaneously, the engine, mounted in the airframe with a fan substituting for the rotor, ran for 30 hours.

On 9 May 1947 ground running at low rotor speeds began and it was quickly realized that tabs on the blades were needed. On 20 June the rotor was run up to full speed and a significant degree of flutter was experienced. The rotor was returned to the tower for further tests, the problem being cured by moving the centre of gravity nearer to the leading edge by fitting weights to the blade tips. On 27 July Marsh, borrowed from Cierva, took the first prototype, VL 958, off the ground. The machine could not be displayed at the annual SBAC show at Radlett because it was powered by an American engine and in those days all aircraft had to be of purely British manufacture. In February the next year, by which time VL 958 had been airborne for

Below: A Sycamore Mk 14 drops troops during an exercise. (Westland Helicopters)

40 hours, the second prototype Mk I, VL 963, flew. Eric Swiss carried out most of the test flying on the Type 171 prototypes and it was he who flew from the City of London to Biggin Hill in less than ten minutes on 30 September 1948 in the 'Hare and Tortoise' demonstration of speedy transit between centres of population.

The Sycamore, carrying a message of greetings from the Lord Mayor of London to the President of the Municipality of Paris, was followed by a Gloster Meteor fighter, which flew to Orly Airport; thence a Dragonfly flown by Alan Bristow, Westland's chief test pilot, took the message on to the heart of Paris. Total elapsed time was under 46 minutes. On 20 January 1949 VL 963 was demonstrated to the three Services with a view to a casualty evacuation version being built. This was the first hesitant step in satisfying a growing desire for a helicopter to remove casualties from the jungles of Malaya where a campaign against Communist terrorists was in progress. Just two months later an urgent requirement from Malaya was addressed to the Chiefs of Staff in London calling for three helicopters for medical evacuation trials. With the 'Buy British' policy in mind, the Fairey Gyrodyne (page 58), the Type 171 and the S-51 Dragonfly were all considered but only the latter, the least favoured of the three, was able to get reasonably close to the deadline of autumn 1949.

By this time it had already been appreciated that civil airworthiness requirements should be determined for commercial British helicopters and on 25 April 1949, after satisfactorily passing the necessary tests, VL 963 was registered as G-ALOU and granted the first ever Certificate of Airworthiness to a British-designed helicopter. VL 963 was on display at the Paris Air Show the next month, thereafter being used for research and development at the RAE Farnborough for the next four years before crashing there on 8 September 1953.

As soon as an engine specially designed for helicopters had become available it was installed in the prototype Mk 2, built to Specification E.34/46. The new engine was a 550hp Alvis Leonides 71 (LE.21 HM) 9-cylinder radial with its crankshaft mounted vertically; this arrangement saved space and weight. Ready in the summer of 1948, the Mk 2 was on static display at the Farnborough Air Show that year but, because of the need for comprehensive testing of the new engine, its first full flight did not occur until 3 September 1949. This was successfully accomplished and Swiss, the pilot on this occasion, landed. Having reduced power he elected to take-off again and began to increase engine rpm. Rotor blade acceleration was too fierce due to a defect in the clutch design, the blade roots sheared and the blades began to scatter themselves over the airfield, disintegrating into hundreds of pieces. A new and stronger rotor system with a diameter of 14.81m (48ft 6¾in) was fitted together with an additional device known as the Same Weller clutch and thereafter the Mk

2, of which only one example was ever built, flew regularly as a Service vehicle (VW 905) for research and development purposes.

The Type 171 Mk 3 was the production model, differing from the Mk 2 in having a 520hp Alvis Leonides Mk 173 engine with a dry weight of 331kg (730lb), a less protuberant nose to improve downward vision and the fuselage width increased by 20cm (8in) to allow some comfort for the three passengers on the bench seat. Safety was enhanced by transferring the accessory drive from the engine to the main rotor gearbox, which was driven through a freewheel clutch, so that essential services would remain available in the event of an engine failure.

The first production batch of fifteen aircraft began building at Filton during 1949; thirteen of them were retained by the Ministry of Supply for test and development work. One was lent to British European Airways (BEA) in 1953 for two years before being handed on to the RAF. The fifteenth was retained as a Company demonstrator and communications aircraft, although it had a short spell in Uganda with Williamson Diamonds Ltd. A number of the original thirteen later became Service helicopters. By the end of 1949 the Army had called for a helicopter that could be used for medical evacuation, the direction of artillery fire, and communications; the Navy envisaged various naval tasks such as anti-submarine warfare (ASW), and search and rescue (SAR). A helicopter operational requirement was thus written in the second half of 1950 for a four-seat helicopter with a speed of 140kph (87mph), a range of 740km (460 miles) and the ability to hover out of ground effect at 1,524m (5,000ft). The primary role was to be casualty evacuation with a quick role conversion to passenger and freight carrying. A Mk 3 was thus modified as a prototype ambulance version for the RAF in support of Army operations. Designated the Sycamore HC Mk 10, it completed trials at Boscombe Down and in early 1953 was taken to Malaya for tropical trials and an operational assessment. It was able to carry two standard stretchers, one above the other, athwart the rear of the cabin, but perspex blisters were required to accommodate the carrying handles. Much earlier, between May 1951 and May 1952, the Army had accepted four copies of a variant, the HC Mk 11, for AOP and liaison duties; they joined 1906 Flight at Middle Wallop, the first one arriving on 21 September 1951. Three HR Mk 12 went to RAF Coastal Command for SAR trials and communication duties, the first reaching St Mawgan, Cornwall, in February 1952. The three different versions could be distinguished by minor modifications, the HC Mk 11, for example, having sliding doors.

A second production batch of ten was ordered. This included four Mk 12, one of which was modified to carry a sonar and a crew of two; the other three had a taller undercarriage and were procured by the Royal Australian Navy which designated them HR Mk 50. They were the first helicopters to be operated by the RAN, which used them for basic helicopter flying training and SAR. Two, designated HR Mk 13, came with a hydraulic winch for air-sea rescue trials with RAF Fighter Command. Two civil versions were built for BEA (named Sir Gawain and Sir Geraint) and, with a conspicuously larger baggage space behind the engine, were designated the Mk 3A. The ninth aircraft was retained as a Company demonstrator and completed as a Mk 4 with four cabin doors, extended landing gear, the larger baggage compartment and the pilot's seat moved to the starboard side in accordance with American practice; detachable rear loading doors could be fitted. Indeed, an attempt was made in the Mk 4 to construct the ultimate Type 171 embodying all the best features in the previous versions. It was sometimes known as the 'universal' Sycamore and was designed for rapid conversion from one role to another. The final aircraft in this production batch was an HR Mk 14, similar to the Mk 4, for the RAF. This became the standard Service machine, intended for a wide variety of tasks. Two particularly interesting features were the transverse throttle on the collective which was aligned laterally rather than longitudinally, the normal direction; and a pilot-operated fluid transfer system to adjust the trim to cater for centre of gravity changes.

In the overloaded condition the Mk 4/HR Mk 14 weighed 2,540kg (5,600lb) with a payload of some 454kg (1,000lb). It possessed a few idiosyncracies. When at rest it was quite noticeable how low the rotor blades hung – no more than about 1.37m (4ft 6in) above ground level – and even when in motion they were thought to be a considerable risk to passengers entering or leaving the helicopter; height to the top of the main rotor head was only 2.84m (9ft 4in). The Sycamore had been designed to cruise with a level fuselage attitude at a speed of 148kph (92mph). To achieve this aim the rotor shaft was tilted slightly forwards. It was thus essential to position the cyclic stick properly on start-up and to prevent the aircraft moving forward or rolling to port on take-off. There was, despite this simple procedure, a number of accidents caused by rolling on take-off. Another unusual feature was that full lateral control was only available when the cyclic stick was central. As it came aft lateral control became less effective. This was critical when landing with the centre of gravity forward and the cyclic therefore aft. The crisp response to control inputs, however, was more than adequate compensation for the unusual stick forces. As a replacement for the Dragonfly, particularly in Malaya, its slightly larger cabin and better performance and handling characteris-

Right: Rescue with a Sycamore Mk 14 using its winch. (Westland Helicopters)

Above: An RAF Sycamore Mk 14 on a small site in Cyprus during the conflict with EOKA. Although few in number they contributed greatly to the campaign. (Avia)

Opposite page, top: A Sycamore Mk 14 overflies the Malayan jungle. (Westland Helicopters)

Opposite page, bottom: A Sycamore Mk 14 about to launch from HMS *Ocean* during the assault on Port Said in November 1956. (Museum of Army Flying)

tics were greeted with enthusiasm. Serviceability was high despite recurrent problems with the rotor blades caused by high temperature and humidity; two fatal crashes were caused by blade disintegration. Modified blades eventually appeared in 1960. Until then, however, the blades achieved an average life of only 100 hours against the 1,000 hours planned.

In all, by the time production ended in 1959, three prototypes and 175 production Type 171 had been built, although 177 production models had been laid down. Apart from the British Armed Forces the largest customer was West Germany which bought fifty, designating them the Mk 52; these were very similar to the Mk 14. Forty-six joined the Bundeswehr. The first Mk 14 Sycamores to enter RAF squadron service joined 275 Squadron in April 1953, re-forming under Squadron Leader D. C. L. Kearns as the RAF's first SAR squadron in the UK. From this somewhat unambitious start, to provide cover for operational and training aircrew in trouble, has grown what amounts to a form of public service. The annual average number of people rescued or flown in some medical emergency by helicopter in the UK now amounts to about 1,000. In 1984 the figure was 1,034 removed alive by service helicopters from a hazard or assisted in an urgent medical incident; helicopter call-outs for the same year totalled 1,216 – including 915 for the RAF and 265 for the Royal Navy.

As a result of the successful trials in Malaya in early 1953 it was decided that the Far East Air Force Casualty Evacuation Flight should be expanded into 194 Squadron and operate the Mk 14 to supplement the Dragonflies. Deliveries began before the end of the year but the machine did not become operational until the spring of 1954. In May 1955 the Sycamore arrived in Cyprus and in late 1956 284 Squadron was formed there. Meanwhile, trials had been completed in Canada and Kenya, and the Joint Experimental Helicopter Unit (JEHU) had been established on 1 April 1955 with six Mk 14 at Middle Wallop. The activities of JEHU are described on page 208.

The Unit dropped its 'E', however, for Operation 'Musketeer', the assault on Port Said, in Egypt, in 1956. By that time it also had on strength six larger Westland-built Whirlwind Mk 2. On the morning of 6 November the twelve JHU helicopters and nine naval Whirlwinds, all led by Squadron Leader Kearns, began to ferry ashore from HMS *Ocean* and HMS *Theseus* the men of 45 Commando RM with the area of the De Lesseps Statue

as the landing zone despite the fact that it was by no means secure. Because the Whirlwind could only carry seven men and the Sycamore three the aircraft made successive journeys. Within two and a half hours 415 troops and 25,400kg (56,000lb) of equipment and stores, much of which was underslung, had been transferred from ship to shore. All troops, their weapons and ammunition were moved within one hour and 25 minutes. On each return trip casualties were taken back, one Marine being in the carrier's sick-bay just twenty minutes after leaving the ship.

Space was at a premium, the troops sitting on the floor cradling mortar bombs in their laps as the helicopters flew in 'vics' of three, at low level over the water at 130kph (81mph). Only six could touch down simultaneously on the landing zone so succeeding formations had to time their run in to land as their predecessors climbed away. Stretchers were not available for the wounded, but there is no doubt that the helicopters saved many lives besides sustaining high morale among the fighting troops. No Sycamores were lost although one Whirlwind had to ditch when it ran out of fuel with wounded aboard; all were saved. On 7 November low-level reconnaissance of forward areas was conducted and one Sycamore was placed at the disposal of the Corps Commander for him to move around the battlefield quickly and easily.

Operation 'Musketeer' was the first time that helicopters had been used in an opposed amphibious assault anywhere in the world. A new dimension had been introduced into amphibious warfare and the lessons were taken to heart with the emergence of the Commando carrier. Recognition of JHU's part in the operation was evidenced by the award of the DSC to Squadron Leader Kearns – the first to be awarded for helicopter operations.

The Sycamore also participated in the Mau Mau operations in Kenya, the EOKA campaign in Cyprus, the early part of the Borneo fighting and, of course, in Malaya. It was the first helicopter into Aden in 1956 for SAR and, although with a limited range and carrying capability, it was popular with the injured who were spared the rough ride over the desert to the nearest airstrip. Before the Sycamore arrived in Cyprus EOKA terrorists, hiding in the mountains, had ample warning of the approach of British patrols as they slowly wound their way up towards them. The Sycamore greatly simplified the matter by dropping small numbers of men close to identified hides and thus cutting off any escape.

The last British Sycamore made its final flight on 11 August 1972. But the Sycamore lives on; it is believed that six ex-German Air Force helicopters are still flying commercially in the Federal Republic today. Despite its undoubted success the Sycamore was never able to make a significant breakthrough into the world helicopter market and in particular to challenge the supremacy built up by the contemporary Sikorsky S-55. Nevertheless, it proved itself a good deal more capable than the Westland/Sikorsky Dragonfly and rendered sterling service, often in difficult circumstances, in many corners of the world.

Type 173

In 1946 the Ministry of Supply had been asked by the Air Ministry to put some funds into the research and development of the three helicopter classes already mentioned, one of which was an 8–10-seater. Bristol responded by starting the design of a twin-engined, tandem-rotor helicopter able to carry ten passengers and designated the Type 173. It was to be Britain's first twin-engined helicopter and first fore-and-aft tandem-rotor helicopter. In 1948 the construction of the first two prototypes to Specification E.4/47 began. The first prototype, the Mk I, was completed quite quickly thanks to the use of two sets of the same well-tried engine and rotor systems as in the Sycamore; indeed, the Sycamore's rotor system had proved itself to be most efficient and now the only change was to reverse the direction of rotation of the front rotor. Nevertheless, serious ground resonance was experienced during ground tests in 1951 and modifications had to be made.

The Type 173 had a long, slim, metal fuselage with two three-bladed contrarotating rotors, one just aft of the cockpit and one atop the tail fin. A shaft and gearbox arrangement permitted synchronization of the engines to ensure matching rpm and to drive both rotors in the event of a single engine failure. This did not mean that the Mk I could fly on only one engine; it could not, but safety was clearly enhanced. On each side of the rear fuselage was a tail plane set at a marked dihedral angle for longitudinal and lateral stability. Overall length of the Mk I was 23.83m (78ft 2in) and maximum take-off weight was 4,808kg (10,600lb), twice that of the Sycamore.

As work on the Type 173 progressed so did study on the use of helicopters by the three Armed Services. In 1951 the Army formulated a requirement for a helicopter able to lift 4,536kg (10,000lb) over a radius of action of 161km (100 miles). To gain experience, a trials unit of three Type 173 was proposed although the 173's payload did not approach that required. By no stretch of the imagination could the Type 173 be classed even as a medium lift helicopter, its payload being less than 1,200kg (2,646lb). Shortly afterwards both the Royal Navy and RAF stated their need for a maritime helicopter with a similar performance to the Type 173. BEA was not to be left out and visualized a 30/40 seater. In mid 1952 the procurement of three Type 173 for evaluation was approved by the Air Ministry, but approval was not given to develop a helicopter with a 10,000kg (22,046lb) payload, first proposed in 1946,

Above: The first prototype Bristol Type 173. As XF 785 it was evaluated by the RAF in 1953 and undertook naval trials on board HMS *Eagle*. (Avia)

because of the projected research and development costs.

The first 173 prototype, G-ALBN, made its maiden flight on 3 January 1952 in the hands of C. T. D. (Sox) Hosegood. It was not intended to move into trans-lational flight and the story that the helicopter would only fly backwards is apocryphal. On landing, Hose-good had to contend with ground resonance, and he had to make half a dozen attempts to land before he eventually got the helicopter down securely. Modifica-tions to the undercarriage were made and these cured the problem. But another problem arose when the helicopter entered forward flight on its third flight. Hosegood found that he had to apply left rudder to maintain a straight course until at about 50kph (31mph); he had full left rudder applied and was still turning to starboard. The rotor blade angles were offset and the angle of the tail fin changed. These and other setbacks took some eight months to sort out, but on 24 August 1952 the machine was able to clear the Filton circuit for the first time. Sufficient confidence existed now to display the helicopter at the Farnborough Air Show the following month. The RAF evaluated the Mk I in 1953; three days of trials aboard the aircraft carrier HMS *Eagle* were also undertaken. Further modifications were made subsequently, including the installation of four-bladed rotors to reduce vibration in the fuselage and controls in certain flight conditions, and the replacement of the dihedral tailplanes with a flat tail plane with endplates.

The second prototype, the Mk 2, had a new undercarriage with castoring front wheels and, more importantly, stub wings to off-load the rotor in cruise flight by about 30 per cent. The first flight of Britain's first compound helicopter took place on 31 August 1953. The stub wings did not remain in position for long, however, since the Admiralty was keen to explore the potential of the aircraft for use from Royal Navy carriers. The ability to hover efficiently was of special importance and the stub wings merely de-graded hover performance. They were removed, a dihedral tail plane was re-introduced and, as XH 379, the Mk 2 carried out trials for the Royal Navy. These convinced the Admiralty of the need for a developed version, later designated the Type 191, and a substantial order was envisaged. The Mk 2 then found its way to BEA for trials in August 1956, but it was written off in 1957 during a demonstration flight, when the forward rotor system and nose struck the ground while the helicopter attempted to transition into forward flight from the hover. Nevertheless, it was the first twin-engined helicopter in the world to join an airline.

The major shortcoming of the Mk 1 and 2 prototypes had been the lack of power of the engines and in particular the single-engine capability. The Mk 3 there-fore boasted two 850hp Alvis Leonides Major 14-cylinder radial engines. This version, of which only three copies were built, had a taller rear rotor pylon to allow greater forward tilt of the rotor to improve longitudinal stability and reduce interference from the forward rotor. The main passenger cabin was length-ened by 77cm (2ft 7in) and volume rose by 1.41cu.m (50cu.ft). Maximum take-off weight increased to

6,124kg (13,500lb). These three helicopters were ordered by the Government in 1953 for further research and development since it was thought that a derivative of the 173 could meet the Army's requirement for a general-purpose helicopter. They did not prove to be very successful, only one of them getting airborne for short-lived hovering trials in November 1956. The demise of the Type 173 was due in the main to engine over-heating and transmission problems. While attempts were being made to resolve these the realization slowly dawned that turbine engines might offer some advantages that piston engines could not, particularly as regards single-engine operation in flight at high-density altitudes.

Nevertheless, even as these problems with the piston engine were beginning to surface three requirements for derivatives were tabled:

- HR 146 by the Royal Navy for a ship-based, general-purpose, anti-submarine and anti-surface ship helicopter. The Leonides Major engines were to be replaced in the production version by two 1,650shp Napier Gazelle free turbines.
- HR 149 by the Royal Canadian Navy, matching the HR 146.

- HR 150 by the RAF for a general-purpose helicopter for casualty evacuation and troop transport to meet an operational requirement issued in April 1954. Two months later another requirement was issued for a turbine-engined version of the Type 173.

To meet these requirements the Bristol Company offered three tandem-rotor designs, two of which were virtually the same:

- Type 191 was proposed for HR 146 in two variants: a Series 1 with two Leonides Major piston engines and a Series 2 with Napier Gazelle turbines – the first turbine designed primarily for helicopter use.
- Type 192 was put forward for HR 150, also with Series 1 and 2 engine options.
- Type 193, similar to the Type 191, for HR 149 but only with Gazelle engines.

It may seem obvious that tandem-rotor designs would be submitted, given the experience gained from the Type 173. While this, of course, was a major factor, thought was given to other configurations and in particular to the requirements for centre of gravity range, minimum external noise (because of the potential civil market), the single-engine capability over the whole speed range and the rotor size in relation to

Above: The first Type 173, here sporting XF 785 in place of its civil registration of G-ALBN, with new four-bladed rotors and tail plane with endplates. (Avia)

disposable load. Superficially these three designs closely resembled the Type 173, but in fact they differed in many important respects, notably the transmission and the turbine engines which were all completely new.

In April 1956 all three designs were accepted and contracts were awarded as follows:

– Type 191: three prototype Series 1 and 65 production Series 2.
– Type 192: 22 with Series 1 or 2 engines.
– Type 193: four.

At about this time, the Helicopter Department of Bristol became a company in its own right, Bristol Helicopter Ltd, and moved to Weston super Mare.

The engine and transmission problems of the Type 173 Mk 3 were, however, instrumental in the cancellation of all Type 191 in the 1957 Defence Review. The Royal Navy had by now also begun to think that the Type 191 was too large and heavy and was unlikely to have acceptable deck handling characteristics. The single turbine-engined version of the Sikorsky S-58 was preferred. For reasons of financial stringency the

Canadians cancelled their order shortly afterwards. In April 1957, as a very minor compensation and largely to ensure that production went ahead, the order for the Type 192 was increased to 26 to include a single development aircraft for the Ministry of Supply; work on the piston-engined version was to be discontinued and all efforts devoted to the Gazelle-engined version. The first three 191 fuselages had been built by this time and so the first two were converted to Napier Gazelle ground test rigs and the third to a control fatigue test rig. In early 1958 the first Gazelle engine of 1,650shp, the 2½-minute emergency rating, and 920shp continuous power became available and, with almost double the power of the 173, the potential problems of single-engined flight were largely overcome.

Type 192 Belvedere

The so-called prototype 192, XG-447, made its maiden flight at Weston super Mare on 5 July 1958. It had manual controls, four wooden rotor blades in each system and an anhedral tail plane with endplates. Because of the large scale of the original naval order Bristol had proceeded with the design best suited to meet naval requirements: a short fuselage designed,

not to carry passengers but ASW equipment and a number of torpedoes, and a heavy duty undercarriage, longer in the front than at the rear, to facilitate torpedo loading from the front without lifting jacks and to take deck landings. One of the unhelpful results of this was that the cabin floor was too high above the ground to permit easy freight loading. Another was that the engines were located in, rather than above, the fuselage at each end of the cabin – hardly the most satisfactory arrangement for a passenger/cargo helicopter. Nine pre-production aircraft were built for development and type clearance trials. Various different types of tailplane were tested and the manual control system gave way to fully duplicated power-operated controls. Other modifications concerned the wheels, doors and rotor blades which were replaced with constant chord metal ones, although the same rotor diameter was retained.

On 23 March 1960 Westland Aircraft Ltd acquired Bristol Helicopter Ltd but development continued uninterrupted at Weston-super-Mare. Indeed, only three months later, in June 1960, XG-452 flew from Gatwick to Tripoli in Libya via Rome and Malta for hot weather trials and in doing so set an average speed record of 209kph (130mph). The distance of 2,242km (1,393 miles) was covered in an elapsed time of twelve hours and six minutes. Very shortly afterwards an initial

Above: A pre-production Belvedere, XG-451, transports a Bloodhound surface-to-air missile. (M. J. Hooks)

Certificate of Airworthiness was granted for limited Service use. In October three pre-production aircraft, still with manual controls, wooden blades and long chord tail plane, were handed over to the RAF Trials Unit at Odiham. Intensive trials including participation in exercises in BAOR were then undertaken before deliveries of the first production aircraft began in August 1961 following the full airworthiness release in March. This was possible only because of the earlier decision to dispense with the normal procedure of prototype development leading to a production aircraft and instead building to production standard from the drawing-board. Of the 26 Type 192 built, only two (the 'prototype', XG-447, and XG-450 retained for test flying) were withheld from the RAF; all the pre-production models were brought up to production standard which included metal rotor blades and duplicated power controls. 66 Squadron was the first to receive the Belvedere on 15 September 1961 and in 1962 both 26 and 72 Squadrons took their deliveries. By now the machine was named the Belvedere HC Mk 1.

The RAF operational requirement had called for a twin-engined general-purpose helicopter able to carry, over a range of 148km (92 miles), 15–20 passengers or 2,722kg (6,000lb) of freight internally or on a cargo hook; it had to be capable of rapid conversion for the carriage of twelve lying casualties or the dropping of parachutists and supplies. The Air Staff did not want the maximum take-off weight to exceed 8,165kg (18,000lb), but it did in fact creep up to 8,618kg (19,000lb) as the normal maximum with an overload condition of 9,072kg (20,000lb). The conventional semi-monocoque fuselage was of light alloy and, besides a window in the sliding doors, only two other windows were provided, one on each side of the fuselage, a throwback to the naval design which was not intended to carry passengers. Fuel tanks with a capacity of 2,610 litres (574Imp gall) were installed under the floor. In its final form the tail plane consisted of a conspicuous inverted V stabilizer to counteract any Dutch roll tendencies: aerodynamically sound, but militarily restricting in that the Belvedere could only land on ground free from all but the shortest undergrowth. The quadricycle under-carriage was not retractable, the forward wheels being fully castoring. The cabin, whose length was 7.32m (24ft), nearly 1.5m (5ft) shorter than that of the 173 Mk 3, could accommodate between 18 and 25 troops if the seats were removed; the actual number carried depended of course on the range to be flown. Up to

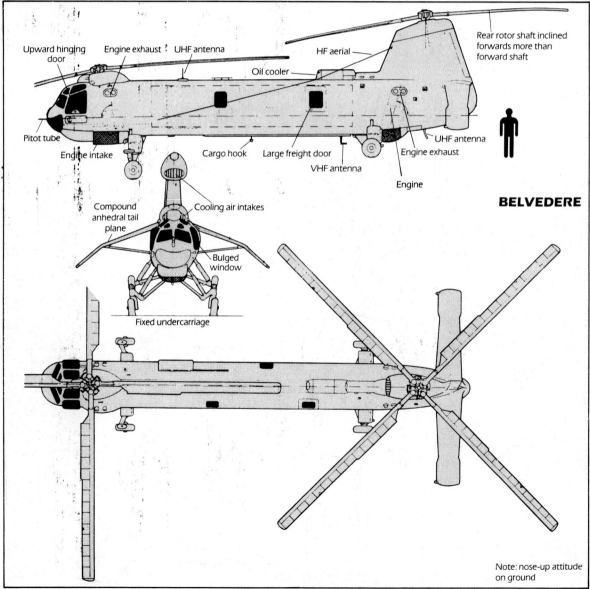

Upward hinging door

Engine exhaust

UHF antenna

HF aerial

Oil cooler

Rear rotor shaft inclined forwards more than forward shaft

Pitot tube

Engine intake

Cargo hook

Large freight door

VHF antenna

UHF antenna

Engine exhaust

Engine

Compound anhedral tail plane

Cooling air intakes

Bulged window

Fixed undercarriage

BELVEDERE

Note: nose-up attitude on ground

twelve lying casualties and two sitting attendants could be carried. Hafner's spider control and tie-rods system used in the Sycamore's rotor head were retained, but to enhance stability at speed the rear rotor was inclined forward 2° more than the front rotor.

The RAF had demanded a high standard of flight performance even in extremes of climate. Thus the transmission and engines were designed to meet the worst 'hot and high' condition and single-engine flight by the virtual doubling automatically of engine power as soon as a failure occurred. This resulted in a certain 'over-engining' in less extreme climatic conditions and a consequent weight penalty; but high contingency ratings were available in the event of an engine failure even if height could not be maintained en route unless weight was below maximum or climatic conditions less than the most severe. This ability to maintain height in most circumstances with only one engine operative was unique at the time. At normal take-off weight with both engines operating, constant payload/range was available up to about 760m (2,500ft) and a temperature of 37°C (100°F), with a positive vertical rate of climb. Above this height payload was reduced. Maximum level speed was 222kph (138mph) and range 716km (445 miles).

Left: A Belvedere brings forward an underslung load during the Radfan operations in 1964. (Avia)

Below: A Belvedere removes the fuselage shell of a Wessex Mk 1 from Nanga Ghat, Borneo. (Westland Helicopters)

Above: The attitude of the Belvedere on the ground did not make for easy loading. Even without endplate fins on the tail plane its pronounced two-stage anhedral precluded landing in dense undergrowth. (Avia)

The Belvedere was withdrawn from RAF service in March 1969 by which time it had served in the UK, North Africa, the Middle East, Malaya and Borneo during the Confrontation with Indonesia. In some respects the Belvedere was unsuited to tactical operations, particularly East of Suez. It was really too large to get into any but the biggest jungle clearings and its rotor downwash was so great that it could stir dust and leaves at heights of 61m (200ft) or so. It might have been better used in BAOR for underslung loads, but the pressure of events further East precluded this. In April 1962 the first Belvedere deployed to the Far East and not many months later made a 725km (450 miles) non-stop flight over the South China Sea from Singapore to Kuching in Borneo. Dubbed 'flying long-houses' by the Ibans and Dyaks, they contributed greatly to the campaign by lifting large, heavy and awkward loads into and out of inaccessible areas; such loads included 105mm howitzers and other helicopters which had crashed. They were similarly used in Radfan where they arrived in 1963. In January 1964 they took part in Operation 'Nutcracker', the first serious venture into the area of Radfan, where they were used to lift troops to picquet the heights above the Wadi Rabwa and to move howitzers, their crews and ammunition. The dissidents realized their importance by the priority they accorded the Belvederes as targets.

Tactically, the aircraft was a resounding success, lifting loads to heights that no other helicopter could manage – sometimes above the ceiling for such loads. Technically, it did not stand up too well to the tough conditions and suffered badly from engine problems caused by sand ingestion and engine fires on start-up. Oil was sprayed on to permanent landing sites to relieve the situation, but in 1964 two Gazelle engines per week were being replaced and a serious shortage of engines resulted. The explosive engine starter system was far from satisfactory and part of it was known to whistle past the ear of the co-pilot on occasion! Engine fires, especially from the Avpin starter fuel, were comparatively common. The design of the Belvedere demanded sophisticated servicing techniques which simply were not available everywhere and the aircraft proved difficult to maintain. The importance of completing technical development and fully training air and ground crew before operational deployment became quite obvious.

For much of its service life the Belvedere received an undeservedly bad Press. Given its naval origins and the fact that many modifications recommended for it, even at the Trials Unit stage, were not embodied, this is hardly surprising. It is also fair to say that the machine rather drifted into military service without the usual scrutiny and firm operational requirement; there were

CHARACTERISTICS: BRISTOL TYPES

Designation	Type 171*	Type 173***	Type 192
Engine	Alvis Leonides 173 520hp	2 × Alvis Leonides Major 850hp	2 × Napier Gazelle 1,650hp
Rotor diameter	14.81m (48ft 6¾in)	2 × 14.81m (48ft 6¾in)	2 × 14.91m (48ft 11in)
Fuselage length	12.8m (42ft)	16.5m (54ft 2in)	16.53m (54ft 3in)
Height	3.0m (9ft 10in)	5.03m (16ft 6¼in)	5.26m (17ft 3in)
Empty weight	1,842kg (4,060lb)	4,463kg (9,840lb)	5,028kg (11,086lb)
Max gross weight	2,449kg (5,400lb)**	6,124kg (13,500lb)	8,618kg (19,000lb)****
Max speed	204kph (127mph)	246kph (153mph)	222kph (138mph)
Range	431km (268 miles)	483km (300 miles)	716km (445 miles)
Service ceiling	4,724m (15,500ft)	?	4,039m (13,250ft)

*Mk 4/HR Mk 14. **Max. overload weight: 2,540kg (5,600lb). ***Third prototype. ****Max. overload weight: 9,072kg (20,000lb).

good reasons for persevering with it but, in the event, it was only in RAF squadron service for seven and a half years because of its absurdly short airframe life of 1,600 hours.

When the helicopter industry amalgamated under the Westland flag, the Bristol designs were abandoned and Hafner's team was disbanded. The venture into helicopters by Bristol could not be called an unqualified success. Only two types had reached production, the Sycamore and the Belvedere, and only 209 helicopters, including prototypes, had been built and flown during the fifteen year period from 1947 to 1962. Very few had reached the civil market and export sales were disappointing.

In 1962, however, Hafner himself was appointed Director of Research at Yeovil where he continued his research into convertible rotor aircraft. He retired in 1968 at the age of 63. He won many awards for his truly innovative and outstanding work in furthering the cause of rotary-wing aircraft: in particular the Louis Breguet Memorial Trophy in 1957 and the Royal Aeronautical Society's Silver Medal in 1961. Hafner had an original turn of mind and always sought the elegant solution in his pursuit of the highest standards. He was an enthusiast and a born leader. Genial and hard-working, he won the respect of all those who worked with him. Tragically, he died on 14 November 1980, aged 75, when he was swept overboard while sailing his yacht.

Above: Eleven Belvederes fly off into oblivion near Singapore in 1969. (Avia)

BRISTOL TYPES AND VARIANTS

TYPE 171 Sycamore: 178 built.

Mk 1: First prototype of 5-seat utility helicopter with 450hp engine; 2 built. First flight (FF) 27 July 1947.

Mk 2: Second prototype with 550hp engine; 1 built. FF 3 September 1949.

Mk 3: Production model with 520hp engine; 8 built.

Mk 3A: Civil version with larger baggage space behind engine; 2 built for BEA.

Mk 4: Standard civil model; 5 built.

HC Mk 10: Military version similar to Mk 3 for casualty evacuation trials; 1 built for RAF.

HC Mk 11: Similar to Mk 10 for AOP and liaison; 4 built for Army.

HR Mk 12: Similar to Mk 10 for SAR; 4 built for RAF.

HR Mk 13: Similar to Mk 12 with winch; 2 built for RAF.

HR Mk 14: Standard Service version; 87 built, 86 for RAF.

HR Mk 50: Similar to Mk 12 with taller undercarriage for SAR and training; 3 built for Royal Australian Navy. FF 25 October 1952.

HR Mk 51: Similar to Mk 4 for SAR and plane guard duties; 9 built for Royal Australian Navy. FF 12 November 1953.

Mk 52: Similar to Mk 14; 50 built for West Germany.

Foreign Users: Australia (13), Belgium (3), West Germany (50).

TYPE 173: 5 built.

Mk 1: First prototype with twin 520hp engines and tandem rotor for 13 passengers; 1 built. FF 3 January 1952.

Mk 2: Second prototype with temporary stub wings; 1 built. FF 31 August 1953.

Mk 3: Third prototype with four-bladed rotor systems and twin 850hp engines; 3 built. FF 9 November 1956.

TYPE 192 BELVEDERE: 26 built.

Type 192: Prototype of twin-engined, tandem-rotor helicopter for 18 troops; 1 built. FF 5 July 1958.

HC Mk 1: Production model; 25 built for RAF.

Fairey Rotary-Wing Aircraft

The Fairey Aviation Company was founded in 1915 and from that year on it had devoted itself almost exclusively to designing and building Service aircraft with the majority being for the Royal Navy. In June 1945 a Helicopter Division was established with Dr J. A. J. (James) Bennett in control. Even before the Second World War had started, while still with Cierva, Bennett had put forward a design to meet Specification S.22/38 for a ship-based observation aircraft. The war intervened and the requirement was shelved, but Bennett's ideas were not, and he brought them with him to Fairey. His Gyrodyne, a combination of the words 'gyratory' and 'aerodyne', aimed to combine the advantages of both the helicopter and the autogiro while trying to minimize the effects of their disadvantages. Today such a machine would be called a compound helicopter obtaining lift from the rotor and propulsion from another source, usually a propeller.

In the USA Sikorsky had selected the tail as the correct position for the counter-torque rotor because it provided a greater moment arm and thus required less power to do its job. This was particularly attractive in the days of the piston engine when the need for power in the hover was paramount; in forward flight, however, the tail rotor contributed little but extra weight. The gyrodyne, on the contrary, dispensed with the tail rotor as the usual method of counteracting torque by producing a lateral force and instead mounted a propeller on the end of a stub wing. By generating a forward force it was not only able to provide yaw control and torque reaction but also propulsive power. Propulsion was therefore not required of the rotor, only lift, and even here it was off-loaded slightly by means of the stub wings. This unique arrangement required much less power for the main rotor in forward flight and, to the joy of the designers, the loads on the rotor and transmission were much reduced compared to a conventional helicopter. A large proportion of the power needed went to the propeller although, of course, the rotor demanded a little more for its share when in the hover or hover taxiing.

Because the rotor had no propulsive function the flight control and rotor system could be comparatively simple. There was no need of a feathering hinge as there was no cyclic pitch. Movement of the throttle, up and down rather than twisting, automatically controlled collective blade pitch and so the throttle took the place literally of the collective lever in a conventional helicopter. Instead of the usual swashplate to transmit control movements from the cyclic stick to each blade, the rotor head became to all intents and purposes its own swashplate. To provide longitudinal and lateral control the rotor head, universally mounted on a fixed rotor pylon, tilted with respect to the axis. In a conventional helicopter a change in rotor torque produces lateral forces as well as rolling and yawing moments. This 'cross coupling' demands some skill on the part of the pilot, but no such skill was required of the Gyrodyne pilot.

Disc loading was low and blade loading high. With the relatively small angle of blade incidence the axial flow through the non-propulsive rotor was low in forward flight and did not increase with forward speed. There was thus no need to compensate for reduced angle of attack as axial flow increased, as would be normal in a conventional helicopter. This in turn gave a lower level of vibration and decreased probability of retreating blade tip stall which therefore permitted higher forward flight speeds.

The control arrangements had another attraction – enhanced safety. In the event of engine failure the Gyrodyne flew like an autogiro: the main rotor blades were always, or almost always, within the autorotative pitch range and therefore the pilot was not faced with the need to react rapidly to get them into this state as with a conventional helicopter.

Gyrodyne

The Fairey Gyrodyne was a four/five-seater with a moulded steel tube structure, a fixed tricycle undercarriage and a tail plane with twin endplate fins and rudders, but no elevators. The reason for having rudders was to provide some degree of directional control when in autorotation after an engine failure. The three-bladed rotor had a diameter of 15.77m (51ft 9in) and the two-bladed variable pitch propeller was mounted on the starboard wing tip; the span of the stub wings was 5.08m (16ft 8in). The power plant was a 525hp Alvis Leonides 9-cylinder radial installed just behind the cabin and driving both the rotor and propeller. Empty weight was 1,633kg (3,600lb) while maximum take-off weight was 2,177kg (4,800lb).

Existence of the FB-1 (Fairey-Bennett 1) project was first publicly announced in April 1946 as a private

Above: The first Gyrodyne prototype, G-AIKF. In June 1948 this aircraft set a world speed record, the first ever by a British rotary-wing machine. (Avia)

venture to meet Specification E.4/46. Revision to this Specification followed later.

The first public view of the static first prototype, given the military serial number VX 591 and the civil registration G-AIKF, was at the SBAC Display at Radlett, Hertfordshire in September 1947. On 7 December Squadron Leader Basil Arkell made the first untethered flight at White Waltham and thereafter testing was continued, the flight envelope being gradually expanded. This phase ended in March 1948 when the prototype was dismantled for a thorough investigation. By this time the second prototype, G-AJJP, was ready to fly.

After re-assembly and more testing it was decided to use G-AIKF in an attempt to set a world speed record over a 3km (1.86 miles) straight line course. No such record in this class had ever been set before so Arkell was not in fact attempting to break a previous record. Nevertheless, the best unofficial speed at that time

stood at 184.4kph (114.6mph), achieved by a Sikorsky R-5. On 28 June 1948 Arkell made four runs, two in each direction, along the London-Reading railway line north of White Waltham. He achieved an average speed of 200.066kph (124.3mph). Arkell's record, the first ever set by a British rotary-wing machine, stood for just ten months until broken in April 1949 by an American in a Sikorsky S-52.

At this very time, April 1949, G-AIKF was being prepared for an attempt on the 100km (62.14 miles) closed circuit world speed record at that time standing at 197.545kph (122.752mph) and held by the same American, H. E. Thompson, who in ten days' time was to break the three kilometres record. On 17 April, during a rehearsal and just two days before the official attempt was to be made, G-AIKF suffered a fatigue

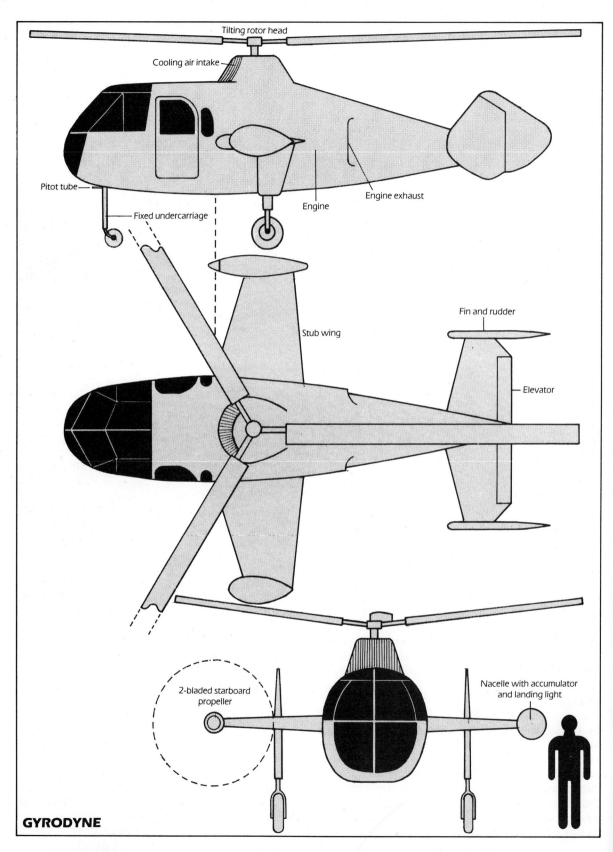

Tilting rotor head

Cooling air intake

Pitot tube

Fixed undercarriage

Engine

Engine exhaust

Stub wing

Fin and rudder

Elevator

2-bladed starboard propeller

Nacelle with accumulator and landing light

GYRODYNE

Above: The propeller on the starboard wing counteracted torque and provided thrust in forward flight. (Avia)

failure in the rotor head and crashed, killing both the crew.

The second prototype was grounded while intensive investigation and fatigue testing were undertaken and the decision to cease development was not all that long in coming. G-AJJP was not scrapped but instead was put to good use as a testbed for the Rotodyne which was already absorbing increasing effort at Fairey. Some four years later, after considerable modification, the Jet Gyrodyne appeared under the aegis of Dr G. S. Hislop who had become Chief Designer for helicopters in 1953.

Although a private venture, the Gyrodyne had attracted the interest of the Air Ministry who saw it as a possible contender to meet an AOP and casualty evacuation requirement. Its projected performance was better than that of both the Sycamore and Dragonfly; furthermore, stretchers could be carried internally, unlike the Dragonfly, and fore-and-aft, unlike the Sycamore. Neither the Gyrodyne nor the Sycamore could however meet the Air Ministry timescale and so the Dragonfly was sent to the Far East. But the Air Ministry nurtured the desire to replace that helicopter as soon as the Gyrodyne became available. The crash of the prototype ended these hopes and by the time the Jet Gyrodyne took to the air four years later both the Royal Navy and RAF had made other arrangements.

Jet Gyrodyne

In early 1949 the design of the Fairey Rotodyne had become more or less firm and a Ministry of Supply contract was signed with Fairey to explore the use of a rotor system driven by tip jets. After the crash of the Gyrodyne it made sense to modify the second prototype as a testbed for the Rotodyne to flight-test the tip jets after they had completed ground tests. Besides the testing of the tip jets themselves, handling procedures needed to be devised for this compound helicopter, Britain's first rotorcraft of this type.

The Jet Gyrodyne retained the same basic configuration of the Gyrodyne while incorporating a number of substantial changes. The most obvious was the replacement of the three-bladed shaft-driven rotor by a larger diameter (18.28m; 60ft) two-bladed rotor with a Fairey pressure jet at the tip of each blade much like the German wartime Doblhoff WNF 342. This arrangement was most appealing in that there was no call for a transmission or gearbox and thus a good power-to-weight ratio was available. The use of tip jets also meant that there was no torque to counter. Disadvantages included the ducting of hot compressed gas up through the rotor head and along the blades, the high specific fuel consumption and the noise level. The tip jet system was for take-off, landing and hovering. The starboard propeller was removed; to provide forward propulsion and some directional control at low speed a variable pitch pusher propeller was mounted at the tip of each stub wing. These propellers were driven by a modified Alvis Leonides 9-cylinder radial piston engine. The Gyrodyne's flight control system was removed and a conventional system installed.

An additional task for the engine was to drive two Rolls-Royce centrifugal compressors positioned under the rotor pylon. Air supplied by these compressors passed down the hollow blades to the tips where kerosene was introduced and the mixture burnt. This fuel was cleverly metered along the blades by centrifugal force. As forward flight speed was gathered the amount of compressed air to the tips was decreased by coarsening the pitch of the propellers which resulted in

more power being transferred to them. Finally the jets flamed out, the compressors were de-clutched and without drive the rotor freewheeled in autorotation. The procedure was reversed as speed was decreased and transition to helicopter flight made – and herein lay the major difficulty: the maintenance of height while the tip jets were re-lighted.

The first tethered flights began in early January 1954 with John Dennis at the controls. These went well

Top: Adapted from the Gyrodyne, the Jet Gyrodyne had a larger tip jet-driven rotor and two engine-driven pusher propellers. (Avia)

Above: Originally G-AJJP as the second prototype Gyrodyne, the Jet Gyrodyne was then given the serial XD 759 before receiving the correct XJ 389. (Avia)

enough for the first free flight to be made in the same month. Some 545kg (1,200lb) heavier than the Gyrodyne, the Jet Gyrodyne was underpowered and, to the consternation of Dennis, it could not make the transi-

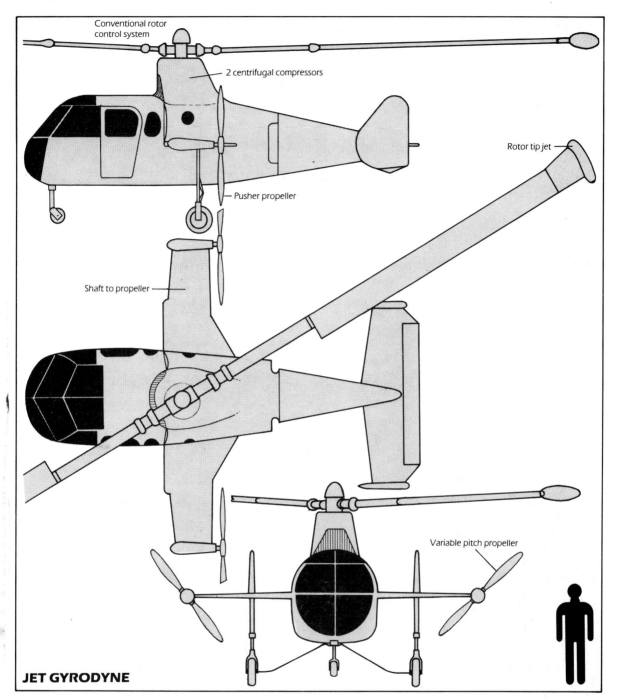

Conventional rotor
control system

2 centrifugal compressors

Pusher propeller

Rotor tip jet

Shaft to propeller

Variable pitch propeller

JET GYRODYNE

tion into forward flight without losing height. It was
more than a year before he was able, on 1 March 1955,
to make a full transition from rotor-borne to propeller-
driven flight and back again. Once the optimum
procedures had finally been worked out transition
could be achieved without loss of height. This required
fairly sensitive and adroit handling, but turned out to
be less demanding than initially feared. By the time the
Jet Gyrodyne was demonstrated at the SBAC Show at
Farnborough in September 1955 there was full confidence in the re-lighting procedure. A good deal of trial
and error had gone into establishing the most effective
sequence of events: the throttle was retarded and then
the compressor clutch engaged and the fuel and jet
ignition switched on. Propeller pitch was progressively
moved into fine and this automatically permitted more
air to the compressors. The tip jets re-lighted as soon as
the required head pressure had been obtained at which

time collective pitch was increased to prevent the rotor overspeeding. Finally, the propeller pitch was fined off completely to permit the maximum delivery of air to the jets.

Because the Jet Gyrodyne was only an experimental aircraft and there being no intention to put it into production, and because of the problems associated with its weight, it was decided to limit the fuel load to some fifteen minutes' flying time – just enough to allow any required test to be undertaken. The test programme was terminated once the techniques to be employed on the Rotodyne were considered satisfactory. It had been carried out largely by Squadron Leader Ron Gellatly and Lieutenant-Commander John Morton who were also to fly the Rotodyne.

Rotodyne

The outcome of the Rotodyne affair was both sad and short-sighted: publicly acclaimed as a 'winner' in the House of Commons on 16 July 1959, it was cancelled less than three years later. Not many years after that, in 1968, the fact that this decision had been unwise was confirmed when the RAF ordered some Boeing-Vertol Chinook helicopters and then cancelled them very soon afterwards to 'save' £10M. Besides incurring cancellation charges, the funds allocated to the Chinook order could have been devoted to solving the outstanding problems of the Rotodyne and bringing it into service before 1968. As a result of all this manoeuvring the RAF was left without a VTOL aircraft remotely in the Rotodyne/Chinook class. To be fair, however, it should be added that the RAF did have some reservations about the Rotodyne's hovering

performance and its tactical applications: it was thought to be too noisy and the display from the tip jets at night were expected to be, if not dazzling, decidedly non-tactical. There were other drawbacks to any compound helicopter: to enjoy the vertical flight and hovering characteristics of the helicopter and the high cruise speed available from a machine whose rotor is unloaded in cruise flight, it must pay the price in having a vertical take-off capability less good than that of a helicopter and decreased payload because of the additional weight of the structure.

The origins of the Rotodyne could be traced back to 1947 when Dr Bennett and Capt A. G. Forsyth, Fairey's Chief Helicopter Engineer, proposed a large transport aircraft capable of vertical take-off – a compound helicopter. A good deal of study and refinement at the Fairey plant at Hayes in Middlesex led to a firm proposal being submitted in January 1949. This design envisaged a fifteen-seater with a maximum take-off weight of 7,258kg (16,000lb) with the rotor being driven by tip jets for slow speed manoeuvring; in the cruise propellers would provide forward thrust. The machine would thus be the world's largest autogiro. Study continued and larger versions were examined. All were to use tip jets, but a number of different wing, fuselage and engine configurations were assessed. The choice finally fell on two Napier Eland turboprops and a capacity to carry 23 passengers.

This arrangement more or less suited BEA who issued a specification in December 1951 for a short/

Below: The Rotodyne, clearly showing one of the rotor tip jets and a folding upper tail fin. (Westland Helicopters)

medium-haul flying 'bus' which could challenge twin-engined fixed-wing aircraft in this weight class. Five companies* submitted designs capable of carrying between 30 and 40 passengers, but it was Fairey's that was accepted. After some changes this envisaged a maximum take-off weight of 14,969kg (33,000lb) for a compound helicopter powered by two 2,800shp Napier Eland N.El.3 turboprop engines, each driving an auxiliary compressor through a hydraulic clutch to deliver air to the tip jets for take-off and landing. To provide for engine failure each engine delivered air to two opposite blades to ensure continuing balanced rotation of the rotor. These engines also each drove a propeller for forward propulsion and at low speed, when the propellers were set at zero pitch, they provided yaw control by differential pitch change. The RAF indicated some interest but it was not until August 1953 that the Ministry of Supply finally ordered a single prototype, XE 521. A second prototype, XH 249, was ordered later but was never completed.

The prototype consisted of a rectangular monocoque fuselage with a cabin for 40 passengers and a volume of 93.45cu.m (3,300cu.ft), a cockpit for two pilots, seated side-by-side, and rear clamshell doors which permitted the loading of vehicles. Attached amidships were two stub wings, mounted high, which had a span of 14.17m (46ft 6in). In two underwing nacelles were located the engines. The single four-bladed 27.43m (90ft) diameter all-metal rotor system, with each blade tip having a pressure jet unit, was mounted on a tall faired pylon. The tail unit was atop

the fuselage and consisted of twin fins and rudders; in 1960 a third fin was added. After simulated ground resonance tests the original retractable undercarriage was replaced by a fixed tricycle one. The early flight tests were carried out with this undercarriage, but during the latter half of 1958 a retractable gear was re-installed. Conventional control surfaces were employed and the Rotodyne's method of flight was the same as that of the Jet Gyrodyne; the compressors were engaged for take-off and landing with just sufficient power being absorbed by the propellers to provide yaw control. In horizontal flight the compressors were de-clutched with all power being transferred to the propellers. The rotor, now turning purely in autorotation, provided about 50 per cent of the lift while the wings provided the rest.

After the usual ground running tests, Gellatly and Morton made the first three flights on 6 November 1957, some ten years after the initial start of the project. For the first 70 landings or so they were limited to a rate of descent of 25cm/s (50ft/min) at touchdown but in fact a rate of less than 15cm/s (30ft/min) was achieved over the first 50 landings – a remarkable feat in a machine weighing nearly 15,000kg (33,000lb). Until 10 April 1958 all flights, about 70, were made purely as a helicopter but on that day, at 1,220m (4,000ft), the first transition to the autogiro mode was carried out. This was taken quite gingerly and was completed successfully. Apart from some re-lighting difficulties at higher altitudes no problems were experienced. In September

*Bristol, Fairey, Hunting Percival, Saunders-Roe and Westland.

Below: In this picture note the addition of a third fin in the centre. All the fins had rudders. (Avia)

ROTODYNE

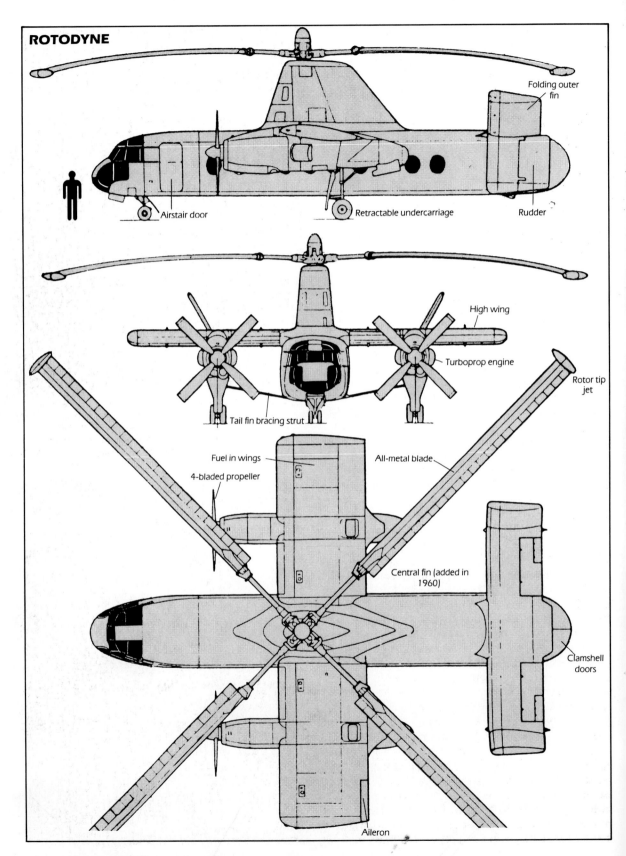

Folding outer fin

Airstair door

Retractable undercarriage

Rudder

High wing

Turboprop engine

Rotor tip jet

Tail fin bracing strut

Fuel in wings

All-metal blade

4-bladed propeller

Central fin (added in 1960)

Clamshell doors

Aileron

the Rotodyne was demonstrated at Farnborough. So well was the test programme going that it was decided to make an attempt on setting a world speed record in the E.2 (Convertiplane Class) over a 100km (62 miles) closed circuit course. On 5 January 1959 with Gellatly and Morton as pilots and two observers, the Rotodyne achieved an average speed of 307.22kph (190.90mph) over the course between White Waltham and Hungerford. This speed was 78.83kph (49mph) faster than that for a helicopter over the same distance. Because Gellatly was a New Zealander this record was credited to New Zealand, that country's only world helicopter record. It still stands although the Soviet Ka-22 Hoop set a record of 356.3kph (221.4mph) over a 15/25km (9.32/15.5 miles) straight line course in October 1961. The Rotodyne's cruise speed was 298kph (185mph) and maximum range 724km (450 miles).

In June 1959 the Rotodyne was exhibited at the Paris Air Show. By this time it had been modified to give the wings ailerons. For some time BEA had been contemplating a larger version in an effort to decrease operating costs. They now proposed a production version, known as the FA-1 or Type Z (XE521 had earlier been called the Type Y), with space for 54 passengers or 70 troops, or a load of 8,165kg (18,000lb), to give a maximum weight of 27,216kg (60,000lb); rotor diameter was to be 31.7m (104ft). Clearly the Elands could not cope with this and so two 5,250shp Rolls-Royce Tyne turboprops were proposed. To provide yet more power, needed in some adverse circumstances, Rolls-Royce considered a separate light gas turbine to drive an auxiliary compressor for the tip jets. BEA, in requiring flight between city centres, demanded a vertical rate of climb at maximum weight of 3.05m/s (600ft/min) and set maximum noise levels – some 17 decibels below the expected level of the Type Z. It was obvious that re-design of the tip jets would be needed.

When taking over Fairey in the early months of 1960, Westland abandoned their own very promising twin-engined Westminster, which had flown in 1958, in favour of developing the Rotodyne. The Government had invested £4M in the Rotodyne programme and announced that it would contribute £1.5M towards the cost of introducing the aircraft into BEA service. At much the same time serious foreign interest, civil and military, was surfacing to the extent that the Canadian helicopter Company, Okanagan, had already formalized an intent to buy one machine for delivery in 1960/1 with options to buy two more. The Kaman Aircraft Corporation in the USA had also reached agreement for the sale of the Rotodyne in the USA and possibly even its manufacture there. In an interview Gellatly claimed that the US Army was interested in ordering up to 200 Rotodynes. This was unlikely to be realized, however, unless the production programme could be launched with a minimum British order for 25

Above: In the Rotodyne the captain sat in the right hand seat. Instrumentation was similar to that in a fixed-wing aircraft with the addition of instruments for rotor rpm and low airspeed. (Westland Helicopters)

Below: From left to right: test pilots Ron Gellatly and John Morton together with two Rotodyne flight test engineers, Blackie Blackburn and Alan Blower. White Waltham, June 1958. (Westland Helicopters)

Above: The Rotodyne first flew in November 1957 and fourteen months later set a world speed record in the Convertiplane class. (Fairey/Westland Helicopters)

aircraft. Indies Air of Puerto Rico had also evinced interest. In June 1959 a model of the production Rotodyne was exhibited at the Paris Air Show in the colours of New York Airways as a result of a letter of intent to buy five of the Z model with delivery in 1964 and options for a further fifteen. The unit cost was estimated at £500,000. The New York Airways order was, however, conditional on the aircraft not exceeding a certain noise level. In Britain both BEA and the RAF maintained their interest and began negotiations for an order for six and twelve aircraft respectively. BEA contemplated an eventual order for twenty aircraft.

As Westland struggled to absorb their new responsibilities during 1960 progress was inevitably slow. The noise problems were not amenable to ready solution and more Government funds, conditional on a firm BEA order, were not forthcoming. The first sign of misfortunes to come was when Okanagan cancelled their order in April 1960 and New York Airways not long after voiced their concern at the lack of progress. Nevertheless work continued, if less optimistically than before. Behind the scenes, however, some soul-searching had been going on in Government circles and on 26 February 1962 the Minister of Aviation, Mr Thorneycroft, announced that, for financial reasons, the RAF was no longer able to support the project; furthermore, BEA had come to the conclusion that the Rotodyne would not meet its requirements. Without any firm orders Westland had no choice but to terminate work.

There was little dispute that the Rotodyne was far in advance of its time and had performed well. In the early stages the noise from the tip jets was indeed deafening, but this was being progressively reduced with the use of suppressors. In March 1961 noise tests were conducted over central London and during take-offs and landings at Battersea Heliport. But the environmental lobby had seized on the noise problem and publicized it widely. Indeed, it was the propaganda that was excessive and ill-judged, not the noise. Most of the other technical problems had a solution in sight and the capabilities of the production Rotodyne were no longer a mystery. It was true, however, that yaw control in the helicopter mode was insufficient, certainly for a military machine. Engine performance was also disappointing. It was clear that more time and money were needed. Furthermore, there was little doubt that it would have taken many months, or even a year or two, for the aircraft to demonstrate its airworthiness to the extent that it could obtain clearance to fly between city centres. Consequently, taking their cue perhaps from potential foreign customers who had become impatient with the slow progress, the Government began to lose faith. This resulted in late decisions and spasmodic and insufficient funding. It was a sad end to an exciting and challenging project to which had been devoted much effort and money.

Ultra-Light Helicopter
At the end of 1952 the War Office had taken another look at its requirements for an AOP helicopter which were then enshrined in an official paper and subsequently in a formal operational requirement for an ultra-light reconnaissance helicopter. An in-service date of June 1957 was stipulated. In July 1953, when the fortunes of the Skeeter were at a very low ebb and the contract with Saunders-Roe had been suspended, the Ministry of Supply received the specification for a small, simple and cheap helicopter to meet the Army's

requirements for reconnaissance, casualty evacuation and other duties. Specification H.144T was sent to all helicopter manufacturers who might be interested. Six designs were submitted by Bristol (Type 190), Fairey, Percival (P.91), Saunders-Roe, Short Brothers (S.B.8) and Westland (Brochure B.145) and from these that of Fairey's was chosen. A contract for four prototypes was signed in July 1954.

In stating their requirements the Army had set quite a challenge: a helicopter that could be dismantled and re-assembled quickly and could travel on a standard 3-ton vehicle. While endurance, strangely, and speed were of comparatively minor importance, a good vertical rate of climb in both temperate and tropical conditions was demanded. The Jet Gyrodyne had already gone some way to proving the efficacy of tip jets and so the decision was taken to employ a rotor tip-drive system for the new helicopter. A very small and light gas turbine was required and the French Turboméca 250shp Palouste BnPe 2 was chosen. This was suitably modified by Blackburn and General Aircraft Ltd and mounted under the tail boom. This engine provided air at the blade tips by means of a centrifugal compressor; this air was then mixed with metered fuel from the same fuel tank supplying the engine.

The aim was to keep the helicopter as small and light as possible and it was therefore dubbed the Ultra-Light Helicopter (ULH). A two-seat plexi-glass cockpit, from which there was excellent visibility, was mounted on a metal shell and a skidded undercarriage. The short tail boom had two fixed endplate fins and a movable central rudder which, by being positioned in the engine exhaust, provided directional control. Later modifications embodied two rudders and an adjustable tail plane. Fuselage length was just 4.57m (15ft) while the two-bladed rotor had a diameter of 8.62m

(28ft 3½in); this was increased to 9.75m (32ft) in two later machines to improve performance. In the prospective version for the Army the observer's seat on the port side could face aft.

Gellatly made the maiden flight from White Waltham on 14 August 1955, just thirteen months after the contract had been signed. The very next month the ULH was demonstrated at Farnborough and impressed the spectators with its agility and climb capability. The first flights, according to Gellatly however, had been 'disastrous'. This was because the rotor system originally had no drag or flapping hinges but instead a direct tilting head. Within three months hydraulics were introduced to the cyclic pitch control and the blades themselves were re-designed. The ULH, unfortunately, failed to impress the Ministry of Supply which withdrew support from the project – for the usual financial reasons – even before the third prototype had flown on 20 March 1956. A second, and more fundamental, reason may have been the German evaluation and possible procurement of the Skeeter. Provided the British Government supported that programme there was a good chance that the German Government would purchase the Skeeter; a sale of as many as 90 was contemplated. In any case, the decision was made to withdraw military support for the ULH and in May 1956 27 Skeeters were ordered for the British Army. As we have seen the Germans eventually purchased only ten Skeeters the following year.

Fairey elected to continue with the ULH on a private basis and were able to get the machine evaluated by the US Army although to no avail. Two were built for civil evaluation in addition to the four military prototypes. G-APJJ was the second of these, the first being used

Below: Fairey's trials Ultra-Light Helicopter demonstrating its manoeuvrability and small size by landing on the back of a lorry during the 1956 Farnborough Show. (M. J. Hooks)

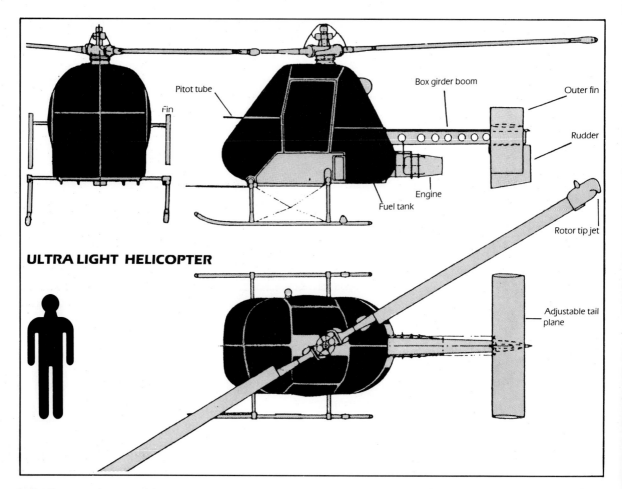

Pitot tube

Fin

Box girder boom

Outer fin

Rudder

Engine

Fuel tank

Rotor tip jet

ULTRA LIGHT HELICOPTER

Adjustable tail plane

only for ground tests. Additionally, the second military prototype (XJ 928) was modified to become G-AOUJ and fitted with hydraulic controls. It is thought that parts of the first and third prototypes (XJ 924 and XJ 930) might have contributed to the building of G-APJJ and G-AOUK. However, another source believes that XJ 936, the fourth military prototype, was simply re-registered as G-AOUK. The situation is remarkably opaque.

G-AOUK, Fairey's demonstration and trials aircraft, appeared at the 1956 SBAC Show and it was joined by G-AOUJ the following year. This latter aircraft made the ULH's final appearance at the Show, alone, in 1958. In dark-blue colours and Royal Navy markings, it gave a stunning demonstration of its manoeuvrability. In an attempt to interest the Royal Navy in the ULH as a light torpedo-carrying helicopter, G-AOUJ carried out trials in the English Channel in 1957 from the frigate HMS *Grenville*. The weather was terrible, the ship rolling 40° and heaving up to 3.65m (12ft) while the wind reached 115kph (71mph). More than 70 take-offs and landings were made while the ship rotated round the roll, pitch and yaw axes and, in the words of one observer, simultaneously heaved (the deck moved up and

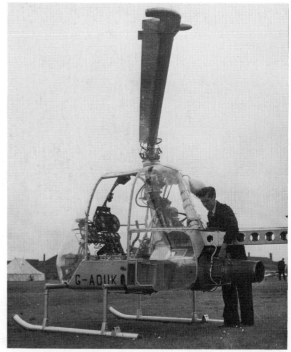

down), swayed (moved side-to-side) and surged (moved backwards and forwards)! In 1958 this aircraft and G-APJJ undertook further trials with the Royal Navy. In the same year one ULH was taken to Canada for cold weather trials and demonstrations to the Canadians who had expressed interest in the helicopter.

In September and October 1958 Certificates of Airworthiness were awarded to G-AOUJ and G-APJJ but these expired in the spring of 1959 by which time the project was doomed; not a single order had been placed for the aircraft despite the fact that it had been flying for nearly four years. The project was halted in 1959.

Regrettably the ULH falls into the category of technical successes which were unable to generate sufficient political enthusiasm and support. Gellatly was quoted as saying that the ULH was the helicopter that he enjoyed flying most of all. Nobody could carp at its

performance: a cruise speed of 153kph (95mph) and a maximum rate of climb at sea level of 6.9m/s (1,350ft/min). Endurance was two and a half hours.

The fate of retired helicopters is often very obscure. All the more surprising then that G-AOUJ, reported to have been broken up, was discovered on an Essex farm in 1979!

FAIREY TYPES

FB-1 GYRODYNE: Experimental compound helicopter with three-bladed single rotor and propeller on starboard wing; 2 built; First flight (FF) 7 December 1947.

JET GYRODYNE: Experimental compound helicopter with single two-bladed tip jet-driven rotor and 2 pusher propellers; 1 modified from Gyrodyne. FF January 1954.

ROTODYNE: Prototype compound helicopter for 30/40 passengers with four-bladed tip jet-driven rotor and 2 propellers at mid-wing; 1 built. FF 6 November 1957.

ULTRA-LIGHT HELICOPTER: Two-seat observation helicopter with two-bladed tip jet-driven rotor; 6 built. FF 14 August 1955.

CHARACTERISTICS: FAIREY TYPES

Designation	Gyrodyne	Jet Gyrodyne	Rotodyne	Ultra-Light Helicopter
Engine	Alvis Leonides 525hp	Alvis Leonides 525hp	2 × Napier Eland N.El.3 2,800shp	Turboméca Palouste BnPe.2 250shp
Rotor diameter	15.77m (51ft 9in)	18.28m (60ft)	27.43m (90ft)	8.62m (28ft 3½in)
Fuselage length	7.62m (25ft)	7.62m (25ft)	17.88m (58ft 8in)	4.57m (15ft)
Wing span	5.08m (16ft 8in)	5.08m (16ft 8in)	14.17m (46ft 6in)	–
Height	3.1m (10ft 2in)	3.1m (10ft 2in)	6.75m (22ft 2in)	2.49m (8ft 2in)
Empty weight	1,633kg (3,600lb)	?	10,886kg (24,000lb)	526kg (1,160lb)
Max gross weight	2,177kg (4,800lb)	2,722kg (6,000lb)	14,969kg (33,000lb)	817kg (1,800lb)
Max speed	200kph (124mph)	?	298kph (185mph)*	158kph (98mph)
Range	402km (250 miles)	?	724km (450 miles)	298km (185 miles)
Service ceiling	?	?	?	?

*Max cruise speed.

Left: G-AOUK, also registered as XJ 936, shows off its unique features. It was the first ULH to be fitted with hydraulic controls. (M. J. Hooks)

Right: One of two ULH built as a private venture, G-APJJ had a larger cabin for emergency load carrying. It was also used for Royal Navy trials. (Westland Helicopters)

Westland turns to the USA

The Westland Aircraft Works was formed in April 1915 out of the Yeovil engineering firm of Petters Ltd. Offering to make 'munitions of war' for the Government, Petters were a little surprised to be ignored by the War Office but asked instead by the Admiralty to make seaplanes – for which they had neither the expertise nor the tools. Nevertheless, they chose a new site on Westland Farm, changed their name and set to with a will. For the next 30 years or so they concentrated almost exclusively on military fixed-wing aircraft; their brief flirtation with two autogiros in the 1930s has already been noted (see page 18).

As the Second World War ended some difficult decisions lay ahead for the Company which was without a single major contract. Prospects in both the military and civil markets looked bleak but appeared more promising as far as helicopters were concerned. The first practical helicopters, the Sikorsky R-4, R-5 and R-6, had already entered production in the USA and the Westland Board, after due deliberation, decided that the best way to ensure the future of the Company was to build helicopters. This was a brave step into the unknown, given the history of the helicopter and its general lack of success over many years, and because nobody could be certain of its ultimate success.

In implementing the decision Westland realized that, whatever course they chose, they would not be able to make a profit for some years. To start from scratch would obviously take longer than building another Company's helicopter under licence – probably the quickest way to build up experience in the various disciplines and to challenge the other British manufacturers. Westland attracted some criticism for their decision to build under licence rather than design their own helicopters, but it appeared sound at the time and now 40 years on can be seen to have been the right one. Nevertheless, the Government was trying to encourage a national helicopter industry and this move seemed uncooperative. In assessing the factors a Westland visit to Sikorsky in 1944 may have played a part. It was decided to approach the United Aircraft Corporation, of which Sikorsky was a part, for a licence agreement initially to build the S-51, a developed version of the R-5D, intended originally for the US civil market and first flown in February 1946. In December 1946 a licence was issued to construct the S-51, to modify it in any way and to sell it world-wide except in the USA and Canada. These were exceedingly favourable and generous terms for which Westland will always be grateful.

The British Services had all been experimenting with the R-4, known as the Hoverfly Mk 1, and the R-6, the Hoverfly Mk 2, but by the end of 1946 it was becoming clear that neither of these helicopter types had a true operational application and a more capable helicopter was required. The S-51 seemed as though it might fit the bill but Bristol, Cierva and Fairey all had their own projects in hand and the competition was likely to be fierce. Realizing that they were lagging, Westland included in their agreement with Sikorsky the delivery of six already built S-51 for demonstration and trials for the Company, the Ministry of Supply and Pest Control Ltd, and three for BEA. This was a shrewd purchase.

WS-51 Dragonfly

As the Services, and particularly the Royal Navy, waited somewhat impatiently for an operational helicopter, Westland began work on the Dragonfly, as it was called by the Royal Navy and subsequently by all operators. Any idea that it would be a simple matter to build an anglicized version of the S-51 was quickly dispelled. Dollars were in very short supply and their lack prevented the importation of any Sikorsky parts or components; the Westland-Sikorsky-51 (WS-51) had to be built purely from British materials and equipment and these differed greatly from the American. According to O. L. L. Fitzwilliams, who had become the Chief Helicopter Engineer, there were only fourteen people in his team and this number included the secretary and tea boy! The first Sikorsky drawings arrived in May 1947 but, when issued to the shop floor, they had to be accompanied by a Westland drawing showing how to anglicize the part. In some cases original Westland drawings were required. All this took much more time than expected and construction was made no easier by the desire to use a British piston engine, the 520hp Alvis Leonides 50, rather than the 450hp Pratt & Whitney Wasp Junior. Finally, on 5 October 1948, just three days before the Skeeter, the prototype G-AKTW flew for the first time, some sixteen months after work had first started in earnest. With the British engine, the WS-51 was designated the Dragonfly Mk 1A.

Anticipating military orders, Westland began hand-building a batch of 30 aircraft, full production tooling

Above: A Dragonfly Mk 1A in manufacturer's colours. This aircraft was retained at Yeovil for customer pilot training. (Avia)

not being undertaken because this was very much a private venture and something of a risk. When the Royal Navy and RAF placed large orders later, a delay of about eighteen months occurred before full tooling could be achieved and the first aircraft delivered. In January 1949 the Royal Navy borrowed one of the six original S-51 for three months for trials on board the aircraft carrier HMS *Vengeance*. Confirmation of their order for 12 HR Mk 1 followed and the RAF ordered three HC Mk 2. These aircraft were generally similar apart from special items of role equipment, the Mk 1 being equipped for air-sea rescue and the Mk 2 for casualty evacuation.

The first production WS-51 flew on 22 June 1949. It and two more were subsequently handed over to the Ministry of Supply for military trials. These were sufficiently successful for the Royal Navy and RAF to place further orders.

The Dragonfly was an ungainly-looking four-seat utility helicopter. Maximum take-off weight was nearly 272kg (600lb) more than the less powerful Sikorsky S-51 at 2,663kg (5,870lb); disposable load with the later metal rotor blades was 567kg (1,250lb). The pilot sat

Above: The simple cockpit of a Dragonfly. (Westland Helicopters)

Below right: A Dragonfly with a stretcher pannier descends into a clearing in Malaya. (Avia)

and Norwich. On 1 June 1950 BEA inaugurated the world's first scheduled helicopter passenger service, between Liverpool and Cardiff – not a route that one would have automatically chosen. None of these ventures caught on as they were plainly uneconomical. The civil versions of the British-built WS-51 were the Mk 1A with the 520hp Alvis Leonides 521/1 engine and the Mk 1B which had the 450hp Pratt & Whitney Wasp Junior radial.

Only about ten civil-registered Dragonflies were operated in the UK and of these six were held at Yeovil for the training of pilots whose Governments or organizations had ordered the machine. Unhappily, BEA did not elect to continue with their helicopter services and thus never operated a British-built Dragonfly. In view of their interest in crop-spraying from helicopters, it was no surprise that Pest Control Ltd ordered two Dragonflies which were delivered in 1949. Within three years both had crashed. The *Evening Standard* took delivery of a single aircraft in 1953 and, while it was considered most useful for publicity and photographic purposes, the problems of operating it into and out of London were so great that in 1955 it was reluctantly sold to Fairey as a communications machine. It crashed at Netheravon in 1959. Silver City Airways briefly ran a trial cross-Channel service with a single Dragonfly in 1954.

centrally in the front part of the cabin and had excellent all-round vision. There was a bench for three passengers behind him. The centre section housed the engine and transmission and the tail boom comprised the rear section. The three-bladed main rotor consisted of a tubular metal spar, wooden leading edges and fabric covering. This sometimes ripped in flight and in very cold weather hardened and cracked. The tricycle landing gear had a castoring nosewheel and was not retractable.

In all thirteen HR Mk 1 for the Royal Navy, of which one was flown with an experimental four-bladed rotor, and four HC Mk 2 for the RAF were built. Of the HR Mk 3, 58 were built and of these 50 found their way to the Royal Navy. This version had all-metal rotor blades with a rotor diameter increased by 30cm (1ft) and hydraulic servo controls as did the HC Mk 4, of which twelve were produced for the RAF. The final mark for the Royal Navy was the HR Mk 5 with a little more engine power, more modern instruments and some additional role equipment. At least 25 Mk 1 and 3 were brought up to Mk 5 standard.

The Dragonfly was not limited to British military service, but it never really made its mark in the commercial world. Three of the original US-built S-51 had gone to BEA in 1948 for an experimental mail service in East Anglia. On 21 February 1949 this was extended to a nightly service between Peterborough

Above: The Prime Minister, Sir Anthony Eden, disembarks from a Dragonfly at the start of his visit to the Farnborough Show on 6 September 1955. (M. J. Hooks)

Twenty-seven Dragonflies were entered on the British civil register, but the majority of these were exported together with others which did not go on the register. In all 39 went to nine foreign countries with Yugoslavia placing the largest order for ten which were delivered in 1953/54; France took nine for service in Indo-China. All were Mk 1A except for three for the Belgian Congo and two for Egypt which were Mk 1B. It is thought that the last Dragonfly in operation was one of the two delivered to the Royal Ceylon Air Force; it was retired in 1969. Westland built 139 Dragonflies.

It did not take long for naval staffs to appreciate the advantages that a helicopter could offer. By operating from small ships and even merchant ships it could obviate the need of expensive aircraft carriers and fixed-wing aircraft to provide convoy escort. Destroyers were normally used for plane guard duties, but it was quite obvious that a helicopter could reach a ditched aircraft much more quickly than any destroyer which, in wartime, would itself become a target when it stopped. The transfer of personnel from ship-to-ship when under way was also simplified by helicopter.

The first Royal Navy helicopter squadron was 705 which formed at Royal Naval Air Station (RNAS) Gosport in May 1947 with Sikorsky R-4B and two R-6, the first naval helicopter squadron to form outside the USA. It was also the first to take permanent delivery of the Dragonfly when the first one arrived on 13 January 1950. As the only British helicopter squadron 705 was used for training pilots who were to take command of SAR units afloat and ashore. The Squadron was also much in demand for trials, demonstrations and actual rescue work. As a replacement for the amphibian Sea Otter the Dragonfly's primary operational role was SAR, particularly aboard aircraft carriers when they acted as 'plane guard' during flying; they were also highly valued for ship-to-ship and ship-to-shore communications. To pick up downed pilots the Dragonfly was equipped with a pilot-operated winch with a permitted maximum load of 172kg (380lb) and a 21m (70ft) long cable. Although the Dragonfly offered a significant advantage in SAR and established the helicopter in this role it had severe limitations. Its cruise speed was only 137kph (85mph) and in any strong head wind progress was slow; still air range with twenty minutes fuel reserves was 400km (248 miles). Despite the fact that it was classed as a four-seater and only carried a crew of two, the Mk 1 could only rescue one person at a time; later a fuel dumping modification permitted two people to be rescued on a single flight but with the penalty of reduced range. Rescues at night or in very bad weather were extremely difficult as the Dragonfly had no true instrument flying capability or automatic flight control system.

The RAF were not far behind the Royal Navy. As we have already seen, the anti-terrorist campaign in Malaya was the catalyst with an urgent demand for three helicopters to be in that country by the autumn of 1949 to form a Far East Casualty Evacuation Flight. Whose idea this originally was has been lost in the mists of time, but Lady Mountbatten can take some credit: returning to the UK after a visit to Malaya in 1948 she pressed the case strongly for medical evacuation by helicopter. It was in fact impossible to meet the 1949 deadline, but the Navy agreed that after their first six Dragonflies had been delivered the RAF could have the next three off the production line. At a production rate of four aircraft a month the RAF received their three Mk 2 in March 1950 after which they were shipped immediately to RAF Seletar in Singapore. By the end of April they were ready to fly and undertake operational trials. The Far East Casualty Evacuation Flight was formed on 1 May under the command of Flight Lieutenant Ken Fry and was therefore the first operational British helicopter unit.

It was agreed that helicopter pilots flying in the Far East should have at least 100 helicopter flying hours. In the RAF there were only four such pilots and one was about to leave the Service. The remaining three formed the Flight initially, but one of these was not permitted to fly operationally in helicopters fitted with radio – and then there were two! The search for pilots with just 50 hours on helicopters began and at one stage this limit was reduced to 25 hours.

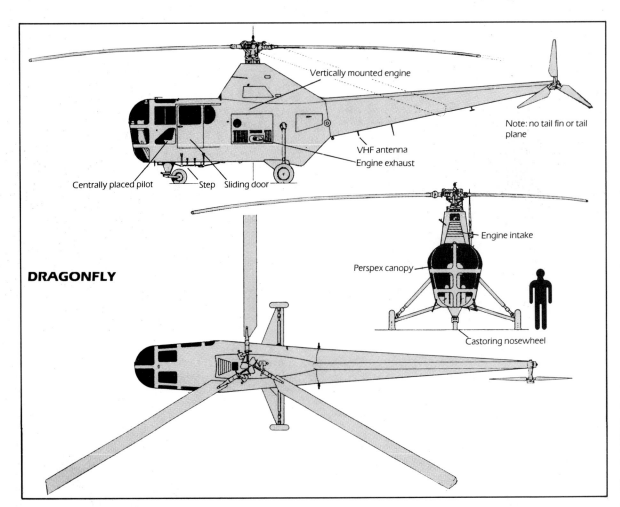

DRAGONFLY

Vertically mounted engine

VHF antenna

Engine exhaust

Note: no tail fin or tail plane

Centrally placed pilot

Step

Sliding door

Engine intake

Perspex canopy

Castoring nosewheel

Such was the level of inexperience that it was not thought that the tropical conditions would have much effect on flight performance. Little thought was given to the problems that might be associated with tropical weather, high temperatures and humidity, high-lying terrain and small clearings surrounded by tall trees. Since only the first few Dragonflies would operate in Malaya where the climate was considered to be comparable to very hot weather in England (!), Ministry of Supply advice was that full tropical clearance would not be needed initially. A full world-wide clearance would be needed in due course, however. In Malaya the normal maximum operating weight was limited so that a vertical take-off and climb to 55m (180ft) AGL out of a jungle clearing could be achieved. Occasionally this meant that fuel was restricted to only 30 minutes' flying time and the payload to 91kg (200lb), i.e., one passenger/casualty, when a hover out of ground effect was unavoidable. The aim, however, was always to have fuel for two hours in case bad weather forced a diversion or a reduction in speed. Refuelling generally was not a problem as fuel in cans was dumped at sites throughout the country. Centre of gravity problems were frequent and for any major weight changes in the cabin the centre of gravity had to be moved by re-locating lead weights – a laborious business at best and impossible when the aircraft could not land because of the terrain. Theoretically, the Dragonfly was flown solo with six weights positioned in front of the instrument panel. For every passenger carried two weights were supposed to be moved aft. In practical terms this procedure was largely ignored because the aircraft had to be shut down while moving the weights there being no crewmen to do the job; the result was that usually only two weights were carried, both ahead of the pilot. Not surprisingly there was a penalty; without forward ballast the pilot could quickly reach the forward limits of cyclic stick travel. In turbulent conditions the nose would rise and power would have to be reduced to lower it. Continual juggling with the manual throttle was thus necessary to maintain a reasonable forward speed and constant rotor rpm. All these factors, the heat and humidity, vibration and the uncomfortable cockpit contributed greatly to pilot fatigue.

To carry lying casualties the panniers designed in the UK and mounted on each side of the fuselage (and which together weighed 95kg (210lb)) were discarded in favour of a 16kg (35lb) wicker basket, designed and manufactured locally. This was inserted athwartships in the cabin, although about 0.6m (2ft) of it was left projecting through the open doorway.

Bad weather, particularly heavy rain, restricted the Dragonfly's operations. It was simply not easy to fly in such rain as the curvature of the canopy did not permit the fitting of windscreen wipers. Flight speed was reduced, typically, to 48kph (30mph). With virtually no forward visibility this at least allowed a useful view of the ground and check points. Globules of water would sometimes stick to the canopy and it would be necessary to yaw the aircraft from side to side to remove them. An artificial horizon was fitted at the top of the instrument panel to assist in flying level in heavy rain and eventually an area of canopy perspex in front of the pilot was treated with water repellent. The fabric-covered rotor blades, nominally with a 1,000 hour life, rarely averaged more than 100 hours before the fabric began to lift. The blade problem was overcome when the first of nine Mk 4 arrived at Seletar in September 1952. Nevertheless, serviceability in the exacting climatic conditions in Malaya was remarkably good – better, paradoxically, when the aircraft were left out overnight on operations than when housed in a hangar when condensation was the main problem.

The first casualty evacuation took place on 14 June 1950 when a soldier, shot in the foot, was lifted out of a waterlogged light aircraft strip. One helicopter was always on immediate stand-by to extract battle casualties or sick men from the jungle. Such a service not only increased morale but offered the added advantage of removing casualties from a patrol so that it could continue its task, its mobility having been restored. It was not long before many other uses for helicopters were found. Well-trained troops can exist and fight in the jungle for weeks at a time; it is their support in terms of combat supplies, ammunition, radio batteries and so on which is difficult. Movement through the jungle can be very slow and arduous – the helicopter was the answer. As a light communications vehicle it was invaluable for the carriage of commanders visiting sub-units and patrols in the jungle, for carrying desperately needed supplies and to assist in the 'hearts and minds' campaign; on one occasion refrigerated vaccine was flown into a remote village when the occupants were found to be suffering from TB. Some chronically sick people were flown out.

Intelligence, naturally, was a key element in the struggle and it was vital to interrogate captured and surrendered terrorists as quickly as possible. Patrols did not have trained Chinese-speaking interrogators and so questioning sometimes could not take place for days thus precluding any effective follow-up operations. The helicopter changed all this and was frequently used to fly out the captured or surrendered and also dead terrorists for quick identification and examination of any documents carried. When the policy of denying food to the terrorists forced them to grow their own in the jungle the Dragonfly was used to destroy their

Left: A Royal Navy Dragonfly Mk 3, WG 706, crashes into the sea close to HMS *Glory* on 16 December 1952 while carrying out plane guard duties off the Korean coast. (FAA Museum)

crops by means of spraying them with a strong weed-killer. Operating over terrorist territory the helicopter was highly vulnerable on these sorties but they were often preceded by ground attack Hornets making strafing runs.

Reconnaissance over the jungle is very difficult, but helicopters, with their ability to fly slowly, were used occasionally for this task as their numbers grew; fixed-wing Austers were the normal reconnaissance aircraft. Peering through the jungle canopy a pilot could expect to get no more than a fleeting glimpse of what appeared to be a cleared area of the jungle floor. With luck he might see a hut or shelter which might confirm the existence of a camp. In circling the area to pinpoint the position on his map and to obtain confirmation, the pilot would undoubtedly alert any terrorists present and cause them to melt away into the jungle. Searching for crashed aircraft also absorbed flying hours and was, perhaps surprisingly, equally difficult.

The Dragonfly was too small to be used regularly for troop-lifting, but when a journey which might take five days on foot took only twenty minutes by air the temptation was always there to 'misuse' it in this role. On one occasion Flight Lieutenant John Dowling extracted twelve soldiers, a civilian reporter, a captured terrorist and a tracker dog from a very small clearing cut in a jungle swamp. The troops had been in the jungle for 29 days, were exhausted and sick, and threatened by terrorists. Fourteen times Dowling went in to lift them all out, one by one. For this and other feats he was awarded the DFC.

The final Dragonfly sortie in Malaya was flown in June 1956, some two years after the Casualty Evacuation Flight had been absorbed by 194 (Helicopter) Squadron with fourteen aircraft. The Dragonfly was finally withdrawn from service in the RAF in May 1962.

A number of naval squadrons and flights operated the Dragonfly, the last one being withdrawn from Royal Navy service in June 1967. In seventeen years it had given sterling service and taken part in some events which had captured the world's headlines. The two best-known were the fight for survival of the US steamer *Flying Enterprise* in January 1952 and the flooding in the Netherlands in February 1953. On the first occasion two Dragonflies were despatched to rescue the Captain and his Mate but neither was able to reach the stricken vessel, one through unserviceability and the other because a very low cloud base and 96kph (60mph) winds forced it to turn back. The fact that the Dragonfly was able to fly at all in such weather was a surprise to many. As heavy seas breached the dykes of the Dutch coast all available Dragonflies from 705 Squadron, Boscombe Down and Westland undertook a two and a half weeks' operation during which more than 800 people were rescued. One Dragonfly carried

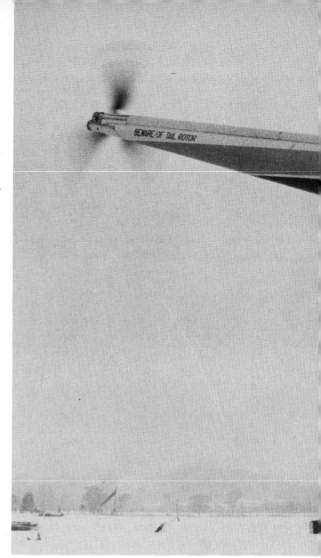

Above: In 1955 Westland introduced the Widgeon, a Dragonfly conversion with a re-designed cabin. (Westland Helicopters)

seven waterlogged people in a single lift; 64 were winched from rooftops. Just a month later, on 26/27 May, HRH The Duke of Edinburgh made the first helicopter flight by a member of the Royal Family when he flew in a Dragonfly on a visit to military units in West Germany. At the time of the Coronation in June 1953 twelve Dragonflies led the massed flypast in the Royal Naval Coronation Review at Spithead. In September 1955 a Dragonfly, based on the survey ship HMS *Vidal*, was used in the annexation of the Island of Rockall in the North Atlantic off the West coast of Scotland. The climb to the top of the precipitous rock to erect a flagpole would have been supremely difficult, if not impossible, on foot.

In Malaya, along the coasts and at sea, the Dragonfly pioneered new helicopter rescue techniques and saved many lives. In carrying out other tasks, particularly in

Malaya, it had proved that the helicopter had progressed from being an experimental machine to an operational one.

Widgeon

The extra 70hp in the Westland-built Dragonfly meant that, in temperate climates at least, a greater payload could be lifted and by a certain redesign of the fuselage the ever-present centre of gravity problems might be solved. After much study and the examination of a number of options it was decided by Westland to go ahead as a private venture on a project to upgrade substantially the Dragonfly's capabilities. The opportunity was taken simultaneously to embody some other quite radical modifications. The new machine was to have a new name: the Widgeon.

The most obvious change was the shape of the front fuselage. This was completely new, had five seats and could take two stretchers internally. A clamshell door on the port side of the nose facilitated stretcher loading. The new, and more pleasing, shape allowed for the pilot and passenger to sit side-by-side with three passengers sitting behind on a bench.

The Dragonfly's rotor head was dispensed with and instead the Whirlwind's, suitably modified, was adopted. Rather than have centre-line hinges similar to the Dragonfly, this head had offset flapping hinges, which were more efficient and which expanded the centre of gravity range, thus eliminating the tiresome ballasting arrangements. The main rotor blades were all-metal while the three-bladed tail rotor was of laminated wood construction. The machine was offered as a multi-role helicopter, capable of rapid role conversion from passenger-carrying to air ambulance, to freighter with a 454kg (1,000lb) external load, to rescue aircraft with a hydraulically operated winch. It could be used for ASW, and for overwater flights inflatable pontoons were available. The load of 454kg (1,000lb) could be transported over 190km (118 miles) or 288kg (635lb) could be moved over the maximum range of 480km (298 miles); four passengers could be flown 440km (273 miles) or three passengers over the full range. Although this payload/range was better than that of the Dragonfly it was not a big enough improvement to encourage the conversion of many Dragonflies to Widgeon standard.

The first Widgeon to fly was a converted Dragonfly Mk 1A. It made its maiden flight on 23 August 1955 and during the next two days ten more hours were flown so as to permit display at the imminent SBAC Show. Two other Dragonflies were converted to Widgeon standard and twelve were built new; the programme ended in 1959. This was perhaps partly because of the introduction of the Westland-built WS-55 Whirlwind in 1954 with its altogether greater capacity and performance. Indeed, certainly in retrospect, the prospects for the Widgeon could never have been very bright given the quest for greater capabilities and the appearance of the French Alouette 2 which flew with a turbine engine for the first time on 12 March 1955. Even before the Widgeon had flown, the Alouette 2 had set a new world altitude record of 8,209m (26,932ft).

None the less, two Widgeons, equipped with loud-hailers, were used in Hong Kong for crowd control and of five bought by Bristow Helicopters Ltd, four were employed on oil exploration in the Persian Gulf. The

Brazilian Navy ordered three while the Jordanian Air Force took one. Operated by Sabena World Airlines, yet another provided a local service round Brussels during the 1958 World Fair and a further one was used in Japan for electrical installation work.

Potentially the most exciting development – sadly to come to nothing – was a requirement to convert 24 Dragonflies to Widgeon standard for the Royal Navy. The designation was intended to be the Dragonfly Mk 7. In September 1957 Specification HCC.188P was issued by which time the first Dragonfly had already been sent off to Westland for conversion. But it was a short-lived affair, falling foul of a Government savings exercise before the end of the year.

WS-55 Whirlwind

The maiden flight of the Sikorsky S-55 took place on 10 November 1949, an auspicious day given that almost 1,800 copies were subsequently built by five different manufacturers. It had been patently obvious for some time that the bigger a helicopter's payload the more useful it would be and it did not take Westland long to

Below: The attractive appearance of the Widgeon was not enough to generate many orders; three Dragonflies were converted and only twelve new Widgeons built. (Westland Helicopters)

Opposite page: The small clamshell nose door of the Widgeon permitted easy loading of two stretchers. (Westland Helicopters)

expand their agreement with Sikorsky to include the licence-building of the S-55. Negotiations began in June 1950 and the licence was issued on 15 November that same year. Exports to other countries were permitted. In order to get an early start at examining the problems of 'anglicization', Westland bought a single Sikorsky-built S-55 in 1950. It was delivered in May 1951 and flew the following month. In addition, 25 Sikorsky-built S-55 were purchased for the Royal Navy as part of the Mutual Defence Aid Programme: ten HAR Mk 21 for rescue and general duties and 15 HAS Mk 22 equipped with a short-range active dunking sonar, the American AN/AQS-4, for ASW. These aircraft adopted the name Whirlwind, the first ten reaching Portsmouth by sea on 20 November 1952. The Mk 21, operated by 848 Squadron RN, found themselves in Malaya in January 1953, supplementing the few RAF helicopters in that country. 706 Squadron formed as a trials squadron in September 1953 as the Mk 22 arrived and was promptly despatched to Northern Ireland whence it was easier to exercise with submarines. As a result of these trials 706 Squadron was disbanded and 845 Squadron formed on 1 March 1954 with eight Mk 22 – and moved to Malta.

Much thought had gone into the design of the S-55 and the eventual result was a shape quite unlike that of any previous helicopter. The central issue had been how to carry a decent payload, in this instance the S-55 was required to carry 1,270kg (2,800lb), in a helicopter with a single main rotor. Because lift has to be applied close to the centre of gravity, i.e., the centre line of the main rotor, the load and fuel must be located in much the same place. It followed that a cabin of some size was needed and that this had to be under the rotor so that variations in the load would have virtually no effect on the centre of gravity. With only bulky piston engines available, the next question was where to put the engine. The answer was in the nose, at an inclined angle, which gave the added bonus, as far as servicing was concerned, of being at a height requiring no ladders or let-down platforms; the engine was made accessible to technicians by means of two clamshell doors. The fuel tank was placed under the floor of the cabin. The only place left for the crew was above and behind the bulbous nose, sitting side-by-side, with the drive shaft passing diagonally up between them to the gearbox under the hub. This hub was little more than a larger version of the R-5 hub with an offset flapping hinge to allow greater freedom in the centre of gravity position.

Three Series of Whirlwind were built. They were referred to by their Series number (1, 2 or 3) by civil operators and, more specifically, by Mark numbers by military operators:

– Series 1: Mks 1 to 4, with American piston engines.

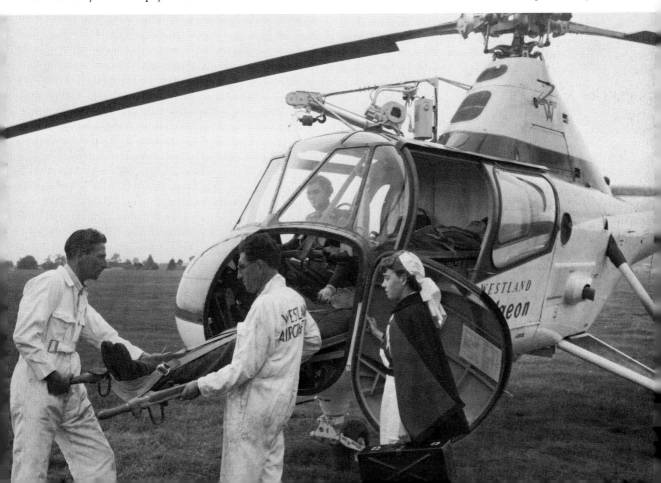

- Series 2: Mks 5, 7 and 8, with British piston engines.
- Series 3: Mks 9, 10 and 12, with British shaft turbine engines.

The Series 1, built at Yeovil, differed little from the Sikorsky-built versions. The first hovering tests started on 12 November 1952. Extraordinarily, the first full flight did not take place until some ten months later – on 15 August 1953. The intervening time was consumed by transmission tests which had to be undertaken on this first aircraft while tied-down, there being no suitable test rig. Ten HAR Mk 1 for the Royal Navy and, initially, ten HAR Mk 2 for RAF Transport and Coastal Commands, both with a 600hp Pratt & Whitney Wasp R-1340-40 engine, were built. The Navy did not receive its helicopters until July 1954 while the RAF took delivery of its first Mk 2 the following month.

Five Mk 1 were despatched to Malaya in September and October 1954 to support the Mk 21 of 848 Squadron, but their performance was so poor that they were returned to the UK less than a year later. In October 1955 HMS Protector, converted for duties in the Antarctic, sailed southwards with two Mk 1; for the next ten consecutive winters Mk 1 visited the Antarctic until replaced by two Mk 9 in 1966. The base for these patrols was normally the Falkland Islands. The Whirlwinds themselves were given the best radio and navigation fits available and, additionally, they had flotation gear installed. A handful of Mk 2 soon found themselves in Malaya where they turned out to be a huge disappointment. Designed as a troop-carrying helicopter with space for ten men, they could frequently take no more than two. The effects of the Malayan climate had again been underestimated.

Twenty-seven Mk 3, roughly equivalent to the HAS Mk 22, were then built for the Navy with a more powerful 700hp Wright R-1300-3 Cyclone engine. These aircraft were intended to take over from the Dragonfly on plane guard duties aboard aircraft carriers and this role was assumed from September 1955. The Mk 3 served aboard HMSs Albion, Ark Royal, Bulwark, Eagle, Victorious and Warrior. For the RAF many Mk 2 were converted to HAR Mk 4 standard with a 600hp Pratt & Whitney R-1340-57 Wasp engine. The supercharger ratio of the Wasp, however, was increased from 10:1 to 12:1 and this offered a much needed improvement in flight performance in tropical conditions over the Mk 2 although it was still by no means really satisfactory. It is a matter of some surprise, though, that the Mk 4 did not have the 700hp engine. This may have been because it was heavy and because the Mk 3 had been a disappointment compared to the Navy's Mk 21.

Some of the Series 1 aircraft were flown by BEA, notably on the experimental passenger service between Heathrow and London's South Bank which began on 25 July 1955. Large floats were fitted in case of an emergency landing in the Thames. Trials with long

silencers took place before the service started but they were not retained.

The Whirlwind appeared large, standing 4.03m (13ft 2½in) high and with a fuselage length of 12.7m (41ft 8½in). A single sliding door was on the starboard side and the distinctive stabilizer at the tail had pronounced anhedral. The three-bladed all-metal main rotor had a diameter of 16.1m (53ft). Because the pod and boom semi-monocoque fuselage was of light alloy the empty weight of the Mk 1 was only 2,398kg (5,287lb) and maximum take-off weight only 3,402kg (7,500lb). A standard twist-grip throttle and duplicate hydraulically assisted cyclic and collective controls were provided. The hydraulic systems were by no means 'total' and failures occurred at which time great skill and some strength were needed to fly in manual control. Later modifications only eased the problem slightly. A winch, similar to the Dragonfly's, was fitted to these early versions, but it was barely adequate because the boom to which it was attached was too low and this made it difficult to swing the person being lifted into the cabin. A raised boom was designed by a Royal Navy officer, Lieutenant-Commander Sproule, and later installed in all Royal Navy marks of Whirlwind. An electrically controlled removable hoist was fitted to the Mks 7 and 9. The cabin was 1.83m (6ft) wide by 3.05m (10ft) long by 1.5m (5ft) high and could accommodate seven civilian passengers or, because they are permitted less comfort, ten fully armed soldiers; six stretchers could be installed. The Series 1 Whirlwind was thus a great improvement on the Dragonfly as far as load carrying in temperate climates was concerned; flight performance was slightly better.

As with the Dragonfly, the anglicizing of the Whirlwind was not an easy task and was at first underestimated. Almost every part of the helicopter was affected to a greater or lesser degree and this was to have profound implications in Malaya later. Because British parts were used, which in some cases were heavier than their American equivalents, the British Whirlwind was some 5 per cent heavier than the S-55 and this naturally affected the payload/range and, critically, vertical rate of climb. To make matters much worse the fuel system was re-designed and this resulted in about 182 litres (40Imp gall) being unusable. Anglicization was taken further when it was decided to replace the American engine with a more powerful British Alvis Leonides Major, a decision brought about by the very poor performance of the Series 1 aircraft in Malaya. This engine and various modifications would enable the Whirlwind to carry a torpedo, thus solving the mismatch problem of submarine detection by helicopter and later destruction by ship if one were available. Besides the new (derated) 750hp engine, the only modifications were to the engine-bay doors and to the tail boom which was given 3° of droop to enhance

Above: Although apparently belonging to the Army, this Whirlwind Mk 2 was actually on the strength of the Joint Experimental Helicopter Unit during the second half of the 1950s. It was later converted to a Mk 10 and found its way to Cyprus where it served in United Nations colours before being retired in 1982. In this photograph it is air-lifting an Auster Mk 6. (Westland Helicopters)

main rotor blade clearance; the stabilizer lost its anhedral. Only one HAR Mk 5 was built in 1955 although three aircraft at one time or another were claimed to be of this type.

Two Mk 3 were taken from the production line and fitted with an Alvis Leonides Major engine for trials purposes; they could perhaps be called prototype Mk 5, but they were later re-engined with the Gnome gas turbine, thus forfeiting their Mk 5 tag. The only other Mk 5 actually started life as a Mk 6 with a French Twin Turmo engine, built under licence by Blackburn, in Westland's first attempt to convert the Whirlwind to turbine power. It did not succeed, the project being cancelled in 1956 and the aircraft being re-engined with an Alvis Leonides engine. Most of the development work for this engine was actually undertaken on production Mk 7. The new installation was not without its problems, particularly with regard to cooling, and these delayed the introduction into service of the Mk 7. Even then this version was plagued by a series of engine failures in its early years. It was, nevertheless, the HAS Mk 7 that was to become the definitive Series 2 version with 129 being built.

Ordered as an ASW helicopter for operation from carriers to replace Gannet fixed-wing aircraft, the Mk 7 flew for the first time on 17 October 1956. It had the same engine as the Mk 5, but in addition, radar and the anglicized version of the AN/AQS-4 dunking sonar for submarine detection. Other Mk 7 carried a lightweight homing torpedo, the Mk 30 to start with and eventually the Mk 44, or bombs or depth-charges in a ventral weapons bay for submarine attack; this bay was only made possible by re-positioning the under floor fuel tanks. The Mk 7 was the first British helicopter to become operational in the ASW role when 845 Squadron RN completed its work-up in August 1957. It had eight aircraft, having turned in its Mk 22. In January 1958 all eight aircraft had to be returned because of engine problems and another eight were issued. Indeed, between April and November 1959, all Mk 7 were grounded except for essential flights so that modifications to the engine and transmission could be carried out. Indeed the loss rate within the two ASW training squadrons was alarmingly high by today's standards. The story is told, perhaps apocryphally, that a diver was sent down to examine a ditched Whirlwind only to find one lying on top of another. The life of the Mk 7 as an ASW helicopter was in fact short-lived, the six front-line squadrons converting to the Wessex Mk 1 in the early 1960s. At much the same time the carriers' ship's flights began to replace their Mk 3 with Mk 7.

In October 1959, 848 Squadron re-equipped with the Mk 7 but with the ASW gear removed so that up to eight Royal Marine (RM) Commandos could be accommodated instead. 846 and 847 Squadrons followed suit as Commando squadrons although 847 remained at RNAS Culdrose for training and test purposes. The Mk 7 of 848 Squadron participated in the Kuwaiti crisis of July 1961 when they were used to land a large number of Commandos close to the Iraqi border when that country moved troops forward in support of a territorial claim on Kuwait. During 1963 and 1964 846 Squadron's Mk 7 were in Brunei and Sarawak helping to fend off Indonesian cross-border attacks. They filled the gap between Army light aircraft and the bigger Wessex and Belvedere, thus conserving flying hours. Because of uncertain reliability they often flew in pairs on specific transit routes for safety reasons. As with all helicopters operating in Borneo, these Mk 7 flew many thousands of hours over mountainous and

Top: Three Whirlwind Mk 3 on El Gamil airfield during the Port Said operations in November 1956. Parachute debris can be seen in the fore-ground. (Museum of Army Flying)

Above: A Whirlwind Mk 7 of 848 Squadron RN flies low level along a river in Borneo. (FAA Museum)

inhospitable terrain with unreliable weather forecasts, totally inadequate maps and little in the way of ground-based aids. Low cloud in the early morning and torrential rain in the afternoon cut visibility drastically and made flying very hazardous for much of the time.

The Mk 7 was finally withdrawn from service in the Royal Navy in August 1975 although some continued in other establishments beyond this date. One, for example, was on the strength of the Joint Helicopter Tactical Development Unit at Old Sarum, near Salisbury until July 1976; it (XN 299) was known affectionately as the 'Iron Chicken'.

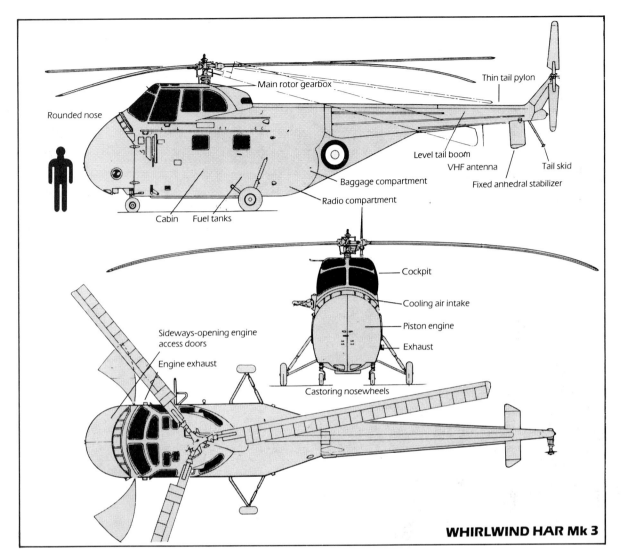

Rounded nose

Main rotor gearbox

Thin tail pylon

Level tail boom

VHF antenna

Tail skid

Fixed anhedral stabilizer

Baggage compartment

Radio compartment

Cabin   Fuel tanks

Cockpit

Cooling air intake

Piston engine

Exhaust

Sideways-opening engine
access doors

Engine exhaust

Castoring nosewheels

WHIRLWIND HAR Mk 3

The final version in the Series 2 was just two HCC Mk 8 aircraft built in the 4/7 seat configuration for the Queen's Flight. The engine was a 740hp Alvis Leonides Major 160. It is interesting to note that, despite being only too well aware of the shortcomings of the Mks 2 and 4, the RAF decided not to procure any Series 2 versions with British engines although considerable pressure to do so was applied. It proved to be a wise decision.

On 17 May 1957 Westland flew a Sikorsky S-58 with a gas turbine engine. This proved to be such a success that it was decided to re-engine the Whirlwind once more and give it a lighter and more powerful turbine engine which would provide a much improved performance and enhanced reliability and flight safety. The decision was taken in 1958 and the second prototype Mk 5 was converted to take an American General Electric T-58 turboshaft; this aircraft became the prototype for the Series 3, flying for the first time on 28

February 1959. The conversion was kept as simple as possible with the turbine mounted in the nose so that it could use the existing transmission. The lengthening of the nose itself and the large circular exhaust were conspicuous, but there was no other obvious external difference to the Series 2.

Bristol Siddeley now built the 1,050shp Gnome H.1000, a licence-built version of the T-58, and this was installed for trials in a Whirlwind in September 1959. It weighed less than 181kg (400lb), less than half the weight of the piston engine it replaced. It could use kerosene rather than the usual high-octane aviation gasoline. Significantly the aircraft's power-to-weight ratio was improved to 1:7.6 compared to the Mk 1's 1:12.5. Following the successful conclusion of the trials a large order for Gnome-engined HAR Mk 10 for the RAF was announced in April 1960. These comprised some new machines and some Series 1 and 2 aircraft upgraded to Series 3. The first Mk 10 flew in the Spring

Above: Two Royal Navy Whirlwind Mk 3 fly over the Royal Mosque in Brunei. (FAA Museum)

Opposite page, top: A different environment: a Mk 7 takes off from a desert site in the Aden Protectorate in 1961. (Avia)

Opposite page, bottom: Originally a Mk 7, this aircraft was converted to a Mk 9. (Westland Helicopters)

of 1961 with deliveries to 225 Squadron of RAF Transport Command beginning in November 1961. These aircraft could carry four Nord AS-11 anti-tank missiles on twin launchers on each side of the fuselage. Firing trials were completed in the Summer of 1962. Twin 7.7mm (.303in) Browning machine-guns were also tested. More Mk 10 went to Coastal Command in February 1962 to be used for SAR. The last one was retired from active SAR duties on 30 November 1981.

Operationally, the Mk 10 gained its laurels in Malaya and Borneo. Like the Belvedere and Wessex it was essential for the movement of men and supplies over the jungle. The versatility of these helicopters prompted Air Vice-Marshal Foxley-Norris, the Commander of 224 Group, to write: 'The Borneo campaign was a classic example of the lesson that the side which uses air power most efficiently to defeat the jungle will also defeat the enemy.'

Some truly outstanding and dramatic rescues at sea were achieved by RAF Whirlwinds. Representative of these was the reaction to the sinking of the oil rig Sea Gem in December 1966. A Whirlwind from 202 Squadron at RAF Leconfield in Yorkshire was scrambled in mid-afternoon and battled its way through snow flurries and strong winds to the scene. Two ships were already taking on survivors and the Whirlwind began to search for those still in the water. Sergeant Leon Smith manoeuvred the helicopter down to about 9m (30ft) and held it steady in the gale. As soon as the first survivor was located Flight Sergeant John Reeson, the winchman, was lowered. In the heavy seas Reeson had great difficulty in getting the rescue strop round the survivor but he eventually managed to do so. The two

men were winched up and Smith then inched his way across to one of the ships. Great skill was required as Smith came in very close to lower Reeson and the survivor on to the pitching deck. They became entangled in some rigging but Reeson freed them, deposited the survivor on the deck and was himself winched back into the helicopter. Another person was discovered in the water and again Reeson went down. Another struggle ensued with the survivor, panic-stricken, making his own rescue even more difficult. The debris and oily water complicated matters, but Reeson eventually succeeded in getting both of them into the helicopter and the survivor subsequently transferred to one of the ships. Reeson, having swallowed a quantity of oily water, was now being sick which added to his exhaustion. Nevertheless, he went down yet again on the winch when another man was sighted. He, however, was unconscious and trapped in the wreckage and Reeson was too weak to free him. Flight Lieutenant John Hill, the navigator, brought Reeson up and went down on the winch himself. A momentous struggle followed as Hill did all he could to disentangle the survivor and get the strop around him while the oily water foamed and thrashed about and over both of them. He succeeded finally but the man died not many minutes later as the helicopter sped back to land. For their supreme efforts Reeson was awarded the George

Medal, Hill the AFC and Smith the Queen's Commendation for Valuable Services in the Air.

The RAF led the way in converting to the Series 3. The Navy followed by converting some of their Mk 7 to HAR Mk 9 standard with the same Gnome engine, starting in September 1964; the first flight of the production Mk 9 took place on 15 October 1965. These aircraft were to be used for training, rescue and general duties; the first entered service in 1966. They were based mainly at Royal Navy Air Stations in the UK but HMSs *Protector* and *Endurance* were each equipped with a Mk 9 for ice patrol duties in the Antarctic. The Mk 9 remained in service until April 1977.

There was no Mk 11, but again two HCC Mk 12 were produced for the Queen's Flight.

The advantages of the turbine engine were numerous besides simplifying the business of flying. The most important, perhaps, was the vastly improved power-to-weight ratio; that it was also smaller, lighter and required no cooling were added bonuses. Indeed, 347kg (765lb) were saved. The excess power indicated that the degradation in flight performance at high-density altitudes would be much less than previously. The Gnome engine came with a new electronic control, developed by Lucas in place of the Hamilton Standard control system, which had the effect of maintaining a constant free turbine speed despite power demands. The Mk 10 was therefore the first RAF helicopter in which rotor rpm were controlled automatically rather than by the pilot with his twist-grip throttle.

The Series 3 was lighter when empty than either the earlier Series yet had a 227kg (500lb) greater maximum take-off weight than the Series 1, thus giving a substantial increase in payload. Economic cruise speed for the Series 3 was 29kph (18mph) faster than the previous Series aircraft, and rate of climb, hovering and service ceilings were all better; range for the Series 3, however, was between 32 and 56km (20 and 35 miles) less than the Series 1 and 2. Series 3 production ended in the spring of 1969.

Besides the military duties described, civil Whirlwinds were used for a wide variety of tasks: whaling, assisting in the exploration for oil and acting as airborne cranes using their cargo hooks. The BEA passenger service absorbed some machines for a time while others were engaged in crop-spraying and, equipped with loud-hailers, in crowd control. Bristow

Opposite page, top left: A Whirlwind Mk 8 of the Queen's Flight at the AAC Centre, Middle Wallop in 1965. (Author)

Opposite page, bottom left: An RAF Whirlwind Mk 10 practises winching drills. (Rolls-Royce)

Top left: Whirlwind Mk 10 participating in operations in Borneo in the 1960s. (Avia)

Bottom left: A Mk 10 flies over the Malayan jungle. This version of the Whirlwind was the first to have a turbine engine. (Avia)

Helicopters Ltd at one time operated eighteen Series 3 machines. For a time during the 1970s one machine provided a search and rescue service in the Dover Straits; in 1972, for example, 83 people were rescued.

The Whirlwind's military service life extended over 25 years during which time it proved its great versatility and displayed its undisputed shortcomings. Useful lessons concerning ASW were learned: for example, autostabilization was necessary because without it pilots found it extremely difficult to maintain the steady and precise hover so important for sonar operations. Only six Mk 22 were fitted with an autopilot for trials purposes. With limited navigation aids the helicopter could not stray far from its mother ship. Despite these shortcomings, the Whirlwind was a satisfactory platform from which to develop ASW doctrine. It was a Mk 3 which carried out the first trials of vertical replenishment (Vertrep) in February 1962 between HMS *Victorious* and the Royal Fleet Auxiliary *Resurgent*. These trials confirmed the concept and demonstrated the need for stronger cargo hooks and certain design changes in future RFAs to permit Vertrep. Four Mk 3 formed part of the ship's flight of HMS *Warrior* in mid 1956 when the first British hydrogen bomb tests took place off Christmas Island in the Pacific. They were used as plane guards for the Avengers on board and for general transport duties. In 1955 a Mk 1 took part in somewhat inconclusive trials of helicopter minesweeping.

In the Malayan jungle the Navy's US-built Mk 22 was able to carry only four combat-equipped troops and so was employed on casualty evacuation duties and small-scale troop movements. The first RAF Whirlwind squadron was 155 which formed at Kuala Lumpur in September 1954 with Mk 4 with a view to relieving 848 Squadron RN. 155 Squadron was originally intended for troop-lift, but because the Mk 4 were limited by the climatic conditions to carrying only two combat-equipped soldiers, the Squadron was unable to assume this role in any useful sense for another eight months when certain modifications to the aircraft had been completed. These included changes to the fuel system to reduce fuel tank weight and the amount of unusable fuel, and increasing the supercharger ratio from 10:1 to 12:1; another step taken to increase payload was to remove as much on-board equipment as possible, e.g., doors and some cowlings. While the modifications were being embodied the Mk 4 remained a disappointment: with a cabin large enough to take ten men it could not, in fact, even match the Sycamore in payload and was hardly better than the Dragonfly!

As the Emergency began to peter out in the second half of 1955 the Mk 4 became available for troop-lift, being used successfully from time to time in this role and for parachute operations by the 22nd Special Air Service (SAS) Regiment and Jungle Rescue Teams. When dropping into a confined space with static line,

as opposed to today's steerable parachute, it was easier for a patrol to jump from a helicopter moving at about 33kph (22mph) because the distance covered by the helicopter between each exit was comparatively short and therefore separation on the ground was equally short. In August 1957 a Valetta crashed into the jungle in central Malaya and fortunately was found by an Auster. A Far East Air Force Jungle Rescue Team and a SAS rescue team were then flown to an appropriate area close to the site in a Whirlwind and parachuted into the trees. Within two hours all members of the twelve-man team had reached the wreckage. The aircrew had died, but the four Army despatchers had survived and were found some way away. A helicopter landing site was prepared using plastic explosives and mechanical saws supplied by helicopter parachute drop and by midday on the third day it was possible for a Sycamore to inch its way into the site to extract the survivors.

Despite the inadequacy of the Series 1 Whirlwind, the Navy's experience in Malaya convinced the Naval Staff and the Royal Marines that helicopters could be used profitably for amphibious operations. The Army and RAF also recognized their value and established the Joint Experimental Helicopter Unit at Middle Wallop on 1 April 1955 to examine the tactical employment of helicopters and to pioneer new helicopter techniques for land operations. A year later six Whirlwind Mk 2 joined the six Sycamores in the Unit.

Operation 'Musketeer', the assault on Port Said in November 1956, confirmed the belief that the helicopter was a suitable Commando carrier when Sycamore Mk 14 and Whirlwind Mk 22 and 3 carried 45 Commando RM ashore from two fixed-wing light Fleet carriers. This successful use of helicopters was to have a considerable influence on naval policy: the value of the Commando carrier was readily appreciated and action quickly taken. HMS *Bulwark* was the first light Fleet carrier to be converted to a Commando carrier and she was commissioned in mid 1959.

The ubiquitous employment of the Whirlwind round the world, starting with the disappointments of the early versions and ending with the much more effective Mks 9 and 10, testified to the success of its basic design philosophy. The incorporation of a turbine engine into the later versions was a most significant and important step for the future – both in terms of performance and pilot handling.

By the mid 1950s Westland had firmly established themselves as the largest helicopter manufacturer in Europe, but it was a title they were later to surrender to S.N.I.A.S., now commonly known as Aérospatiale, of France.

Right: A Series 3 Whirlwind operated by Bristow Helicopters Ltd during the 1970s for SAR in the Dover Straits. (Westland Helicopters)

DRAGONFLY, WIDGEON AND WHIRLWIND TYPES AND VARIANTS

WS-51 DRAGONFLY: 139 built
HR Mk 1: Westland-built Sikorsky S-51 4-seat utility helicopter for air-sea rescue; 13 built for Royal Navy. First flight (FF) 22 June 1949.
HC Mk 2: Similar to Mk 1 for casualty evacuation; 4 built for RAF.
HR Mk 3: Similar to Mk 1 but with larger rotor and all-metal blades; 58 built, 50 for Royal Navy.
HC Mk 4: As for Mk 3; 12 built for RAF.
HR Mk 5: Upgraded Mk 3; all conversions from Mks 1 and 3.
Mk 1A: Commercial version with Alvis Leonides engine; 47 built of which at least 24 were used by foreign military forces. FF 5 October 1948.
Mk 1B: Commercial version with Pratt & Whitney engine; 5 built.
Foreign Users: Belgian Congo (3), Ceylon (2), Egypt (2), France (9), Iraq (2), Italy (3), Japan (5), Thailand (3), Yugoslavia (10).
WIDGEON: Much modified and different-shaped version of the Dragonfly; 3 Dragonflies converted and 12 new built. FF 23 August 1955.
Foreign Users: Brazil (3). Hong Kong (2), Japan (1), Jordan (1).
WS-55 WHIRLWIND: 436 built.
HAR Mk 1: Westland-built Sikorsky S-55 for SAR and general duties; 10 built for Royal Navy. FF 12 November 1952.
HAR Mk 2: Similar to Mk 1; 32 built for RAF and some later converted to Mk 4 standard.
HAR Mk 3: Similar to Mk 1 for plane guard duties with more

powerful engine; 27 built for Royal Navy. FF 24 September 1954.
HAR Mk 4: Similar to Mk 2 with different engine for tropical conditions but still of 600hp; 31 built for RAF.
HAR Mk 5: Similar to Mk 3 but with drooped tail boom and first Whirlwind to have a British engine, of 750hp; 1 built. FF 28 August 1955.
HAS Mk 7: ASW helicopter with radar, dunking sonar and torpedoes; 129 built for Royal Navy. FF 17 October 1956.
HCC Mk 8: VIP configuration for Queen's Flight; 2 built.
HAR Mk 9: For SAR, training and general duties with turboshaft engine; 17 converted from Mk 7. FF 15 October 1965.
HAR Mk 10: First turboshaft-engined variant of Whirlwind, for tactical troop-lift with optional armament; 68 built for RAF and 45 converted from Mks 2, 4 and 8. FF Spring 1961.
HCC Mk 12: VIP configuration with turboshaft engine for Queen's Flight. 2 built.
Series 1: Commercial version with American piston engine; 79 built. FF 12 November 1952.
Series 2: Commercial version with British piston engine; 37 built.
Series 3: Commercial version with turboshaft engine; 18 built. FF 28 February 1959.
Foreign Users: Austria (10), Bahamas (2), Brazil (8), Brunei (3), Canada (2), Cuba (2), France (43), Ghana (6), Iran (2), Jordan (2), Kuwait (4), Norway (1), Qatar (2), Saudi Arabia (1), Spain (4), Yugoslavia (19).

CHARACTERISTICS: DRAGONFLY, WIDGEON AND WHIRLWIND TYPES

Designation	Dragonfly HR Mk 3	Widgeon	Whirlwind HAR Mk 3	Whirlwind HAS Mk 7	Whirlwind HAR Mk 10
Engine	Alvis Leonides 50 520hp	Alvis Leonides 521/2 520hp	Wright R-1300-3 700hp	Alvis Leonides Mk 155 750hp	Bristol Siddeley Gnome H.1000 1,050shp
Rotor diameter	14.94m (49ft)	14.99m (49ft 2in)	16.1m (53ft)	16.1m (53ft)	16.1m (53ft)
Fuselage length	12.53m (41ft 1¾in)	12.75m (41ft 10in)	12.71m (41ft 8½in)	12.71m (41ft 8½in)	13.46m (44ft 2in)
Height	3.95m (12ft 11½in)	4.06m (13ft 4in)	4.03m (13ft 2½in)	4.03m (13ft 2½in)	4.03m (13ft 2½in)
Empty weight	1,994kg (4,397lb)	2,007kg (4,425lb)	2,272kg (5,010lb)	2,438kg (5,375lb)	2,246kg (4,952lb)
Max gross weight	2,663kg (5,871lb)	2,676kg (5,900lb)	3,402kg (7,500lb)	3,629kg (8,000lb)	3,629kg (8,000lb)
Max speed	153kph (95mph)	175kph (109mph)	159kph (99mph)	170kph (106mph)	170kph (106mph)
Range	483km (300 miles)	480km (298 miles)	515km (320 miles)	540km (335 miles)	483km (300 miles)
Service ceiling	4,030m (13,222ft)	3,658m (12,000ft)	2,620m (8,600ft)	3,962m (13,000ft)	5,060m (16,600ft)

The Westminster and the Wessex

In 1951 Westland turned their attention to the design of some very large helicopters, ambitious projects indeed, which came to nothing. But a strong desire to build a large transport helicopter remained. With production of the Whirlwind well under way in 1954 it was vital to keep the Company's momentum going by re-directing the energies of the design and engineering staffs. Without research and new designs and their development, there could be no subsequent production and without production there was no future for the Company. In December 1953 the first flight of the Sikorsky S-56 assault helicopter, capable of carrying 23 combat-equipped troops, for the US Marine Corps had taken place. It was a short step for Westland to decide to examine the desirability of building the S-56 under licence but with British turbine engines. A number of studies was conducted, one of which envisaged replacing the Pratt & Whitney radial piston engines, located at the tips of the stub wings, with Napier Eland engines. Eventually, after a year of quite fierce debate, it was agreed that the Company should strike out on its own with a new design for a larger helicopter, but attempt to minimize costs and development time by concluding an agreement with Sikorsky to use the main and tail rotors, the transmission and the flying controls of the S-56. The scene was thus set for a new and promising venture. But there was a limitation: little could be made available in the way of financial and manpower resources.

Westminster

Westland were particularly keen to mount two turbines ahead of a single rotor above the cabin roof and this was the form the new machine took. It was called the Westminster – perhaps to shame the Government into providing some support; it never did! Two principal versions were planned: a purely civil, short-range transport for 35/40 passengers and a flying crane with a disposable load of 6,804kg (15,000lb). The most cost-effective stage length was to be 161km (100 miles) and the machine therefore would not be competitive over greater lengths. Further versions were to be contemplated later.

Previous experience had indicated how important were test rigs for the transmission, engine installation and flying controls. Originally, a ground test rig was proposed, but in March 1956 it was agreed to go

straight for a flying rig which would also enable cockpit configurations and handling characteristics to be studied. Because this first prototype was to be a flying test rig it was decided not to cover the fuselage but to have simply an open tubular framework structure. Only the cockpit and the tail pylon had skins. Two 3,150shp Napier Eland 229A turboshaft engines were mounted side-by-side above the so-called cabin ahead of the 21.95m (72ft) five-bladed all-metal main rotor. The main rotor hub had offset combined drag and flapping hinges to increase the centre of gravity range, and hydraulic drag dampers. The tail rotor had four all-metal rotor blades and it was intended that both rotors should have electrical de-icing. The undercarriage was of the tricycle type with a tail wheel.

The first framework prototype, G-APLE, was completed in February 1958 with the maiden flight taking place on 15 June that year, just twelve days after the first engine run. Without an enclosed passenger cabin, but with a single central hook and a useful load of 6,214kg (13,700lb), this particular prototype was seen ultimately as a flying crane. It was demonstrated at the SBAC Show in 1958. While test flying continued into 1959 a second prototype, G-APTX, was built. There were some significant differences. The fuselage had more covering, an external 1,135lit (250Imp gall) fuel tank, and the airframe was a little lighter. The maiden flight of G-APTX was on 4 September 1959.

In January 1960 Brochure No. B 204 on the Westminster Civil Transport Helicopter was issued. At an assumed price of £350,000, an annual flying rate of 2,000 hours and obsolescence after eight years, the direct operating cost per flying hour was calculated at £99.57. A maximum take-off weight of 15,196kg (33,500lb) was planned. The maximum take-off weight of the crane version was intended to be 16,330kg (36,000lb) with the option of having Rolls-Royce Tyne engines. Like the Sikorsky S-60 'Skycrane', which first flew in March 1959, a load or personnel cabin could be suspended from or clutched to the underside of the fuselage between a tall four-point undercarriage. A

Opposite page, top: The framework first prototype of the Westminster. Westland decided to build a large helicopter by applying two Eland engines above the cabin to the Sikorsky S-56. (Westland Helicopters)

Opposite page, bottom: When it first flew in June 1958 the Westminster was the largest single rotor turbine-powered helicopter to be built in the Western world. (Westland Helicopters)

Above: In its crane version the Westminster could lift a disposable load of 6,804kg (15,000lb). (Westland Helicopters)

military version of the Westminster with a rear-loading ramp was also proposed: a crew of two and 45 troops or 32 stretchers or a load of 6,804kg (15,000lb) to be carried. A leaf was taken out of the Soviet book whereby a 1,818lit (400Imp gall) cylindrical fuel tank could be attached to either side of the fuselage.

Despite the success of the programme so far, it had attracted virtually no outside interest. To generate such interest it was decided to make various modifications, including the skinning of the fuselage, and the first prototype was the object of this exercise. The first flight of the more elegant G-APLE took place on 12 June 1960. It soon demonstrated its ability to fly at 250kph (155mph) with a remarkably low vibration level. G-APTX, meanwhile, was given a Sikorsky-built six-bladed main rotor in place of its original five-bladed one.

The production aircraft were to have two 3,500shp Eland E.211 engines, but such power was thought unlikely to be forthcoming after the failure of the E.229A to reach their full power – particularly in the absence of any outside financial support to maintain further development. To improve the engine out performance it was proposed to install a third engine, a 1,000shp Gnome, above the tail rotor shaft just to the rear of the main rotor gearbox. The 318kg (700lb) weight of this engine was compensated by increasing the maximum take-off weight by 454kg (1,000lb). Besides allowing the Westminster to hover and cruise

more economically with one Eland inoperative, the Gnome could also be used as a form of auxiliary power unit to start the Elands.

Just as the Westminster was reaching a certain acceptable level of development maturity, the rationalization of the British helicopter industry began. To establish its position as the foremost helicopter manufacturer in the land Westland acquired Saunders-Roe Ltd in August 1959 and its plants at Cowes in the Isle of Wight and at Eastleigh near Southampton. This purchase was followed on 23 March 1960 by buying Bristol Helicopter Ltd located at Weston-super-Mare. A few weeks later, on 2 May 1960, the helicopter element of Fairey Aviation Ltd at Hayes in Middlesex was absorbed by Westland. The result of these mergers was to bring practically the entire spectrum of British helicopter activities under the control of Westland and thereby induce several major headaches. In September 1960 Westland announced that they intended to concentrate their efforts on the P.531, the Gnome-engined Whirlwind and Wessex, and the Rotodyne; work would also continue on the Belvedere.

The Westminster was to be a casualty and two factors in particular caused its demise. With the cancellation of the Bristol Type 191 for the Royal Navy and that Service's desire for the Wessex instead, the private, though limited, effort devoted to the Westminster by Westland upset some senior naval officers. They alleged that the Wessex was not receiving the attention due to it, a charge that was proved to be unfounded when the Wessex made its maiden flight ahead of schedule. Nevertheless, this belief generated positive

Above: The first prototype, now with an enclosed fuselage. It first flew in this form in June 1960. (Westland Helicopters)

opposition to the Westminster which Westland were never able to dissipate. With Fairey came the Rotodyne and Government support for that machine. The project seemed to have great potential in the summer of 1960 and certainly was one which merited continued Company effort. On the other hand, Westland could obviously not support all the projects in hand at the time of the take-overs; those with less certain prospects faced cancellation. The Westminster, with no official interest, was one of these and the project was abandoned in September 1960 after a joint Government/ Westland evaluation between it, the Rotodyne and the Bristol Type 194. The aim was to decide which design was the best for the next generation of transport helicopter. There were many factors to be considered, not least that the Type 194 was only a paper project while the other two contenders had flown. Each design had its advocates and each its shortcomings. The Westminster came last, not being considered a competitor for stage lengths over 161km (100 miles), and even behind the Type 194 which 'emerges from the comparison surprisingly well as a formula on which to base civil transport operations over 370km (230 miles)'.

So, after some 145 flying hours, the project came to an unhappy end. The irony of it all became apparent years later when the first cost-effective passenger-carrying helicopters adopted the basic Westminster configuration rather than that adopted by the Rotodyne or any other helicopter.

WS-58 Wessex

In 1952 the US Navy formulated a requirement for an ASW helicopter to replace its S-55. The S-58 was the result, first flying in March 1954. As the Admiralty viewed with some alarm the problems with the Bristol Type 173, contemplated their re-emergence in the Type 191 and slowly came to the conclusion that the 191 would be too heavy and large for carrier lifts and easy deck handling, Westland negotiated a licence agreement with Sikorsky in 1956 to build the S-58. A single Sikorsky-built S-58 with a 1,525hp Wright piston engine was bought for trials purposes. The Company had already carried out some studies on ASW helicopters, but it was quite clear to all that at that time Bristol had been nominated as the Company to build ASW helicopters and no official interest had therefore been shown in any Westland proposals.

With the cancellation of the Type 191 for the Royal Navy, the Admiralty quickly turned to Westland who were asked how they could fill this ASW gap which had so comparatively suddenly appeared in the Navy's operational capability. Westland believed that a twin-engined aircraft was necessary for ASW, but because of the short time-scale and because the Napier Gazelle free turbine engine had recently passed a Type Test at 1,250shp they felt confident in proposing an S-58 with a single Gazelle engine to meet the Navy's needs, an apparently cheaper solution of much lower risk than anything else. Within a few months a 1,100shp Napier Gazelle NGa.11 turboshaft engine, itself a licence-built version of the American General Electric GE-T58, was cleverly installed at a 35° angle in the nose of the

Top: The prototype Wessex Mk 1 at Farnborough in 1957. Note the circular engine intake in the nose. (Westland Helicopters)

Above: A Wessex Mk 1 of 845 Squadron RN within sight of the Rejang River near Sibu, Borneo in December 1963. (Author)

Westland-owned S-58 where the Wright engine had been. After ground running tests the prototype Wessex, as it was called, made its maiden flight on 17 May 1957. Despite offering less power than the piston engine, the NGa.11 was much lighter and happily matched the power-to-weight ratio of the American engine. The aircraft's performance was good enough to merit further development.

Two pre-production aircraft with a more powerful 1,450shp Gazelle Mk 161 turboshaft were then built for naval trials, the first Westland-built Wessex flying on 20 June 1958 – just five days after the Westminster. The attraction of the Wessex for the Royal Navy was, first, its payload which in theory enabled the machine to combine submarine detection and attack. That this was not realized was because of the need for greater endurance and radius of action and because of im-

proved submarine capabilities; the increased weight of a crew of four, in certain circumstances, and specialist role equipment (radar and navigation systems, etc.) all reduced the payload available for weapons. Nevertheless, when used in the submarine attack role a homing torpedo could be carried on each side of the fuselage. The Wessex also scored over the Whirlwind in having a flight control system which provided automatic stabilization, a night dunking capability, Doppler radar and better flight performance. The sonar was the same as that in the Whirlwind HAS Mk 7.

The HAS Mk 1 entered production in 1959 with the first of 129 being delivered in April the following year. 700(H) Flight RN started trials in June and on 4 July 1961 815 Squadron was commissioned as the first RN Wessex squadron; it embarked in HMS *Ark Royal* in September. In due course the County Class guided missile destroyers, designed with a hangar and landing platform for a single Wessex, came into service.

The S-58, and therefore the Wessex, adopted a similar dynamic system to that of the S-55, but the fuselage shape was quite different. The semi-monocoque light alloy structure had a straight under-surface quite close and parallel to the ground. The top surface slanted downwards towards the tall raked tail fin at the top of which was the tail rotor with four blades rather than the two of the Whirlwind. A small horizontal stabilizer was inset into the leading edge of the fin. The tail unit folded 180° to port and forwards for stowage aboard ship. Because the Gazelle turbine was slightly longer than the Wright engine the Wessex's fuselage had to be lengthened by 0.49m (1ft 7½in). The Wessex had one more main rotor blade than the Whirlwind and a rotor diameter 0.97m (3ft) greater. The light alloy blades themselves had a longer life and offset flapping and drag hinges; the rotor head was increased in size and much strengthened. The other obvious difference from the Whirlwind was the under-carriage: the Wessex had two main wheels and a single wheel at the tail.

The Mk 1 in the ASW role carried a crew of three: a pilot, an observer and a sonar operator. At night two pilots were aboard. The pilots enjoyed good vision from the cockpit which had large forward and side windows, the latter being concave to improve the downwards and rearwards view. Apart from the ASW equipment a new breed of electronic gadgetry was fitted; the first pre-production Wessex had to make do with a simple autopilot and automatic hover in the sonar mode, but it did not have an automatic transition to the hover. Some time later a simplex flight control system Mk 3, Doppler navigational radar and radio altimeter, incorporating a Louis Newmark Mk 19 autopilot, helped to make a vast improvement in the ability to operate effectively by day and night. The autopilot included heading and height holds with provision for an automatic transition from within a height/speed gate to a pre-selected Doppler-controlled hover – something the US Navy's S-58 did not have. The gate conditions were usually 38m (125ft) facing into wind at 167kph (104mph) and, depending upon the sea state, hover height was 12m (40ft). Once in the hover the submersible sonar unit was lowered into the water, while the cable mode of the flight control system maintained the plan position of the aircraft using angular information from the sonar cable and the height was judged from the length of cable paid out minus the depth of the sonar bell.

When required to do so the Mk 1 could undertake SAR missions. In 1963 HMS *Ark Royal* was cruising in the Gulf of Aden when one night one of her Sea Vixens ditched. Lieutenant Vic Sirett was scrambled in his Wessex. Despite extreme darkness and a heavy swell the Sea Vixen crew were located some 32km (20 miles) away. Sirett came to the hover at 9m (30ft) and lowered his sonar cable to help in maintaining an accurate hover. To Sirett's consternation the observer leaped

Above: A pair of 845 Squadron Wessex Mk 1 overfly HMS *Albion*. (FAA Museum)

out of his dinghy and swam towards the cable which he grabbed instead of the rescue hoist. The effect of the waterlogged survivor clutching desperately to the cable while he was blown about in the rotor downwash caused the Wessex to rock violently from side to side. The unnerving sight of what appeared to be a helicopter partially out of control only a few metres above undoubtedly alarmed the survivor and he let go of the cable. He was eventually winched up and the first operational night rescue by a Royal Navy helicopter had been safely accomplished. The pilot, perhaps understandably, preferred to stay in his dinghy and was later rescued by a destroyer!

ASW Mk 1 took part in the RM Commando assault on an Army barracks and the airport at Dar-Es-Salaam, capital of Tanganyika, in January 1964. Invited to help suppress a military mutiny, 340 men of 45 Commando were flown ashore in eight Wessex and two RAF Belvederes in 80 minutes in the face of sporadic

machine-gun fire. One Wessex later rounded up some fleeing, but still armed, mutineers by making menacing dives on them until they turned round and headed back to the barracks and into captivity.

The advantages of the Wessex in terms of payload/range had been realized early on and it was decided to employ it in the Commando role in addition to ASW. Consequently, in April 1962, 845 Squadron reformed in this role with twelve Wessex Mk 1. The sonar, of course, had been removed as had most of the flight control system, but the autostabilization equipment was retained. Up to sixteen fully equipped troops or eight stretcher cases could then be carried, or a load of 1,814kg (4,000lb) internally or as an underslung load. A variety of weapons was sometimes installed: fixed forward-firing machine-guns or 50mm (2in) free flight rockets in pods mounted outboard of the undercarriage struts, or four AS-11 wire-guided anti-tank missiles with the sight inside the cockpit on the port side.

Maximum cruising speed for the Mk 1 was 195kph (121mph) and range with the standard fuel load of 1,364 litres (300Imp gall) was 630km (390 miles). A very attractive feature was the fact that the crew could get into a 'cold' Wessex, start up and take-off in no more than 45 seconds.

It did not take too long for Westland to return to their earlier idea of a twin-engined Wessex. The Wessex Mk 1 had been something of a rush job with a turbine engine replacing a piston engine in the S-58. The Mk 2 was a much more studied affair. The Gazelle engine was removed from a Mk 1 and replaced by two coupled 1,350shp Bristol Siddeley H.1200 Gnome turboshafts, one a Mk 110 and the other a Mk 111, to give a better performance in tropical conditions and at high altitude. The coupling was to ensure that in the event of an engine failure the other engine could drive the rotor system. Although having a total output of 2,700shp, the Wessex HC Mk 2 was restricted to 1,550shp at the rotor head. The maiden flight of this prototype was made on 18 January 1962 and that of the production model on 5 October 1962. Long before this though, in August 1961, the RAF had placed a substantial order for Mk 2 for tactical transport, casualty evacuation and general duties. A crew of three and fifteen troops or eight stretchers and a medical attendant can be carried, but a more normal battle load is ten to twelve troops with one pilot and a crewman.

Besides the engine change and the conspicuous single large exhaust stack on each side of the nose instead of two pairs of smaller exhausts there were no

Top left: A naval Wessex Mk 1 descends into a clearing near Bario in Borneo. (FAA Museum)

Left: Safely down in a very confined area. The tallest trees in Borneo are some 60m (200ft) high. (FAA Museum)

Right: A Wessex Mk 1 kept afloat by flotation bags while another starts the recovery procedure. (FAA Museum)

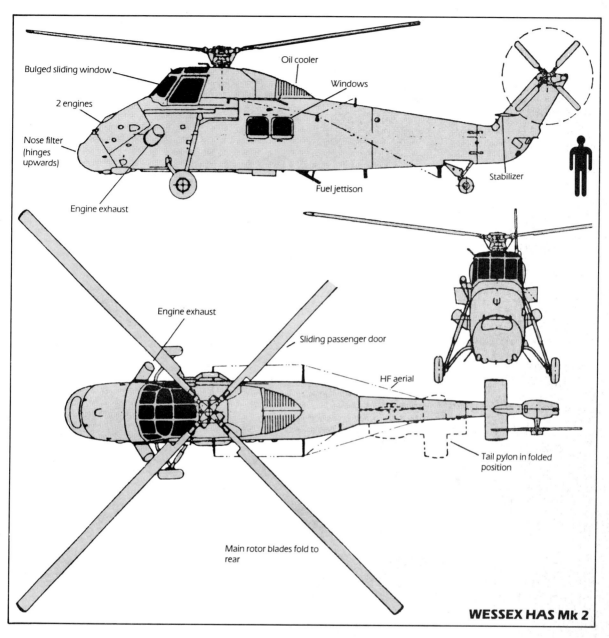

Bulged sliding window

Oil cooler

Windows

2 engines

Nose filter
(hinges
upwards)

Stabilizer

Engine exhaust

Fuel jettison

Engine exhaust

Sliding passenger door

HF aerial

Tail pylon in folded
position

Main rotor blades fold to
rear

WESSEX HAS Mk 2

Top: The Wessex Mk 1 production line at Yeovil in 1965. (Westland Helicopters)

Above: A Wessex Mk 1 during trials with the new Type 195 sonar. So advanced and expensive was the sonar and test equipment that the helicopter was fitted with huge floats so that in the event of it ditching there would be little fear of losing the machine and its equipment. (FAA Museum)

major differences to the Mk 1; the Mk 2, however, has only autostabilization equipment and no autopilot. Maximum take-off weight has crept up by 409kg (902lb) to 6,124kg (13,500lb). Seventy-one Mk 2 have been delivered to the RAF, the first entering service in 18 Squadron in February 1964. Some have been designated HAR Mk 2 for SAR duties, a role in which they are still used in 22 Squadron. Despite having a radius of action of only 185km (115 miles) the HAR Mk 2 is better suited than the Sea King for rescues close to coastal cliff edges by virtue of its available power, manoeuvrability and weaker rotor downwash. Mk 2 are also still in service for advanced flying training and in such locations as Cyprus, Hong Kong and Northern Ireland. They are not expected to be retired for perhaps another ten years.

While the HAS Mk 1 had been a distinct improvement on the Whirlwind HAS Mk 7 it still had some irritating shortcomings. The reliability of the flight control system had been unsatisfactory and the Gazelle engine had not been free from trouble. The ASW equipment was quickly becoming obsolescent. The first Wessex HAS Mk 3 prototype, embodying some major modifications, flew in 1964, and the first flight of

Above: An RAF Wessex Mk 2 embarks troops during an exercise. (Westland Helicopters)

the production model, a converted Mk 1, took place in December 1966. A more powerful engine, a 1,600shp Gazelle Mk 165, was installed, but more noticeable were the large dorsal radome for the search radar which gave rise to the nickname 'Camel' for the Mk 3, the fairing extension aft of the rotor head and an airspeed indicator probe protruding from the nose. For the first time all specialist equipment on board was British-made and the many enhancements over the Mk 1 included:

– A new lightweight search radar.
– The Type 195 dunking sonar.
– A Mk 30 duplex automatic flight control system (AFCS).
– Improved Doppler navigational equipment.

– A tactical plotting display with selective simultaneous display of both radar and sonar target information.

All this sophisticated equipment added up to an ASW helicopter far more capable than any other in the world. When first introduced the sonar was very advanced and very expensive, costing more than the helicopter itself. So special was it that its first trials were conducted by a Wessex with floats as a means of preserving the aircraft and sonar in the event of ditching. The most important element of the package was arguably the new AFCS which permitted operations day and night in adverse weather conditions and indeed the ability to fly automatically from one hover

Above: A Wessex Mk 2 prepares to lift off an underslung load. (Rolls-Royce)

Opposite page, top: An SAR Mk 2. (Author)

Right: Two Mk 2 on the helicopter dispersal at RAF Kai Tak, Hong Kong. Note the nose filters. (Rolls-Royce)

Below: A Mk 2 shows off its folding tail. (Westland Helicopters)

to the next by the simple expedient of pressing just two buttons. But the major shortcoming remained: a single Mk 3 still could not search and attack except over very short radii of action. The fact that it was also single-engined was considered unsatisfactory.

On 9 January 1967 the Intensive Flying Trials Unit (IFTU), 700(H) Squadron, formed at RNAS Culdrose with five Wessex Mk 3 and disbanded nine months later. The following month, October, 814 Squadron became the first operational ASW squadron with six Mk 3. Three other operational squadrons, 700(H) Flight and two training squadrons eventually took delivery of the Mk 3, of which 46 were produced; of these only three were built from scratch, the remainder being converted Mk 1.

The Mk 3 pioneered the technique of in-flight refuelling from the most convenient nearby ship, infinitely preferable to flying back to the aircraft's more distant mother ship. Having got into formation with the ship the helicopter's winch wire would be lowered. To this was attached the refuelling hose which was winched up and plugged into the fuel system. Such a procedure effectively increased the helicopter's endurance.

Embarked aboard carriers, helicopter cruisers and destroyers, the Mk 3 had a fairly uneventful career until the Falklands conflict. Then, on 21 April 1982, the Wessex Mk 3 from HMS *Antrim*, with its sonar removed and flown by Lieutenant-Commander Ian Stanley, led two Wessex Mk 5 loaded with SAS troops to South Georgia. After a night of appalling weather the SAS radioed to be returned to their ships. In the ensuing recovery both Mk 5 crashed and the solitary Mk 3, nicknamed Humphrey, eventually succeeded in rescuing every single man despite the continuing atrocious weather. On his final flight Stanley carried seventeen men aboard his Wessex, which was some 900kg (1,984lb) overweight, to get them back to his ship before nightfall. The helicopter was quite unable to hover and Stanley had no choice but to make a straight-in approach to the deck. For his outstanding skill and determination, Stanley was subsequently awarded the DSO. Four days later, with the sonar re-installed in his aircraft, he was again in action in very poor visibility searching for the Argentinian submarine, *Santa Fe*, which was reported to be approaching Grytviken. The helicopter radar located a contact 8km (5 miles) out to sea and the Wessex turned towards it. At 1.2km (¾ mile) range visual contact was made and Stanley dropped two 136kg (300lb) depth-charges which exploded just off the port side and prevented the submarine from diving. It managed to edge on towards Grytviken harbour while Stanley summoned help and sprayed the boat with fire from the 7.62mm machine-gun mounted in his starboard cabin window before leaving the action to the other helicopters.

Above: A Wessex Mk 3 drops a Mk 44 torpedo. The large dorsal radome houses the antenna for the search radar, and the fairing forward of it the extra electrical power for the radar and sonar. (Avia)

Humphrey's war was not yet over. On the very day that British troops began their re-possession of the Islands HMS *Antrim* was attacked by Argentinian A-4 Skyhawks. Humphrey received a number of 20mm hits but was repaired and continued to fly. When HMS *Antrim* returned to the UK Humphrey went into honourable retirement at the Fleet Air Arm Museum at RNAS Yeovilton. The only other Mk 3 to take part in the Falklands conflict was wrecked on 12 June when a ground-based Exocet missile hit HMS *Glamorgan*. A few Mk 3 soldiered on after the war was over, but the last

operational flight of this Mark took place in January 1984.

Two HCC Mk 4 for the Queen's Flight, with special furnishings and painted red, were delivered to RAF Benson in April 1969. They are still in service. Their red livery makes them most conspicuous, its specific aim.

The final version of the Wessex for the British Services was the HU Mk 5. Termed an assault helicopter it was to be capable of lifting a dozen or more RM Commandos from their carrier or assault ship to capture a beachhead for follow-up forces. Although far from ideal it could be used as a 'gunship' in such instances, equipped with a variety of weapons. Design began in April 1962. The Mk 5 first flight was on 31 May 1963 with the production model flying on 17 November; it began to relieve the Mk 1 in the Commando role from late 1964 although initially going to a training squadron. Similar to the Mk 2, it had two coupled Gnome engines (Mk 112 and Mk 113) and a strengthened rotor head. To cater for heavy-footed Commandos the airframe was made more robust and this also allowed rather more carefree handling at low level, useful in the event of the need to take evasive action from enemy fire. Like the Mk 2, the Mk 5 now usually has a filter attached to the nose when serving overseas – and often in the UK. In addition to the weapons carried by the Mk 1 the Mk 5 can also launch up to four AS-12 missiles, a more effective and longer range version of

Above: A Royal Navy Wessex Mk 5 fires an SS-11 missile at sea in 1970. (FAA Museum)

Left: An Army Sioux is recovered by a Mk 5 in Malaysia. (Museum of Army Flying)

the AS-11; a general-purpose 7.62mm machine-gun can also be fired from the cabin door position. Both these types of weapon were fired during the Falklands War. In 1960 the Naval Staff had raised a requirement for helicopter fire support for amphibious landings and this gave added impetus to the arming of naval Wessex. Besides the crew of three, although the machine can be operated by a single pilot, there is space for up to fifteen seated troops or 1,814kg (4,000lb) freight can be transported in lieu. Artillery pieces, Land Rovers, fuel or ammunition pallets can be underslung with ease.

One hundred Mk 5 were built and, according to the 1984 Defence White Paper, some 50 Mk 5 remain in service with the Royal Navy. By 1986 it is expected that no more than about sixteen will still be serving and these will go on into the 1990s for secondary duties.

Mk 5 played a notable role during the Borneo and Radfan campaigns. Indeed, both the Mks 1 and 5 flew in Borneo, the former being involved at the very beginning of the Brunei rebellion when, on 15 December 1962, Commandos were flown ashore to ambush

rebels near Seria. Many jungle operations could never have been undertaken without the Wessex and their importance was readily appreciated by the Indonesians who were known to implant vertical stakes some 3m (10ft) high in helicopter landing sites. The Wessex was used for all manner of tasks, particularly the move and resupply of patrols as they laid ambushes in the jungle and casualty evacuation. It was a Wessex Mk 1 that was to fire the first missile from a British helicopter in anger. Some Indonesians infiltrated across the border in late April 1964 and then withdrew into inaccessible caves. Standing off out of range of small arms fire, a few Mk 1 pumped SS-11 missiles into the caves. One missile was a rogue and disappeared off into the jungle and presumed oblivion. Some weeks later an Iban tracker stumbled across it and decided that it should be returned to its rightful owners. He struggled manfully through the jungle with it for several days before solemnly presenting it to an RAF helicopter detachment. In some consternation the detachment commander had no option but to close his operations centre until the missile had been dealt with.

Flying operations could be a hazardous business given the frequent low cloud and heavy rain. On one occasion the leader of a section of three Wessex was confronted by the problem of extracting 24 men from a jungle site in a single lift because no men could be left behind in a position liable to attack. The height of the site was 610m (2,000ft) above sea level, the temperature was 27°C (81°F) and the distance to base was 113km (70 miles). With 386kg (850lb) of fuel he could take eight men out in each aircraft but not reach base; with 431kg (950lb) he could just reach base but not extract all 24 men together. As the skies darkened he decided to fly to the nearest refuelling point, make a difficult approach and landing in the dark, refuel and spend the night there, continuing the next morning. The improved performance of the Mk 5 when it arrived in Borneo in June 1966 was very welcome.

In the Radfan campaign Royal Navy and RAF Wessex were used for the same sort of tasks. Some were armed with machine-guns to protect others as they inserted and extracted patrols occasionally under fire. After a Belvedere had been hit from above it became normal practice to fly along ridge lines. Landing picquets on hill tops, sometimes as high as 2,134m (7,000ft) at temperatures close to 40°C (104°F) at midday and when the turbulent wind could change 180° within five minutes was a hair-raising business. Having enough torque available for underslung loads was a major problem and they were simply not accepted if conditions did not meet the strict requirements laid down. To guess the weight of ammunition or rations, for example, is not easy and the Army were prone to underestimation and therefore disappointment. Because roads and passes were frequently mined by the

dissidents, the Belvedere and Wessex were heavily engaged in bringing forward supplies from fixed-wing airfields and in the logistic support of the troops in action. In contrast with the Borneo campaign water was a crucial commodity.

As the Radfan operations were brought to a successful conclusion security disorders began to occur in Aden itself. To provide a deterrent to mortar attacks on the airfield at Khormaksar RAF Wessex Mk 2, equipped with powerful searchlights and machine-guns, patrolled the perimeter by night.

More than 40 Mk 5 from 845, 847 and 848 Squadrons were deployed to the South Atlantic in 1982. Unfortunately six were lost on board the *Atlantic Conveyor* when that vessel was struck by an Exocet missile and later sank; the only other two lost crashed on South Georgia. Like the other helicopters involved they played an important part in that victorious campaign, one firing an AS-12 missile at the police station, an Argentinian HQ, in Port Stanley.

The only Wessex type now in service with the Royal Navy is the Mk 5. The Queen's Flight is expected to retain its HCC Mk 4 and the RAF its HC/HAR Mk 2 until the aircraft chosen to meet Air Staff Requirement 404 enters service. It has been reported that a Royal Auxiliary Air Force squadron is to be formed from ex-Navy Wessex Mk 5.

The reason why the Royal Navy finally procured two separate Marks of Wessex for the ASW and Commando roles can probably be traced back to their experiences with the Mk 1 east of Suez during the early 1960s. The campaigns in both Borneo and the Radfan pointed up the Commando role features that conflicted with ASW requirements. To operate in 'hot and high' conditions required a margin of power at sea level which greatly reduced endurance at that level – a major drawback for ASW operations. On the other hand, to achieve maximum endurance at low level resulted in insufficient power at altitude. Some protection against small arms fire was necessary for Commando operations and this added some 113kg (250lb) to the aircraft's weight, thus reducing useful payload or fuel. ASW aircraft required sonar which, although it could be removed, had to have fixed fittings thereby incurring a weight penalty; the flight control system and navigation aids were not really needed in a Commando helicopter and these equipments also contributed to a further loss of payload. The marriage of the ASW and Commando roles in a single type was therefore not a particularly happy one and was not to be repeated.

Five other Marks of Wessex have been built. The most numerous was the Mk 31, 27 of which were delivered to the Royal Australian Navy from August 1962. This version was basically similar to the Mk 1 but had a 1,540shp Napier Gazelle Mk 162 engine. When afloat these aircraft have been based on HMAS *Melbourne*. They have been progressively updated and are now referred to as the Mk 31B. 816 Squadron operates all the fourteen remaining operable Wessex in the utility role with three in storage.

Between April 1964 and February 1965, twelve Mk 52, a version of the HC Mk 2, with two 1,350shp Gnome engines, were delivered to the Iraqi Air Force. According to *The Military Balance 1984/85*, seven are still in service. In 1966 another variant of the HC Mk 2, the Mk 53, found favour with the Ghanaian Air Force which bought three. Yet another variant, the Mk 54, was ordered by Brunei which took just one aircraft in January 1967 and removed it and another second-hand Wessex from service in 1971.

The civil version of the Wessex is the Mk 60, again similar to the HC Mk 2. Eighteen were built for Bristow Helicopters Ltd and have subsequently operated in many places around the world mainly in support of oil and gas exploitation. They have made a significant contribution to such activities in the North Sea. Designed to carry ten passengers in some comfort, they can carry up to sixteen in austere conditions or eight stretchers, two sitting casualties and a medical atten-

dant. The final delivery was made in 1970 but all were withdrawn from service, leaving Bristows by 1981 without a single British-built helicopter in its inventory. Seven have since been bought by Sykes Aviation.

Rationalization

The lack of knowledge and even interest in helicopters in Government circles during the 1950s had resulted in spasmodic support and encouragement. While the helicopter industry had pursued a number of promising lines of development the dividends were never reaped in the 1960s. What more can be said of the cancelled Rotodyne – a lost opportunity of some magnitude? Fragmented and short of money it was doubtful if any one Company could make a spectacular breakthrough into world markets. Rationalization was therefore entirely logical. However, the success of Westland in producing American designs, although anglicized and modified, under licence, while effective in the short term, gave rise to the thought in many Service pilots' mind that American helicopters must be better than British. The only real Service knowledge of helicopters was vested in officers of comparatively junior rank and, until rationalization, the more senior officers responsible for actually selecting which helicopters should be developed and procured were baffled by the choice and the advice they were being given. The result was delay, confusion and not always

Left: Changing an oleo in the hover; HMS *Bulwark*, 1972. (FAA Museum)

Below: An early morning visit to a Borneo outpost. (Rolls-Royce)

Above: A Royal Australian Navy Wessex Mk 31 with a Bendix sonar below the fuselage. (Westland Helicopters)

the best aircraft entering service. The perfect example of all this was the Belvedere, designed as a naval helicopter but operated only by the RAF. The Royal Navy then chose the Wessex for ASW, subsequently adopting it, like the RAF, as a tactical transport helicopter. It was even fondly imagined as an assault helicopter, a role for which it was really too unwieldy and vulnerable for most levels of conflict. The Mks 2 and 5 were, and are, transport helicopters – and very good ones – and fortunately have never had to be used

Above: A Bristow Wessex Mk 60. This version has been used for offshore support in many parts of the world. (Rolls-Royce)

in a true assault role. They were not designed for assault and could not expect to survive in Europe in the face of aimed enemy fire.

As the 1960s progressed the helicopter industry settled down, the Services built up their expertise and knowledge and a fruitful dialogue between the two began. It is now very close and mutually beneficial.

WESTMINSTER AND WESSEX TYPES AND VARIANTS

WESTMINSTER: Twin-engined transport helicopter for up to 40 passengers; 2 prototypes built. First flight (FF) 15 June 1958.
WESSEX: 369 built.
HAS Mk 1: ASW helicopter with single 1,450shp engine; 131 built, 129 for Royal Navy. 1 converted to Mk 2 and 43 converted to Mk 3. FF 20 June 1958.
HC Mk 2: Transport version for up to 16 troops with two 1,350shp engines; 72 built for RAF. FF 18 January 1962.
HAR Mk 2: Some HC Mk 2 used for SAR by RAF.
HAS Mk 3: Modernized ASW version of Mk 1 with 1,600shp engine and dorsal radar; 3 prototypes built. FF 30 November 1964.
HCC Mk 4: VIP configuration for Queen's Flight; 2 built. FF 17 March 1969.

HU Mk 5: (Armed) assault helicopter for up to 16 Commandos similar to HC Mk 2; 100 built for Royal Navy. FF 31 May 1963.
Mk 31: Similar to Mk 1 with 1,540shp engine; 27 built for Royal Australian Navy.
Mk 31B: Uprated Mk 31.
Mk 52: Similar to HC Mk 2; 12 built for Iraqi Air Force.
Mk 53: Similar to HC Mk 2; 3 built for Ghanaian Air Force.
Mk 54: Similar to HC Mk 2; 1 built for Brunei Air Wing.
Mk 60: Commercial variant similar to HC Mk 2; 18 built for Bristow Helicopters Ltd.
Foreign Users: Australia (27), Brazil (1), Ghana (3), Iraq (12).

CHARACTERISTICS: WESTMINSTER AND WESSEX TYPES

Designation	Westminster	Wessex HAS Mk 1	Wessex HC Mk 2	Wessex HAS Mk 3
Engine	2 × Napier Eland E.229A 3,150shp	Napier Gazelle Mk 161 1,450shp	2 × BS Gnome H,1200 1,350shp	Napier Gazelle Mk 165 1,600shp
Rotor diameter	21.95m (72ft)	17.07m (56ft)	17.07m (56ft)	17.07m (56ft)
Fuselage length	20.83m (68ft 4in)	14.74m (48ft 4½in)	15.24m (50ft)**	14.74m (48ft 4½in)
Height	6.7m (22ft)	4.93m (16ft 2in)	4.93m (16ft 2in)	4.4m (14ft 5in)
Empty weight	9.072kg (20,000lb)*	3,447kg (7,600lb)*	3,538kg (7,800lb)	4,241kg (9,350lb)
Max gross weight	14,969kg (33,000lb)	5,715kg (12,600lb)	6,124kg (13,500lb)	6,124kg (13,500lb)
Max speed	250kph (155mph)	212kph (132mph)	212kph (132mph)	204kph (127mph)
Range	333km (207 miles)	1,038km (645 miles)	770km (478 miles)	483km (300 miles)
Service ceiling	?	4,300m (14,100ft)	?	?

*Equipped. **With filter.

Light Helicopters for the Army and Navy: Scout, Wasp and Sioux

During 1956 Saunders-Roe started simple design studies of a light turbine-powered helicopter. These were to lead eventually to a machine with a 400shp Blackburn Turmo engine de-rated to 325shp so that it could use the transmission, main and tail rotor blades, the blade articulation and a control system all based on those of the Skeeter. A five-seater weighing 1,542kg (3,400lb) and dubbed the P.531, this machine was to be offered by Saunders-Roe on their own initiative as a replacement for the Skeeter. It seemed clear that the Army's and Navy's needs for light helicopters were bound to expand and thus a comparatively large market was about to open up. Although no military specifications had been issued Saunders-Roe intended the machine for military purposes and discussed its uses informally with all three Services. The Army did indeed require a liaison helicopter and it was generally accepted that a five-seater was about the right size. The French Alouette 2, which was already flying, had some

supporters but the War Office and the Ministry of Supply favoured buying British, even though no suitable helicopter was then in existence.

The Royal Navy had always been keen to use helicopters at sea from a variety of different ships and had undertaken trials as early as the 1940s. As has already been noted the Navy had some interest in the Skeeter and a single Mk 4 was built for them, undergoing trials in 1953. In 1957 the RAE at Bedford began to examine in depth the problems of helicopters operating from frigate-sized ships and a Fairey ULH carried out trials on a frigate that same year. Thus, when Saunders-Roe began work on the P.531, the Admiralty watched developments with interest but without actually expressing a firm requirement for such a helicopter. Nevertheless, it was apparent that a requirement for light helicopters to operate from small ships did exist and would be issued in due course. There was, arguably, a distinct advantage to Saunders-Roe in there being no military specifications at this stage as the Company was therefore not held to rigid military

Below: The second prototype of the P.531. Note the slim tail fin and triangular ventral fin. (Westland Helicopters)

requirements. Saunders-Roe believed that existing five-seaters were unnecessarily large and expensive, and they aimed to design as small and compact a helicopter as possible while giving it a good performance world-wide even at high altitudes and temperatures.

Size and weight could be held down by using a turbine engine. But there was no British-designed gas turbine in the 250–1,000shp class. Fortunately the Blackburn Engine Company had earlier had the foresight to sign a licensing agreement with the French Company Turboméca. Thus the French Turmo free power turbine engine was the inevitable choice to power the new helicopter and a Blackburn-built Turmo 603 de-rated to 325shp was used. With the saving of weight that resulted it was possible to retain the Skeeter's rotor diameter and this in turn theoretically saved yet more weight although the disc loading became greater. With the aircraft's greater maximum weight, however, more lift was required from this given rotor diameter and acceptable blade loading and thus the P.531 had four main rotor blades rather than the three of the Skeeter.

Under the leadership of the chief designer, Ted Ciastula, the design of the P.531 was completed at Eastleigh in November 1957 and on 1 January 1958 it was decided to build two prototypes. By using so many Skeeter components construction time was so much reduced that the first prototype, G-APNU, was able to fly only a few months later on 20 July 1958 after ground running had started on 19 June. The second prototype flew on 30 September. These first two prototypes were intended to prove the basic concept of the aircraft, in particular the engine installation and rotor and flight control systems.

P.531 Scout

In January 1959 the Army, having perceived that it needed a helicopter a good deal more capable than the Skeeter, began to consider in earnest what it was that it really wanted. Very short in experience of such matters, considerable flights of fancy were indulged before a rough consensus was reached: the new helicopter had to be robust, reliable and easy to maintain. It had to be as small and as manoeuvrable on the ground and in the air as possible. It had to be able to carry five passengers or a load of 454kg (1,000lb) and be able to operate world-wide, particularly with regard to a vertical climb out of ground effect at 3.5m/s (689ft/min). It was quite obvious that all these demands would result in a breach of the maximum weight rule whereby Army aircraft were not allowed to weigh more than 1,814kg (4,000lb). The Air Ministry refused to countenance such a thing, but eventually the Minister of Defence agreed that the P.531 could be an exception on the grounds that it would be stupid to choose an unsuitable aircraft simply because it weighed less than the

1,814kg limit. Navy and Army pilots by this time had flown the P.531 at Boscombe Down and were impressed by its handling characteristics.

It was quite clear, however, that the Army's requirements could not be met by the existing P.531 and so a major re-design was put in hand by Saunders-Roe, still on their own initiative – but with considerable encouragement! Designated the P.531-2, the new aircraft was nearly 1½ times heavier at 2,268kg (5,000lb) and had a skid undercarriage instead of the earlier four-wheeled affair. To power this machine a Blackburn A.129, an improved version of the Turmo, was installed. This engine was de-rated to 635shp and, with further development, was later to be called the Nimbus Mk 101. The new aircraft, G-APVL, first flew at Eastleigh on 9 August 1959.

Westland were in the process of acquiring Saunders-Roe at this time and they decided to build a second P.531-2 powered instead by an even more powerful Gnome H.1000 engine de-rated from 1,050shp to 685shp, the only P.531 ever to fly with this engine. The maiden flight was on 3 May 1960. Although profoundly unhappy about the growth in weight and the consequent loss in ground mobility, the Army was sufficiently satisfied with the new prototype to place an order for a few P.531-2 Mk 1 for delivery from September 1960. They were intended for familiarization and further Service evaluation. The first of these pre-production aircraft flew on 4 August 1960. A month later a substantial order for the production helicopter,

APVL

Above: Looking much more like the eventual Scout, the P.531-2 was a much heavier version of the original P.531. (Westland Helicopters)

designated the Scout AH Mk 1, was placed by the Army for deliveries to start twelve months later.

The main difference between the P.531-2 Mk 1 and the Scout was the inclusion of powered controls in the latter. The original manual controls had proved unsatisfactory in the main because of the feedback of random forces which, if not controlled by the pilot, resulted in a rapid and disconcerting rolling and pitching of the aircraft. In September 1960 it was therefore decided to isolate all rotor forces from the pilot by introducing powered controls.

The transfer of the programme to the former Fairey plant at Hayes began in 1961. This move, and the difficulties involved in converting the Scout (and Wasp) drawings to enable production to start, resulted in a certain loss of urgency. The major reason for this was the high turnover of key staff for whom the future appeared uncertain. The Army was soon faced with the prospect of not receiving its first Scouts on schedule. So-called 'Intensive' flying trials began in the summer of 1961 but came to an abrupt halt when all the engines had become unserviceable. Although having aspired to be intensive nobody could claim that this was ever an appropriate description.

The first production Scout with the Nimbus Mk 101 engine flew on 6 March 1961, but the first deliveries to operational Army units were not made until two years later. Then they were committed almost immediately to combat in Borneo and the Radfan in some of the most ruggedly inhospitable and violently contrasting terrain and climatic conditions imaginable. That they performed so well without the shakedown period normal for the introduction of a new aircraft type into service is a credit to their design and ruggedness.

With two seats in front and a bench seat for three or four passengers behind, the latter only possible with bulged cabin doors, the Scout has a conventional aluminium alloy, stressed skin fuselage structure of the pod and boom type. The bench seat can be folded flat against the bulkhead or removed to facilitate the carriage of freight. Bulges in both rear cabin doors permit the internal stowage of a stretcher; a stretcher can also be installed in a pannier on either side of the fuselage. It is to be hoped that the casualties are unconscious when so carried because even with the small window inserted in the lid, the resemblance to a coffin for the conscious occupant is overwhelming! The Scouts proved their value in this casualty evacuation role during the Falklands War when they were used to save many lives; indeed, two officers were awarded the DFC for their bravery in extracting casualties under fire.

The Scout has a tubular skid undercarriage with removable ground handling wheels. One of the major worries when the helicopter first entered service was the insufficient issue of these vital wheels. The main rotor has four all-metal blades, attached by a torsion-

rod suspension system to the fully articulated hub; the blades can be folded to the rear. The two-bladed tail rotor is made of wood. The horizontal stabilizer with endplates is mounted under the rear of the tail boom. Since 1966, after various uprating modifications, the power plant has been a 1,050shp Nimbus Mk 105 turboshaft de-rated to 710shp.

A most conspicuous feature of the Scout is the exposure of this engine and transmission to the elements. Ease of access and servicing was one of the main design considerations and it is for this reason that there are no cowlings. This led to the basic 'spinal' structure of the forward section of the aircraft which provided for three interconnected fuel tanks, attachment points for the main rotor gearbox, servicing platforms on both sides of the engine and bays for electrics and other services. All the load-bearing struc-

Top: A Scout on exercise with a stretcher pannier on each side. By mounting the engine on top of the fuselage and leaving it uncovered, accessibility is improved and the platform on each side can be used as a servicing stand for the rotor head. (Rolls-Royce)

Above: With passenger doors removed and flotation gear fitted, a Scout flies over Hong Kong. (Rolls-Royce)

Opposite page: A Scout manoeuvres slowly between the trees in Borneo. Note the small bulge in the rear door. (Author)

ture of the cabin is beneath the floor; the cabin walls and roof act simply as fairings and are not part of the stressed structure. The tail boom is built as a separate unit.

The Scout is a truly general-purpose helicopter. It can be used for passenger and freight carrying, casualty evacuation, command and control, reconnaissance and AOP, and what is termed armed action. On a number of occasions, particularly during the Radfan operations and in Borneo, two fixed forward-firing 7.62mm

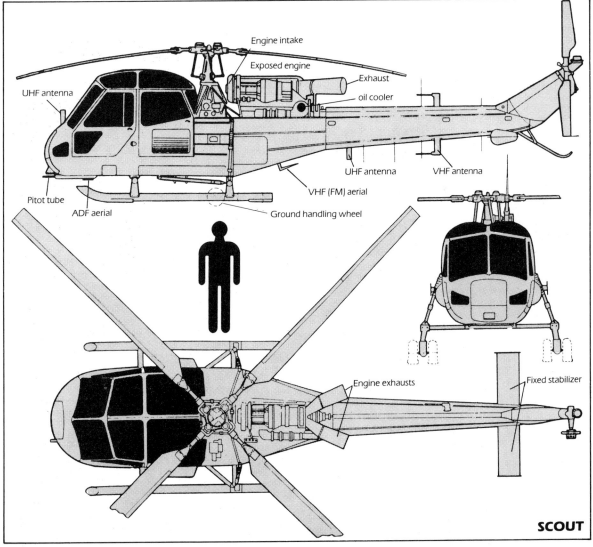

UHF antenna

Pitot tube

ADF aerial

Engine intake

Exposed engine

Exhaust

oil cooler

UHF antenna

VHF antenna

VHF (FM) aerial

Ground handling wheel

Engine exhausts

Fixed stabilizer

SCOUT

Opposite page, top: In 1970 the first Scouts were armed with four SS-11 anti-tank missiles. Note the larger bulged passenger door to permit a longer rear seat. (Museum of Army Flying)

Above: A Scout fires an SS-11 missile. (Museum of Army Flying)

Left: An 8 Flight Scout sports two 7.62mm machine-guns: one fixed, forward-firing and one mounted in the cabin. (Museum of Army Flying)

general-purpose machine-guns were fitted to the landing skid booms, one on each side of the fuselage. The sighting system was somewhat rudimentary: a chinagraph cross on the pilot's windscreen which did not contribute greatly to accuracy! A single traversible machine-gun can be mounted in the cabin either to port or starboard with a field of fire from 30° to 150° in relation to the axis of the aircraft and a depression from 0° to −40°. When roled for anti-tank warfare, two French SS-11 missiles are mounted on each side of the fuselage on booms and an Avimo-Ferranti AF-120 gyro-stabilized binocular sight is located in the cockpit roof above the port forward seat. This sight has two alternative magnifications, × 2.5 and × 10.

After considerable study into the value of anti-tank helicopters the AAC installed four Vigilant missiles on a Scout in 1962 together with a stabilized sight. It was realized from the outset that the 1,375m range of these missiles was much too short for helicopter use, but the trial was sufficiently successful to encourage further development of the concept. Two years later a Scout was fitted with four SS-11 missiles and a French APX/BEZU sight for further trials. In 1966/67 a four-phase trial called 'Helltank' took place to assess the effectiveness of the helicopter in tactical reconnaissance and anti-tank warfare. Its potential in these roles was confirmed and, there being no suitable British missile, it was decided in 1969 to procure the SS-11 with the AF-120 sight for a limited number of Scouts. The first systems came into service in 1970. The SS-11 is a wire-guided missile which takes 23.5 seconds to reach its maximum range of 3,000m. It is a manual, command–to–line-of-sight system; that is to say, the missile has to be flown to the target by the gunner using a miniature control stick. This requires a comparatively high degree of skill – much more than the later generations of anti-tank missiles now widely deployed. Missile launch can take place at any flight speed between 0 and 130kph (81mph). During the Falklands War more than a dozen missiles were fired at stationary targets – mainly bunkers and buildings – and a very high hit rate was achieved.

Some Scouts have been equipped with a variety of specialized equipment. Although it was the original intention for all Scouts to have autostabilization and an autopilot, the need for weight and financial savings precluded this. Nevertheless, a few Scouts have been given a Mk 28 autopilot. An air-driven rescue hoist can be fitted with a cable length of 23m (75ft). A colour TV camera, monitor and associated equipment has been fitted from time to time. The camera is controlled by an operator sitting in the port seat facing aft. The first time such equipment was used in a practical trial was in Londonderry in 1972. At 305m (1,000ft) AGL, the TV

produced excellent pictures on two colour monitors at Brigade HQ. The aircraft was under the direct control of the HQ and thus could be ordered to look in any particular direction and to use its zoom lens for more detail. Two inflatable bags, one on each side outboard of the rear doors, can be stowed in clam-type alloy shells. In Hong Kong, for example, Scouts fly as a matter of course with such flotation gear.

The Scout, rugged and robust, is a delight to fly. Remarkably free of vibration, it is responsive to control inputs and is very manoeuvrable. As far as safety is concerned its one major shortcoming is its high rate of rotor decay after an engine failure. Rotor rpm are normally 410 and it is essential that autorotation be established without delay otherwise the rotor rpm may fall below the minimum power-off figure of 330. Rate of descent in autorotation at 2,268kg (5,000lb) is approximately 15.2m/s (3,000ft/min). An engine-off landing is more difficult in the Scout than in most helicopters, not least because a touchdown speed of about 37kph (23mph) is recommended. Some practice is required to ensure landing with the skids level as the tendency is to land with the rear of the skids touching first. Damage to the skids or a fore-and-aft pitching movement can result.

Above: A Scout on eagle patrol in Northern Ireland. For these patrols the back seat was normally removed. (Rolls-Royce)

Opposite page, top: A missile-armed Scout is well camouflaged against the background. The protuberance in the cockpit roof is the housing for the AF.120 missile-aiming sight. (Museum of Army Flying)

Above: A Scout lands close to an infantry position during the Falklands War. Although over twenty years old it proved itself as a battlefield machine, being rugged and reliable. (Museum of Army Flying)

The Scout had rendered sterling service in many locations around the world. In recent years it has played a notable role in the search for immigrants trying to enter Hong Kong illegally from China and in Operation 'Agila', the transition to independence for Zimbabwe. In March 1964 the first Scouts arrived in Aden and a month later others arrived in Malaya. In Aden, in particular, they were often fired at and hit an uncomfortable number of times. One incident at random gives a flavour of the type of flying undertaken. In May 1967 a number of vehicles was ambushed in a wadi and casualties were sustained. Two Scouts were scrambled to help, one armed with machine-guns and the other in the casualty evacuation role. On reaching the area the armed Scout was hit but the pilot, Lieutenant David Ralls, determined to find the dissidents' position so that he could call in some fighter ground attack aircraft in the area. He located the enemy

position, and though hit again, flew over it to mark it with a smoke grenade. Once the strike was completed Ralls attempted to observe its effects, but again came under fire from another position. His gunner returned the fire. By this time a Wessex with RM Commandos aboard was on its way and Ralls led it to a point just above the position which was then successfully assaulted. This action complete, Ralls returned to the original ambush position and brought out four casualties. It was a display of courage, flying skill and initiative which earned Ralls the DFC.

The Scout's performance in the Falklands provides further proof of its versatility and robustness. Twelve from the RM Commando Brigade and the AAC's 656 Squadron were deployed and only one was lost. While the 2nd Battalion The Parachute Regiment was fighting for Port Darwin, Lieutenant Richard Nunn, a RM pilot, was tasked to evacuate casualties. As he moved forward with his airgunner in the cabin, he was suddenly attacked by two Pucara aircraft with cannon and rocket fire. As they made repeated passes from different heights and directions Nunn did all he knew to take evasive action but, once seen by two comparatively slow-flying but heavily-armed aircraft, there is not much a helicopter can do, especially in the open. The

Scout was eventually shot down. Before he died, however, Nunn had selflessly supported the battalion, bringing forward vital ammunition to the front line and evacuating casualties regardless of fire. For his courageous actions Nunn was awarded a posthumous DFC.

Another Scout pilot, Captain Sam Drennan of the AAC, won the DFC for his support of the 2nd Battalion Scots Guards during their attack on Tumbledown Mountain in June 1982. Flying under fire, over difficult mountainous terrain, in turbulent winds and heavy snow showers, Drennan repeatedly flew forward in full view of the enemy to evacuate sixteen seriously wounded men from exposed positions.

The Scout ceased full-scale production in 1970; none was produced in 1971, but five more were built in 1972. In all, 148 production Scouts were built. It did not sell well abroad, only nine copies being exported: two each to the Royal Australian Navy and the police departments of Bahrain and Uganda and three to the Royal Jordanian Air Force. Some 40 Scouts remain in AAC service and are expected to continue well into the 1990s. The AAC's first Territorial Army Squadron, to form in 1986, will be equipped with twelve Scouts while others are currently serving in the UK, Brunei, the Falkland Islands and Hong Kong.

P.531 Wasp

As a result of the trials at Boscombe Down in 1959, the Royal Navy ordered three prototypes, designated P.531-0/N, with which to develop operating techniques from small ships. During the somewhat protracted trials beginning in November 1959, both a skid undercarriage with four oleos and a long-stroke quadricycle wheeled landing gear were tested during take-offs and landings from HMS *Undaunted*, a wartime frigate modified to have a landing platform. As many as nineteen undercarriage/deck securing systems were tested by day and night including suction pads attached to the fore and aft ends of each skid. To assist in arriving at a decision on the choice of undercarriage a 'rolling platform', 7.3m (24ft) square, was built at RAE Bedford to simulate the motions of a frigate at sea. The undercarriage had to fulfil two particular requirements: a safe landing within prescribed ship motion limits and thereafter immobility of the helicopter as the ship manoeuvred. A harpoon and grid system was also tested in December 1960 on the platform by a dynamic full-scale P.531 model fuselage and by a fully airworthy Dragonfly. A barbed harpoon was lowered from the helicopter and this engaged a grid on the deck. The idea was not pursued because of the perceived technical problems, but interestingly it has since been revived for the Lynx. Eventually it was decided to install a widely spaced, four-wheeled, fully castoring undercarriage which permitted heavy landings on a pitching deck and made for comparatively easy deck handling.

While these trials were in progress the heavier P.531-2 had superseded the original P.531 with the approval of both the Army and the Navy. Thus, in 1961, the Navy placed its first major order for the Sea Scout HAS Mk 1, the name later being changed to Wasp. Flown by Ron Gellatly, the first pre-production aircraft made its maiden flight from White Waltham on 28 October 1962. A second pre-production machine was followed by the first production HAS Mk 1 model in January 1963. Six months later 700(W) Squadron, the Wasp IFTU, formed at RNAS Culdrose. By March 1964 it had completed its task, been disbanded and given way to 829 Squadron, the HQ Squadron for all Small Ships Flights, now based at RNAS Portland.

The Wasp shares the same basic design concept as the Scout and quite closely resembles it. There are, however, some notable differences besides the landing gear. The tail boom, for example, folds and instead of the Scout's full-length tail plane below the tail boom the Wasp has a half-length one at the top of the tail rotor pylon on the starboard side. Unlike the Scout the Wasp has metal tail rotor blades. From quite early on, a de-rated 710shp Nimbus Mk 103 or 104 was used. As we have seen it was originally intended that the Scout and Wasp should both incorporate an autopilot/autostabilization system. While only a very few Scouts

Above: A P.531-0/N, a prototype for the Wasp but with skid landing gear. (M. J. Hooks)

Opposite page, top: A P.531-0/N with suction pads attached to the skids. (Westland Helicopters)

Opposite page, bottom: A Wasp with an AS-12 missile. Note the angles of the wheels, splayed out to minimize movement after touchdown. (Westland Helicopters)

ever received such a system, a Mk 28 four-channel system to provide control in pitch, roll, yaw and height together with a radar altimeter was installed in the Wasp. This was developed on a Skeeter which was re-engined with a Turmo turbine to give a constant speed rotor system which a piston engine could not provide.

The Wasp was developed directly from the Scout to operate from small platforms on frigates and destroyers to extend the range of their anti-submarine operations. This was in line with the Medium Range Anti-Submarine Torpedo Carrying Helicopter (MATCH) concept. The Wasp was to be used as an integral part of the frigate's anti-submarine weapon system, its role being to launch its torpedoes under radar guidance against long-range sonar contacts; this allowed the frigate to stand off out of range of the target submarine's weapons. The Wasp can, of course, undertake a number of secondary roles such as the direction of naval gunfire, the detection and identification of other ships and casualty evacuation.

Above: A Wasp with flotation gear and a rescue hoist on the starboard side. (Rolls-Royce)

Below: The tail fin and stabilizer of the Wasp differ substantially from those of the Scout. (FAA Museum)

Above: With missile sight in the roof but no missiles, a Wasp on patrol in the Far East. (Rolls-Royce)

Below: A few Wasps were equipped with the 6,000m range AS-12 guided missile from 1969. (FAA Museum)

Above left: April 1982: a Wasp with an AS-12 missile faces the icy waters of South Georgia from the deck of HMS *Plymouth*. (FAA)

Above: An 829 Squadron Wasp fires an AS-12. (FAA Museum)

Above right: With an AS-12 missile on each side and flotation gear, a Wasp attends the International Air Show at Middle Wallop in 1984. (Author)

Left: A Wasp from 829 Squadron with two Mk 44 torpedoes flies over HMS *Aurora*. The Wasp was one of the first small ship's helicopters which could carry two torpedoes. (FAA Museum)

The Wasp carries no equipment to detect submarines, but instead a weapon load of some 400kg (880lb) consisting of two Mk 44 or 46 homing torpedoes between the undercarriage legs or an equivalent weight of depth-charges or bombs. Any ship that can control a Wasp by radar can direct it to attack a target detected by the ship's sensors. Because of the growing threat from fast patrol boats, the Royal Navy decided to acquire the additional capability to mount air-to-surface weapons for the Wasp. In 1969 two French 6,000m range AS-12 wire-guided missiles were mounted on outriggers, one on each side of the fuselage, together with an APX/BEZU M.260 gyro-stabilized sight. Three Wasps fired a total of eight AS-12 at the Argentinian submarine *Santa Fe* in April 1982. The first, launched from a Wasp from HMS *Endurance* from a height of 305m (1,000ft) and 6km (3.7 miles) away, was the first guided missile ever to be fired at a ship by the Royal Navy in anger; it hit the conning tower.

In all 98 Wasps were built for the Royal Navy, 96 of which were production models. Some 30 are still in service in 829 Squadron for anti-surface vessel (ASV) attack and survey, the Sea King having taken over the ASW task. It is expected that by 1987 most, if not all, Wasps will have been retired from front-line service. Thirty-five Wasps were exported. According to the Military Balance 1985/86, one ASW helicopter squadron of ten Wasps is still in service in South Africa's Southern Air Command. None of the Dutch Wasps remains in service, but at least ten of them have been sold to the Naval Air Arm of the Indonesian Navy with which they are still in operation. The Brazilian and New Zealand Navies continue to operate the Wasp, both having taken delivery of more refurbished aircraft and more than doubling their original number.

47G-3B-1 Sioux

By the early 1960s the helicopter was firmly established in the AAC and before the decade was out the Army's operational fixed-wing fleet had withered to a handful of Beavers and Auster Mk 9. Despite the shortcomings of the Skeeter it was quite clear that the helicopter was the ideal aerial battlefield vehicle: it needed no airstrip and could land almost anywhere, it could fly very slowly and therefore in worse weather than a fixed-wing aircraft, and it could make use of natural ground cover to hide itself. Because of the delay in development and production of a suitable gas turbine light helicopter to replace the Skeeter, it was decided to conduct a 'fly-off' competition between four existing American helicopter types: the Brantly B.2, the Hiller 12E, the Hughes 269 and the Bell 47G-3. What was required was an aircraft that could be procured quickly and was small, simple, reliable and easy to conceal in the field; a two-seater principally for reconnaissance and observation. The Bell 47G-3 won the competition from the Hiller 12E and in early 1964 an order for 150 was placed to Specification H.240, the first 50 to be built by Agusta in Italy to achieve the earliest possible delivery and the remainder by Westland. Subsequently another 116 were ordered for the Army and fifteen for the RAF as training aircraft and known as the Sioux HT Mk 2. At the same time that the HT Mk 2 was in production for the RAF six Sioux were being built for the South Yemen Air Force. Of these some were sold back in the UK in 1974.

The number for the Army greatly exceeded the number of Skeeters. The reason was the so-called

Above: The Sioux was an American Bell Helicopter design built under licence by Westland in the 1960s. (Westland Helicopters)

Opposite page: The Royal Marines operated a few Siouxs. Here one, attached to 40 Commando in 1973, flies from HMS *Bulwark*. (Author)

Integration Scheme which was approved in 1963. This involved the establishment of a light helicopter platoon or troop of up to six light helicopters in selected armoured, artillery, engineer, signals and infantry units. The scheme had the desirable effects of raising the number of Army aircraft and of providing intimate helicopter support to combat units although the disadvantages of the ensuing decentralization of command and control and technical support are not difficult to imagine. Financial and manpower stringencies caused the scheme to wither and die in less than ten years by which time all these helicopters had been consolidated into AAC squadrons and regiments.

The Army's planned in-service date for the 47G-3B-1, named the Sioux AH Mk 1, and somewhat irreverently called the 'clockwork mouse' in the AAC, was April 1964 and the original intention was to use it for no longer than about five years. In the event the last one was not withdrawn from service until September 1978 because of the delay in the appearance of the Anglo-French Gazelle.

The first version of the Bell 47 had made its maiden flight in December 1945. A multitude of modifications and refinements over the years ensured continuing sales. The 47D was the first variant to introduce the 'goldfish bowl' canopy and to be ordered in significant numbers by the US Army. In 1952 Agusta acquired a licence to manufacture the aircraft in Europe. Westland subsequently acquired a licence from Agusta to build it for the British Armed Services, part of the agreement being to accept certain components from Agusta for the British Company to incorporate into the helicopters it was to build. The first of the Italian-built Sioux was flown to the AAC Centre in the spring of 1964 and the first Westland-built Sioux flew on 9 March 1965.

The Bell 47G-3B-1 was basically the same as the earlier Bell 47G-3 which had first flown in July 1959. It was a helicopter with an exceptional high-altitude performance and powered by a piston engine rated at 225hp from sea level to over 4,572m (15,000ft). The engine in the British Sioux was the Lycoming TVO-435-B1A version of 270hp with a turbo-supercharger which

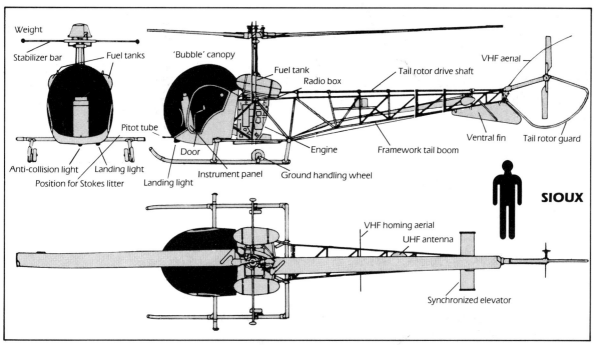

Weight

Stabilizer bar

Fuel tanks

'Bubble' canopy

Fuel tank

Radio box

Tail rotor drive shaft

VHF aerial

Pitot tube

Door

Instrument panel

Engine

Ground handling wheel

Framework tail boom

Ventral fin

Tail rotor guard

Anti-collision light

Landing light

Landing light

Position for Stokes litter

VHF homing aerial

UHF antenna

SIOUX

Synchronized elevator

Above: The two-bladed 'see-saw' rotor with stabilizer bar was not articulated. Note the two fuel tanks behind the 'bubble' canopy and the stripe painted horizontally round it. (Museum of Army Flying)

maintained take-off power to about 3,780m (12,400ft) at a temperature of approximately 40°C (104°F). Despite this constant power to altitude the Sioux was considered underpowered in normal operations. The supercharger also placed an extra demand on the transmission for which it was not designed; this resulted in an unhealthy serviceability record for a time. The noise that the engine made has been particularly popular with the film industry which has been keen to dub it onto many helicopter sequences without regard to the type of helicopter in view! Two interconnected fuel tanks were mounted above the engine, one on each side of the main rotor transmission. One problem experienced in very hot weather was the vaporization of the fuel before it reached the carburettor. This resulted in the engine cutting out in flight or even preventing take-off. In Aden, for example, flying at midday was sometimes not possible.

The most interesting design feature of the Bell 47 was undoubtedly its novel rotor system. Known as a 'see-saw' system, the two blades were connected to the collective and cyclic pitch controls, but the hub was not articulated and there were no drag, flapping or feathering hinges. A 1.5m (5ft) hydraulically damped stabilizer bar, weighted at each end and rigidly attached to the main rotor mast below and at 90° to the main rotor blades, provided instead a degree of autostabilization by means of its inherent inertia and gyroscopic action. If the helicopter's attitude was involuntarily disturbed, the bar tended to remain in the same place. The relative movement between the bar and the mast would then cause the hub and blade assembly to feather and return

the rotor to its original plane of rotation. In other words, the rotor tilted about the drive shaft and mast. The result was a rock steady hover in ground effect. The two all-metal blades had internal 4.5kg (10lb) weights to increase the dynamic inertia of the rotor and this improved the autorotational characteristics of the aircraft. The two-bladed all-metal tail rotor was particularly sensitive to damage. Even strikes against blades of long grass could cause a catastrophic failure and a tail rotor strike indicator on the tip of each blade was fitted. These were inspected for evidence of a strike after each flight. With only two main rotor blades, the rear one tied to the tail boom, there was no need of a blade-folding facility.

The 'bubble' canopy provided excellent all-round vision for the pilot and observer, the pilot sitting, unusually for a helicopter, on the port side. To provide a horizon reference at a glance – the rudimentary instrument panel was in the centre of the cockpit and not opposite the pilot – a thin yellow band was painted horizontally round the canopy. Also attached to the outside of the canopy at the centre was a 15cm (6in) long piece of wool, stuck on with adhesive tape. Once forward speed had been achieved the position of the wool indicated the balance of the aircraft; simple and effective. There were three side-by-side seats in the cockpit although it was comfortable for neither the pilot nor the passenger if the middle seat were occupied. The centre section carrying the engine at the

Above: An Army Sioux in service with the United Nations in Cyprus on landing pad 'Juliet' in the Greek area near Xeros, 1968. (Author)

approximate centre of gravity was of welded steel tube as was the triangular cross-section tail boom. These were both left uncovered, thus improving accessibility to all major components and systems and facilitating the detection of leaks and frayed cables. The skid landing gear had small ground handling wheels which could be raised and lowered by means of a small piece of piping. Two Stokes litters for the carriage of casualties or light stores could be secured to the undercarriage cross-members, one on each side of the cockpit.

Over the years the Sioux was equipped with a variety of role equipment. In Northern Ireland, for example, a Nightsun searchlight was mounted between the landing gear cross tubes on the starboard side and connected to the aircraft's electrical system. For operations in Aden and Borneo, a 7.62mm machine-gun was occasionally fitted to the front cross tube with an ammunition tray on the centre seat. In forward flight there was a notable shift to port when the gun was fired, but as suppressive fire was generally the object this did not matter too much. In the hover the recoil was considerable and substantial right pedal was needed to maintain the aircraft heading.

The Sioux was, of course, warmly welcomed by the Army as a replacement for the Skeeter. It was 295kg (650lb) heavier than its predecessor, offered an extra seat and, more important, an adequate flight performance world-wide. Sioux of the RM and AAC operated in more than 40 countries in all five major continents. It had a most useful radio fit consisting of military VHF (FM), VHF and UHF sets and a simple but effective

VHF (FM) homer. One of the most attractive features of these radios was the fact that they were digitally tuned, thus saving the pilot the traditional and laborious task of regular re-tuning. Where the Sioux did not compare favourably with the Skeeter was in its flight performance in temperate climates. It was slower with a maximum cruise speed of only 138kph (86mph) and was less agile. It was, nevertheless, a pleasant and easy aircraft to fly and it was therefore used for pilot training in addition to its operational roles. On the ground it was somewhat fragile and comparatively easily damaged during ground movement or when carrying rather more robust soldiers.

The Sioux participated in the activities in Belize, Borneo, Cyprus, the Radfan and Northern Ireland to name just some of the most important. It was used for observation and reconnaissance, the carriage of personnel, casualties and light stores, and as an airborne command post in which role it was particularly useful if a little cramped. Many unusual incidents were experienced, but the pilot who had to land in a clearing in Borneo to act as a 'midwife' to the Iban woman he was taking to hospital may have been the most nonplussed. So keenly awaited were these helicopters in the Far East that 26 of the Agusta-built Sioux were delivered direct to Malaya. Sioux were already in Northern Ireland when the State of Emergency was officially declared on 12 August 1969. From then until it was gradually replaced by the Gazelle from 1975 it proved most valuable by day and night, particularly for the

Above: A 666 Squadron AAC Sioux armed with a 7.62mm machine-gun in the starboard seat. (Author)

Above right: A Sioux on patrol in the Radfan in 1965. (Museum of Army Flying)

surveillance of events or areas and the search for culvert bombs and wires leading from suspect bombs.

From 1968 to 1976 six Sioux comprised the AAC Helicopter Display Team named the Blue Eagles while an RAF team of three Sioux from the Central Flying School was called the Tomahawks. With its piston engine and twist-grip throttle the Sioux was not ideal for display purposes, but the skill of the pilots showed the teams off in spectacular fashion.

Westland also built sixteen 47G-4A helicopters during 1969. These were procured by Bristow Helicopters for the basic training of Army pilots at the AAC Centre. They were generally similar to the Army and RAF helicopters but they did have a different engine: an unsupercharged 305hp Avco Lycoming VO-540 derated to 270hp. These aircraft were retired from this particular task in 1982.

SCOUT, WASP AND SIOUX TYPES AND VARIANTS

P.531: First Saunders-Roe prototype of 5-seat utility helicopter with 325shp engine and wheeled undercarriage; 2 built. First flight (FF) 20 July 1958.

P.531-0/N: Similar to P.531, but developed by Westland with skid landing gear as naval prototype; 3 built. FF September 1959.

P.531-2: Much heavier version of P.531; 2 built, 1 with 635shp engine and 1 with 685shp engine. FF 9 August 1959.

P.531-2 Mk 1: Pre-production aircraft with 635shp engine; 8 built. FF 4 August 1960.

SCOUT AH Mk 1: Production utility aircraft, a few later armed with SS-11 missiles, and with 710shp engine; 148 built, 139 for Army. FF 6 March 1961.

WASP HAS Mk 1: ASW/ASV version of Scout with weapons but no sensors, and wheels; 134 built, 98 for Royal Navy. FF 28 October 1962.

SIOUX: 253 built.

AH Mk 1: Piston-engined 3-seat reconnaissance helicopter; 222 built, 216 for Army. FF 9 March 1965.

HT Mk 2: Trainer similar to Mk 1; 15 built for RAF.

47G-4A: Trainer with 305hp unsupercharged engine; 16 built for Bristow Helicopters Ltd.

Foreign Users:

Scout: Australia (2), Bahrain (2), Jordan (3), Uganda (2).

Wasp: Brazil (3), Netherlands (12), New Zealand (3), South Africa (17).

Sioux: South Yemen (6).

CHARACTERISTICS: SCOUT, WASP AND SIOUX TYPES

Designation	Scout AH Mk 1	Wasp HAS Mk 1	Sioux AH Mk 1
Engine	RR (Bristol) Nimbus 105 710shp	RR (Bristol) Nimbus 103/104 710shp	Avco Lycoming TVO-435-B1A 270hp
Rotor diameter	9.83m (32ft 3in)	9.83m (32ft 3in)	11.32m (37ft 1½in)
Fuselage length	9.24m (30ft 4in)	9.24m (30ft 4in)	9.85m (32ft 4in)
Height	2.73m (8ft 11in)	2.97m (9ft 9in)	2.84m (9ft 3¾in)
Empty weight	1,466kg (3,232lb)*	1,566kg (3,453lb)	814kg (1,794lb)
Max gross weight	2,427kg (5,350lb)	2,495kg (5,500lb)	1,338kg (2,950lb)
Max speed	211kph (131mph)	193kph (120mph)	169kph (105mph)
Range	505km (314 miles)	488km (303 miles)	351km (218 miles)
Service ceiling	4,085m (13,400ft)	3,720m (12,200ft)	6,096m (20,000ft)

*Basic operating weight.

The Sea King Family

As the capabilities of the submarine improved – becoming faster, deeper diving and with more effective weapons – so it became ever more necessary to upgrade the means to detect and destroy it. Neither the Whirlwind nor the Wessex had been able to combine these roles over a satisfactory radius of action. What was desperately needed as the 1960s wore on was a hunter/killer helicopter which could fly out to at least

185km (115 miles) from its parent ship, search for an hour or more, find and destroy its target and then return.

The Sikorsky S-61 was the design chosen to fulfil a 1957 US Navy requirement for an anti-submarine helicopter. The first prototype flew in March 1959 and in that same year Westland signed yet another licence agreement with Sikorsky. Their original intention, however, was to build a civil 23-seater powered by two Napier Gazelle engines and called the WS-61 Wiltshire. The rationalization of the helicopter industry and an almost total lack of interest ensured that this idea made

Below: The Sea King Mk 1, a Westland-built version of the Sikorsky SH-3D but with British engines and substantially better avionics. These allowed it to operate autonomously as a submarine hunter/killer. In the background is a Whirlwind Mk 7. (FAA Museum)

Above: By the end of 1969 the Royal Navy had come to the conclusion that the Sea King was the world's most effective ASW helicopter. (Westland Helicopters)

Opposite page, top: A Sea King Mk 1 hover taxis over Royal Navy Phantoms. (FAA Museum)

Opposite page, bottom: A Mk 1 lowers its Type 195 sonar. Four Mk 44 torpedoes are also visible. (Rolls-Royce)

very little headway. As far as an ASW helicopter for the Royal Navy was concerned Westland pursued a triple track policy in the early 1960s: improving existing types, developing an anglicized version of the S-61 (later named the SH-3A Sea King in US Navy service), and continuing with their own designs such as the WG-1/WG-4 and the tandem rotor WG-2 and WG-11.

There was an important distinction in the way that the US Navy and the Royal Navy viewed the role of the ASW helicopter at this time. To the former the ship was the tactical command centre which directed the activities of the helicopter whose sensors could be used for the final and exact location of the submarine and whose weapons could be used for its destruction. The Royal Navy, on the other hand, saw things differently, preferring to give the helicopter the necessary equipment to allow it to operate tactically quite independently of its parent ship; the tactical centre was on board the helicopter, not the ship.

By 1965 the choice of a replacement for the Wessex HAS Mk 3 lay between the WG-11, the Sikorsky-built Sea King or an anglicized version built by Westland. In June 1966 the Royal Navy placed an order for the Westland Sea King and then demanded that the aircraft be brought into service as quickly as possible. There was thus no time to anglicize all the drawings and

Westland ordered four Sikorsky-built airframes to be used for systems integration. The first arrived at Avonmouth in component form in October 1966 and was re-assembled on the dockside and flown to Yeovil. This aircraft had T-58 engines, but the other three were assembled with Rolls-Royce Gnome engines and British avionics.

The first production HAS Mk 1 built by Westland flew on 7 May 1969 at Yeovil and on 19 August that year the IFTU, 700(S) Squadron, was commissioned at RNAS Culdrose. Over 2,500 flying hours were achieved with six aircraft and the Navy came to the conclusion that the British Sea King was the most potent and effective hunter/killer helicopter in existence.

The fuselage of the Sea King is outwardly similar to the American SH-3D with a watertight hull which permits landings on water. The landing gear has main wheels which retract into sponsons, and a fixed tail wheel. Inflatable bags are fitted to the outside of each sponson to improve stability and flotation when the rotor is stopped. The Sikorsky five-bladed all-metal main rotor has an automatic powered folding system while the five-bladed tail rotor is mounted high on the manually folding tail. Where the British Sea King differs from its American counterpart is in its power plants, avionics and role equipment. The two 1,400shp T-58 engines were replaced in the Mk 1 by two Rolls-Royce 1,500shp Gnome H.1400 turboshafts. The Louis Newmark Mk 31 AFCS, a less complicated but highly reliable simplex version of the Mk 30 in the Wessex Mk 3, offered automatic transition from and to the hover which permitted reliable day and night ASW operations. The heart of the helicopter as a weapons system

comprised an Ekco AW391 search radar mounted in a dorsal radome, a Plessey dipping sonar Type 195 and a Marconi AD 580 Doppler navigation system which had already proved itself in the Wessex Mk 3. The output from these equipments was all fed into an automatic tactical plotting display in the cabin; a constant indication of helicopter position in relation to all contacts was thus available. Together with its weapons the Sea King could detect, track, classify and destroy modern submarines by means of this integrated system.

At last the Royal Navy had an ASW helicopter that met their stated needs. A crew of four, two pilots, an observer and a sonar operator, and two externally-mounted Mk 44 homing torpedoes could be carried for up to four hours; by swapping an hour's fuel two more torpedoes could be carried. Up to four Mk 11 depth-charges could be taken instead of the torpedoes. While maximum endurance speed was 138kph (86mph) typical cruise speed was 211kph (131mph) at the normal take-off weight of 9,300kg (20,500lb).

In February 1970 the first Royal Navy Sea King squadron, 824, formed at RNAS Culdrose and in June the Squadron embarked in HMS *Ark Royal*. The normal complement was six Sea Kings per carrier and four for the two converted helicopter cruisers, HMSs *Blake* and *Tiger*. Five operational and two training squadrons were ultimately equipped with the Mk 1. The 56th and final production Sea King was delivered to the Navy in June 1972.

The very first production Mk 1 was used as a vehicle to carry out highly important flight tests with new composite main rotor blades in 1982. These blades offer longer life, reduced cost of ownership and maintenance, and increased safety. A gradual retrofit programme is now underway so that all Sea Kings will eventually have these blades.

HAS Mk 2

So successful had the Mk 1 been that within two and a half years the decision had been taken to order an improved version. In November 1974 thirteen HAS Mk 2 were ordered and two years later this number was increased to 21 while it was agreed to convert the remaining 48 Mk 1 to Mk 2 standard. The only external difference was the addition of a sixth blade to the tail rotor to give better yaw control. More powerful engines, the 1,660shp Gnome H 1400-1, were also installed. The fuel jettison rate was increased while the fuel capacity itself was raised. As a result of these and

Below: The Sea King Mk 2, seen here with Mk 44 torpedoes, employed more powerful engines than the Mk 1 and a sixth blade was added to the tail rotor. (Westland Helicopters)

Opposite page, top: Twenty-one Mk 2 were built and 48 Mk 1 were converted to the new standard. Note the foreign object damage shield in front of the engine intakes to prevent the ingestion of ice and solid objects. This shield was progressively introduced on the Mk 2. (Rolls-Royce)

Opposite page, bottom: The first Westland-built Sea King Mk 1, XV 642, was updated to Mk 2 standard and subsequently used for trials of the new composite main rotor blades, seen here, in 1982. (Westland Helicopters)

Above: The first two Mk 2 converted to carry the Searchwater radar for airborne early warning. The modifications took only eleven weeks during the summer of 1982. Here, the dome is in the deployed position. (Westland Helicopters)

other modifications maximum take-off weight rose by 227kg (500lb) to 9,526kg (21,000lb). The first Mk 2 flew on 18 June 1976 and the last of the 21 was delivered in October 1979. Meanwhile the Mk 1 were converted by the Royal Navy between August 1976 and January 1980.

Fifteen Mk 2 took part in the Falklands War and all returned safely. While those of 824 Squadron were employed mainly on ASW patrol, 825 Squadron was formed only on 2 May for general duties with stripped-out aircraft, their sonars having been removed. Some of these aircraft participated in the heroic rescue efforts associated with the devastating attacks on the vessels Sir *Galahad* and Sir *Tristram* as they furiously burned. Hovering in dense smoke, the helicopters had no normal horizon and the pilots had to use whatever they could see; for example, the name 'Sir Galahad' painted conspicuously on the stern. With great presence of mind the pilots used their rotor downwash to blow the survivor-filled dinghies away from the ships which were liable to explode at any moment.

The Mk 2 has been the platform for a most interesting development. As a result of the lack of a long-range search capability for the Royal Navy at sea, forcibly brought home during the Falklands War, an airborne early warning (AEW) requirement was quickly issued. Action to meet it was swift and two Mk 2

were hurriedly converted to take Thorn-EMI's Searchwater maritime surveillance radar (as in the Nimrod MR Mk 2) during the summer of 1982. This radar is designed to detect, track and classify small targets, even submarine periscopes, against the clutter produced by heavy seas – but it is not really an AEW radar. Nevertheless, its airborne target detection capability has been much improved. The whole process from MoD approval through planning, development, production and flight test to embarkation in HMS *Illustrious* as she left for the South Atlantic on 2 August 1982 took only eleven weeks – an amazing feat! The radar scanner is mounted in an inflatable 1.9m (6ft 3in) diameter drum-like dome on the starboard side just forward of the dorsal radome. When airborne the radar is hydraulically rotated forwards and downwards to provide a 360° scan. Service ceiling for the aircraft is 3,050m (10,000ft) and at this height an acceptable target detection range of more than 161km (100 miles) can be achieved. Flying so high, however, does increase the aircraft's vulnerability.

Besides the primary role of AEW this new version of the Sea King is well able to undertake certain important secondary roles: the direction of Sea Harriers and other fighter aircraft, surface ship surveillance and over-the-horizon targetting for other launch platforms. With a

Left: The Sea King Mk 3 resembles the Mk 2 but is used for SAR by the RAF. (Rolls-Royce)

Opposite page, top: The Mk 3 has a crew of two pilots, a radar/winch operator and a load-master/winchman. The Mk 3's comprehensive navigational equipment includes a TANS in the cockpit whereas the naval variants have the TANS in the observer's position in the rear. (Rolls-Royce)

Opposite page, bottom: Up to six stretcher cases, or two casualties on stretchers and eleven seated, or nineteen seated survivors can be carried by the Mk 3. (Rolls-Royce)

Squadron which was re-commissioned on 9 November 1984; a Flight of this Squadron was commissioned at RNAS Culdrose on 31 May 1985 with three production AEW Sea Kings in a new light-grey colour scheme. These helicopters have better target tracking and data handling facilities than the original two pre-production aircraft, and integrated with the radar are a Cossor Electronics Jubilee Guardsman IFF and Ferranti FIN 1110 inertial navigation system.

HAR Mk 3

As early as 1969 the West German Navy had ordered a variant based on the Mk 1 for SAR. It became the envy of the RAF. But it was not until June 1975 that funds became available at which time an order for fifteen HAR Mk 3 was placed. Based on the Mk 2, the Mk 3 has a sophisticated navigation system which includes a Decca Tactical Air Navigation System (TANS) F which accepts data from a Type 71 Doppler and a Mk 19 Decca navigation receiver. The search radar has been retained. The first Mk 3 flew on 6 September 1977 and the fifteenth aircraft was delivered in February 1979. By this time a sixteenth aircraft was needed and in 1983 another three were ordered for delivery in 1985. The first unit to get the Mk 3 was D Flight of 202 Squadron at RAF Lossiemouth.

The RAF Sea Kings are generally painted a conspicuous yellow and have a crew of four: two pilots, a radar/winch operator and a winchman. The cabin has space for six stretchers or two stretchers and eleven seats or simply nineteen seats. Maximum take-off weight can reach 9,707kg (21,400lb). This SAR helicopter is used mainly for long-range rescue, and short-range when other helicopters are not available, having a radius of action of some 615km (382 miles) although this of course is reduced if a heavy load of survivors is anticipated; a standard planning radius is 463km (288 miles).

Many daring rescues have been carried out with this aircraft. One of the most exceptional took place during the night of 27 March 1980 when the accommodation rig Alexander Kielland capsized in the North Sea. Mk 3 and Royal Norwegian Air Force Sea Kings were scrambled. In appalling weather and gathering darkness with a cloud base at about 30m (100ft) these helicopters flew nearly 320km (200 miles) to locate and rescue most of the 89 survivors. One Mk 3 saved 36. The entire crew received awards, Flight Lieutenant Bob

requirement to operate some 100km (62 miles) from its mother ship and remain airborne for four hours, the gross weight of the aircraft precludes it carrying any weapons and so, for the present at least, the AEW Sea King is unarmed.

Six more AEW Sea Kings have been ordered and these will be Mk 2 converted and brought up to reflect the aircraft performance of the Mk 5. For the moment they are designated Mk 2 (AEW). It is expected that two flights of three aircraft each will be deployed on board the two operational carriers with the other two helicopters used for training. All will belong to 849

Neville, the captain, receiving the AFC and Flight Sergeant Mike Yarwood, the winchman, getting the AFM. Yarwood was lowered into 9m (30ft) seas to assist in the winching up of all 36 people, a most courageous and energy-sapping feat. In September 1984 perhaps the longest-ever rescue mission took place. Scrambling from Brawdy in West Wales, a Mk 3 flew out to a Liberian container ship some 645km (400 miles) west of Land's End. With Flight Lieutenant Ian MacFarlane as pilot the aircraft refuelled first at Cork airport before heading out into the Atlantic and again at the Glomar Arctic II oil rig. Heavy rain and low cloud bedevilled matters and a mechanical problem forced the helicopter back to the rig for a time. However, it was soon able to make an approach to the ship. Winchman Sergeant Mark Tait was lowered to the

deck, placed the injured man on a stretcher and the two were then winched up into the helicopter. Again the helicopter refuelled at the rig and at Cork, the entire operation taking some nine hours.

A single Mk 3 was deployed to Ascension Island during the Falklands War and then moved to the Falklands when the fighting ended; two others joined it later.

The Commando

The Sea King HC Mk 4 for the carriage of Royal Marine Commandos has its origins in a Saudi Arabian purchase to meet an Egyptian Air Force requirement for a transport helicopter. Westland initially offered a simplified version of the Mk 41, itself a version of the Mk 1. The new machine, without a dorsal radome and with seats for 21 troops, was designated the Commando Mk 1. Payload and endurance were enhanced for the new role and the first model flew on 12 September 1973. Only five Mk 1 were built, purely to fulfil an urgent Egyptian requirement, the bulk of the order being met later by the Mk 2.

Twenty-three Commando Mk 2 have been ordered for the Egyptian Air Force, seventeen being the

Opposite page, top: Painted in a conspicuous yellow, the Mk 3 has saved many lives both on land and at sea around the coasts of the UK and further afield. (Author)

Opposite page, bottom: The RAF has ordered nineteen Mk 3 operated by 202 Squadron but deployed in small numbers in different locations. Note the bulged window to the left of the doorway. (Westland Helicopters)

Below: The Sea King Mk 4 Commando is a transport version of the standard Sea King. Clearly visible here are the de-icing strips on the foreign object damage shield. (Westland Helicopters)

Opposite page, top: The Commando can operate in arctic or tropical conditions. (Westland Helicopters)

Opposite page, bottom: Unlike other Royal Navy and RAF Sea Kings the Commando has a fixed undercarriage, no dorsal radome and stub wings in place of the sponsons. (Westland Helicopters)

Above: As a tactical troop transport the Commando can seat up to 28 armed troops. (Westland Helicopters)

Below: By having folding main rotor blades and tail pylon, unlike most other Commandos, the Royal Navy version can be based aboard ship with comparative ease. (T. J. T. Everett-Heath)

standard version for 28 troops with a heavy duty undercarriage, stub weapons platforms in place of the sponsons, the uprated H. 1400-1 engines and associated transmission. These aircraft have large sand filters in front of the engines. Two others were equipped as VIP transports for President Sadat and designated the Mk 2B. In September 1975 Egypt ordered four more Mk 2, this time for ECM duties and designated the Mk 2E. Some time was needed to integrate and check out all the systems and it was not until 1980 that these aircraft were delivered. As might be expected they can be distinguished by extra aerials and various EW fairings on the fuselage. Three Mk 2A and a single VIP Mk 2C were built for the Qatar Emiri Air Force and all had been delivered by the spring of 1976.

These export orders for 32 Commandos prompted the Royal Navy in mid 1978 to order fifteen of the basic Mk 2 to boost its troop-lift capacity by obtaining a helicopter with a greater payload, speed and range than its Wessex Mk 5. To retain some commonality with Royal Navy Sea Kings already in service, the HC Mk 4, as this version for the Navy is called, has folding main rotor blades and tail pylon but keeps the fixed landing gear of the earlier Commandos. The first HC Mk 4 flew on 26 September 1979 and two months later 846 Squadron was receiving its first machine. The refined design, with a cabin capacity of nearly 28cu.m

(989cu.ft), allows up to 28 combat-equipped troops or nine stretchers and eight passengers or 2,722kg (6,000lb) internally or 3,402kg (7,500lb) underslung to be carried over a radius of action of some 260km (162 miles) in a wide range of climatic conditions. So far these aircraft have only been armed with a 7.62mm machine-gun in the cabin door but they have the capability to mount a variety of weapons.

Fourteen Mk 4 of 846 Squadron took part in the Falklands War, three failing to return but none as a result of direct enemy action. On 14 May 1982 two of them ferried SAS troops to and from the successful night attack on Pebble Island when eleven Argentinian aircraft were destroyed on the ground. The crews wore night vision goggles (NVG). These goggles are attached to the helmet and by means of a pair of image intensifying tubes enhance the ambient light. The latest generation of tubes, a few of which were available in the Falklands, permit safe low-level flight when the stars provide the only light. Many missions were undertaken by night, some only possible because of the availability of NVG. A tragedy occurred during the night of 19 May when a Mk 4 with a number of SAS

Opposite page: A Commando above the stern of the assault ship HMS *Fearless.* (FAA)

Below: A Commando helps in the evacuation of HMS *Sheffield* during the Falklands War. (FAA)

Above: The first two uprated Sea King Mk 5 were handed over to the Royal Navy in October 1980. The Mk 5 has a larger cabin to accommodate the more modern ASW equipment. (Westland Helicopters)

troops aboard was thought to have been struck in the tail rotor by a large bird and ditched; 21 men died. 21 May was the day that re-possession of the Islands began and on that day seven Mk 4 moved some 417,000kg (919,312lb) of equipment and stores and 520 troops – a prodigious feat. Some mystery surrounds the loss of a Mk 4 in Southern Chile where it was deliberately destroyed by its crew, led by Lieutenant Hutchings RM who was later awarded the DSC, after, presumably, a clandestine mission. Mk 4 were the workhorse of the War, being used day and night for every conceivable task of which they were capable. Before the main landing took place they were used extensively for the cross-decking of personnel and stores in preparation for the assault. Once the troops were ashore they were often used for night insertions of Special Forces teams, the occasional movement of men forward towards Port Stanley and, more often, their accompanying Rapier SAM systems, artillery, ammunition, fuel and combat supplies. The shortage of all types of helicopters and the higher priority accorded to casualty evacuation and logistic tasks meant that vertical envelopment, or the placing of comparatively large numbers of troops behind enemy lines to cut them off, was rarely used. It was a Mk 4 which took General Menendez and a few of his Staff from Port Stanley back to HMS *Fearless* after the Argentinian surrender.

When British troops were deployed to the war-torn city of Beirut in 1983, three of 846 Squadron's Mk 4 were embarked aboard HMS *Fearless*, transferring in January 1984 to the Royal Fleet Auxiliary *Reliant*. Shuttling between the ships and locations in Beirut, they were used for routine logistic tasks and the carriage of personnel. On 8 February 1984 the evacuation of British troops and their equipment began and this was followed immediately afterwards by the evacuation of civilians of 27 nationalities. Because of the threat and the circumstances the helicopters were emblazoned with large Union Jacks and equipped with chaff and decoy flare dispensers, radar warning receivers and armoured seats.

Two further Mk 4, designated Mk 4X and with dorsal radomes, are used by the RAE for research and development. Partly as a result of the Falklands War eight more Mk 4 were ordered shortly after it finished, another four in 1984 and so far another ten in 1985.

The latest version of the Commando is the Mk 3, eight of which have been procured by Qatar. They incorporate the 1,660shp Gnome H.1400-1T engine, re-rated aerodynamically to meet the requirement for high engine power at high ambient temperatures. These aircraft are equipped with an AM-39 Exocet anti-ship missile on each side of the fuselage.

HAS Mk 5

Before the final Mk 2 had been delivered to the Royal Navy it was already obsolescent. Great progress had been made in ASW technology and it was decided to order some more Sea Kings with the new equipment and designate them HAS Mk 5. So far 30 have been built and the Mk 2 are being progressively brought up to the same standard. The first Mk 5 were delivered to the Navy in October 1980 and were fitted out with a most impressive array of ASW equipment. In a larger dorsal radome is housed the antenna for the MEL Sea Searcher radar which offers good long-range detection and excellent target discrimination even in sea clutter, and a track-while-scan of two targets simultaneously. Also installed in the aircraft are a Type 195 sonar, a GEC Avionics AN/AQS-902 Lightweight Acoustic Processing and Display System (LAPADS) to process information derived from the Jezebel sonobuoys, and a TANS G coupled to the Decca 71 Doppler. The A-size Jezebel sonobuoy weighs some 8.5kg (18.7lb), is passive and omni-directional and its hydrophones can operate at various selected depths. To cater for the additional equipment the cabin's rear bulkhead has been moved nearly 1.83m (6ft) towards the tail. Both the observer and sonics operator sit in the cabin in front of their respective radar and sonics displays. With the additional ability to drop a mix of A-, and the smaller F- and G-size sonobuoys, the Mk 5, using passive sonar techniques, can detect enemy submarines at much greater range than the Mk 2 which only has active sonar. Magnetic anomaly detection (MAD) gear to detect whether a suspicious object is made of metal or not, trailing from the starboard sponson, can be installed; nine kits were supplied for the Falklands War.

The principal weapons carried are up to four Mk 46 or Stingray torpedoes or Mk 11 depth-charges. The Mk 5 has the 1,660shp H.1400-1 engines with a conspicuous anti-iced foreign object damage shield in front of them.

The Mk 5 saw action for the first time when 820 and 826 Squadrons, each with nine aircraft, participated in the Falklands War. As the Task Force left Ascension Island the Mk 5 began their unremitting task of searching for Argentinian submarines. Numerous contacts were reported and a number of torpedo and depth-charge attacks made, but no submarines were claimed to have been hit – only an unsuspecting whale or two! Whether the lack of detection stemmed from an absence of submarines or inadequate ASW sensors is not known, but the waters around the Islands are certainly not conducive to acoustic detection. However, the captain of the submarine *San Luis* has reported that he was harried by ASW helicopters for a period of

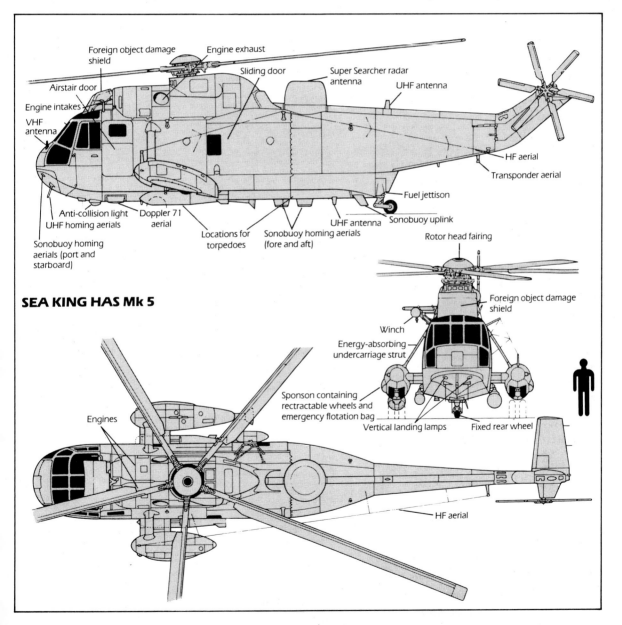

SEA KING HAS Mk 5

Foreign object damage shield
Engine exhaust
Sliding door
Super Searcher radar antenna
UHF antenna
Airstair door
Engine intakes
VHF antenna
HF aerial
Transponder aerial
Fuel jettison
Anti-collision light
UHF homing aerials
Doppler 71 aerial
Locations for torpedoes
Sonobuoy homing aerials (fore and aft)
UHF antenna
Sonobuoy uplink
Sonobuoy homing aerials (port and starboard)
Rotor head fairing
Foreign object damage shield
Winch
Energy-absorbing undercarriage strut
Sponson containing rectractable wheels and emergency flotation bag
Vertical landing lamps
Fixed rear wheel
Engines
HF aerial

Left: The larger flat-topped dorsal radome houses the aerial for the Sea Searcher radar which has significantly better range and discrimination in electronic countermeasures conditions than its predecessor, the AW 391. Here a Mk 5 dips a Type 195 sonar. (Westland Helicopters)

Right: The Mk 5 can carry up to four Mk 46 torpedoes, one seen here, or four Mk 11 depth-charges. (T. J. T. Everett-Heath)

Below: Two Sea Kings, a Mk 5 on the left and a Mk 4 on the right, hover close to the Argentinian vessel *Narwal*. (FAA)

twenty hours during one patrol. Once in the Exclusion Zone Mk 5 were also used to undertake radar reconnaissance patrols to help enforce the blockade. In the early hours of 3 May, for example, a contact was located on radar. The Sea King was engaged by machine-gun fire as it approached, so withdrew and called for missile-armed helicopters. Two Lynx appeared, sank the offending patrol boat and severely damaged a second. No Mk 5 were lost to enemy action but two were forced to ditch because of technical malfunctions.

At the very end of April the senior pilot of 826 Squadron led three Mk 5 off to search for the *San Luis* which was thought to be operating somewhere to the north of the Islands. Unable to land on the two frigates nearby – because their platforms were too small – the Sea Kings refuelled in the hover by winching up a fuel hose and connecting it to their fuel system. While this was going on the ships carried out anti-submarine manoeuvres, the helicopters following rather like balloons being flown by a couple of small boys. At all times the helicopters had to be available for SAR and it was some Mk 5 from 826 Squadron that rescued 55 men from HMS *Coventry*.

On most occasions all the Sea Kings operated at maximum take-off weight and when over land flew at very low level indeed, given the complete absence of any natural cover. The most demanding part of any mission was usually the recovery to the ship and when this had to be conducted in bad weather at night, perhaps in icing conditions, to a darkened, pitching vessel, in radar and radio silence, every ounce of skill,

nerve, good training and teamwork was required. The AFCS did much to reduce crew workload and increase accuracy during the 8, 613 deck landings carried out in April, May and June 1982. To improve performance at high weights an aerodynamic strake was installed at short notice on the port side of the tail cone. This lessened the power required by the tail rotor, thus making more power available for the main rotor. All Royal Navy and RAF Sea Kings have now been retrospectively modified.

The Royal Navy Sea Kings have been so successful that further modifications to enhance their operational effectiveness are being considered. One of the shortcomings of the Mk 5 is that it has active and passive sonics processing requiring separate displays and, in fact, separate stations within the aircraft. This is far from ideal and a combined active and passive suite clearly would be more satisfactory. This is achieved in the AQS-902D-DS which combines the acoustic processing for both passive sonobuoys and active dipping sonar into one system. No plans are yet afoot to replace the Type 195 sonar which is now beginning to show its technological age, although Plessey's Cormorant lightweight sonar can be integrated with the AQS-902 to form the Helicopter Integrated Sonics System (HISOS). Together with other modifications, an upgraded sonar sonics-equipped aircraft will result and will be designated Sea King Mk 6.

Below left: A Mk 5 brings in stores as two Harriers prepare to launch. (FAA)

Below right: A Wessex Mk 5 and a Sea King Mk 5 undertake vertical replenishment from RFA *Resource*. The versatility of both types was well demonstrated during the Falklands War. (FAA)

Sea Kings for Export

As part of the licence agreement Sikorsky had permitted Westland to sell their Sea Kings anywhere in the world apart from North America and Japan where Mitsubishi also had a licence. In May 1969 the West German Navy ordered 22 principally for SAR and they entered service with the Marineflieger in 1974. Based on the HAS Mk 1, these aircraft had the rear bulkhead moved rearwards to provide for 21 seats, and the sonar removed. A winch was fitted over the starboard door and extra fuel tanks increased endurance up to a maximum of 5¾ hours. These aircraft are now to be given an ASV role and are to be equipped with the

Above: An Egyptian Sea King Mk 47 undergoes servicing. (Rolls-Royce)

Ferranti Seaspray Mk 3 radar and the British Aerospace Sea Skua anti-ship missile.

The Mk 42, again similar to the Mk 1, was produced for the Indian Navy in the ASW role. Six were delivered in 1971, six more in 1974 and another three, designated Mk 42A and with the ability to operate from small ships by means of a hauldown system, handed over in 1980; these aircraft had the H.1400-1 engines. In July 1983 another twelve, designated the Mk 42B, were ordered, with options for eight more. These options have now been converted into firm orders. The Mk 42B will have

Above: A Commando Mk 2 of the Egyptian Air Force. Note the large engine intake sand filter. (Rolls-Royce)

Below: A Commando Mk 2 on a test flight in the UK before delivery to the Egyptian Air Force. (Westland Helicopters)

H.1400-1T engines and the MEL Super Searcher radar based on the Sea Searcher but with better clutter suppression and a freeze frame facility among the improvements. Instead of MEL's colour display the Indians have selected monochrome for compatibility with the Jezebel sonabuoy displays. The Mk 42B will be armed with one British Aerospace 600kg (1,323lb) Sea Eagle missile on each side of the fuselage. This missile is an anti-ship skimmer using active radar guidance; it has an advanced and large warhead and a range of perhaps 100km (62 miles). The Sea Eagle has been the subject of successful trials installed on the Advanced Sea King, now itself under trial and the first helicopter to carry the missile. The Mk 42B will have one less tail rotor blade than the standard Sea King – resembling the Mk 1 – and 45kg (100lb) ballast will be removed from the nose. A transport version of the Mk 42B, without mission systems but with a weather radar, is to be built as the Mk 42C. The Indian Navy have ordered three.

Ten Mk 43 for SAR and similar to the Mk 41 were delivered to the Royal Norwegian Air Force beginning in 1972. An eleventh, uprated, aircraft was designated

Above: British and Soviet helicopters in the same air force: an Egyptian Commando Mk 2 with a Mi-6 Hook. (Rolls-Royce)

Mk 43A and delivered in September 1978. Because of the possibility that confusion might arise with the Mk 44 and Mk 46 torpedoes, these designations were not employed for the Sea King. Thus it was that six Mk 45 went to the Pakistan Navy, the first at the end of 1975. Although primarily for ASW, four of them were modified to carry two Exocet missiles and these aircraft did not enter service until 1978.

The Mk 47 was not actually the next export model to fly; that was the Mk 50. Six ASW Mk 47 were ordered by Saudi Arabia for the Egyptian Navy, the first entering service in January 1976. In March 1974 the Belgian Air Force ordered five Mk 48. Mainly for SAR duties, one of the five can be converted for the carriage of VIPs. The fourth export order for ten Sea Kings was placed by the Royal Australian Navy for ASW in May 1973 and this

Below: The VIP Commando Mk 2B for President Sadat of Egypt. (Westland Helicopters)

Above: A Pakistani Mk 45 fires an Exocet missile. (Westland Helicopters)

Left: An unusual paint scheme on a Belgian Mk 48 displayed at the Middle Wallop International Air Show, 1984. (Author)

was particularly significant in that a 'hot and high' performance was demanded. The Mk 50 was thus the first uprated version of the Mk 1 to fly with H.1400-1 engines, an uprated transmission, a six-bladed tail rotor and a different sonar; these engines permitted an increase in maximum take-off weight to 9,525kg (21,000lb). These helicopters had the ability to refuel while airborne from a ship by means of a winchable in-flight refuelling system. Many of these improvements were adopted later for the Royal Navy's Mk 2. The maiden flight of the Mk 50 was on 30 June 1974 and the aircraft joined 817 Squadron in the following year. To replace losses, two more aircraft, designated the Mk 50A to signify various improvements, were delivered in January 1983.

The Westland Sea King has proved to be a remarkably successful and reliable medium helicopter. In the ASW and ASV roles it is an autonomous hunter/killer able to operate day and night in all but the very worst weather. Its great versatility is evident from the number of different roles it can undertake, and its robustness in these roles has been amply proved by its performance during the Falklands War. Its attributes will surely lead to more military orders.

It has, however, made no impact in the commercial market. In September 1974 the Company issued a proposal for a derivative, known as the Type 656, designed specifically to support offshore oil drilling. Similar to the S-61 but with more powerful H.1400-1 engines and a greater fuel capacity, the machine was to be able to out-rival the S-61 by being able to carry 24 passengers and their baggage over 556km (345 miles). This capability, however, was not considered good enough by North Sea and other operators to merit procurement in place of their existing S-61 and the 656 never entered production.

SEA KING VARIANTS

SEA KING: 269 built and 37 on order.

HAS Mk 1: Westland-built Sikorsky SH-3D with 1,500shp Rolls-Royce engines for ASW; 56 built for Royal Navy and 48 later converted to HAS Mk 2. First flight (FF) 7 May 1969.

HAS Mk 2: Similar to Mk 1 with 1,660shp engines and sixth blade in tail rotor; 21 built for Royal Navy. FF 18 June 1976.

HAS Mk 2 (AEW): Eight Mk 2 modified to carry Searchwater radar. FF 23 July 1982.

HAR Mk 3: Similar to Mk 2 for SAR; 19 built for RAF. FF 6 September 1977.

HC Mk 4: Transport version, called Commando, of Mk 2 with seating for 28 troops; 23 built for Royal Navy and 14 on order. FF 26 September 1979.

Mk 4X: Similar to Mk 4 but with dorsal radome, for research and development; 2 built for RAE.

HAS Mk 5: Improved version of Mk 2 with updated ASW equipment; 30 built for Royal Navy. FF 14 August 1980.

HAS Mk 6: Improved version of Mk 5 with further enhancements to ASW equipment.

Mk 41: Similar to Mk 1 but for SAR; some now being given ASV role, armed with Sea Skua missiles; 23 built, 22 for West German Navy. FF 6 March 1972.

Mk 42: Similar to Mk 1; 12 built for Indian Navy. FF 14 October 1970.

Mk 42A: Uprated version of Mk 42 with 1,660shp engines and hauldown system; 3 built for Indian Navy.

Mk 42B: More effective version of Mk 42A with engines modified for high ambient temperature operations, Super Searcher radar and Sea Eagle missiles; 20 for delivery to Indian Navy. FF 17 May 1985.

Mk. 42C: Transport version of the Mk 42B; 3 for delivery to Indian Navy.

Mk 43: Similar to Mk 41; 10 built for Royal Norwegian Air Force. FF 19 May 1972.

Mk 43A: Uprated version of Mk 43; 1 built for Royal Norwegian Air Force.

Mk 45: Similar to Mk 1 but able to carry Exocet missiles; 6 built for Pakistan Navy. FF 30 August 1974.

Mk 47: Similar to Mk 42 but with 1,660shp engines; 6 built for Egyptian Navy. FF 11 July 1975.

Mk 48: Similar to Mk 41 but with 1,660shp engines; for SAR but convertible to VIP configuration; 5 built for Royal Belgian Air Force. FF 19 December 1975.

Mk 50: Similar to Mk 47; 10 built for Royal Australian Navy. FF 30 June 1974.

Mk 50A: Similar to Mk 50 but with various minor improvements; 2 built for Royal Australian Navy.

COMMANDO Mk 1: Transport helicopter for 21 troops based on HAS Mk 1; 5 built for Egyptian Air Force. FF 12 September 1973.

Mk 2: Enlarged version of Commando Mk 1 for 28 troops; 17 built for Egyptian Air Force. FF 16 January 1975.

Mk 2A: Similar to Mk 2; 3 built for Qatar Emiri Air Force. FF 9 August 1975.

Mk 2B: VIP version; 2 built for Egyptian Air Force. FF 13 March 1975.

Mk 2C: VIP version; 1 built for Qatar Emiri Air Force. FF 9 October 1975.

Mk 2E: ECM version; 4 built for Egyptian Air Force. FF 1 September 1978.

Mk 3: Armed multi-role version with Exocet missiles or other weapons, dorsal radar, sponsons and same engines as Sea King Mk 42B. 8 built for Qatar Emiri Air Force. FF 14 June 1982.

Foreign Users: Australia (12), Belgium (5), Egypt (34), India (38), Norway (11), Pakistan (6), Qatar (12), West Germany (22).

CHARACTERISTICS: SEA KING TYPES

Designation	HAS Mk 1	HC Mk 4	HAS Mk 5
Engine	2 × RR Gnome H.1400 1,500shp	2 × RR Gnome H.1400-1 1,660shp	2 × RR Gnome H.1400-1 1,660shp
Rotor diameter	18.9m (62ft)	18.9m (62ft)	18.9m (62ft)
Fuselage length	17.01m (55ft 9¾in)	17.01m (55ft 9¾in)	17.01m (55ft 9¾in)
Height	4.85m (15ft 11in)	4.72m (15ft 6in)	4.85m (15ft 11in)
Empty weight*	7,019kg (15,474lb)	5,700kg (12,566lb)	6,202kg (13,673lb)
Max gross weight	9,300kg (20,500lb)	9,526kg (21,000lb)	9,526kg (21,000lb)
Max speed	220kph (137mph)	210kph (130mph)	222kph (138mph)
Range	1,112km (691 miles)	1,230km (764 miles)	1,230km (764 miles)
Service ceiling	3,050m (10,000ft)	3,050m (10,000ft)	3,050m (10,000ft)

*Equipped.

The French Connection: Puma, Gazelle and Lynx

In 1963, once the dust of rationalization had settled, Westland began to study what designs might be needed to replace the military helicopters already in service. These ranged from the Skeeter through to the Belvedere. The seven types, Westland believed, could be replaced by three new helicopters and, according to size, these were designated:

WG-5: a single-engined, three-seat light reconnaissance helicopter; in 1965 this became the four-seat WG-12.

WG-3: a twin-engined light tactical helicopter in the 3,630–4,990kg (8,000–11,000lb) class; this ultimately became the 3,630kg (8,000lb) WG-13 Lynx.

WG-4: a twin-engined medium transport for 24 troops and ASW helicopter in the 7,710kg (17,000lb) class; in 1964 this became the 5,670kg (12,500lb) WG-7.

A great deal of discussion centered on these projects but little actual progress could be recorded despite the desire of all the Services for new helicopters. The Royal Navy eventually turned to the Sea King as a replacement for the Wessex Mk 3 while retaining an interest in the WG-3 to take over from the Wasp. At about the same time it became clear that the French also needed a similar family of helicopters and so discussions were undertaken to ascertain the degree of commonality possible. On 17 May 1965 the two Governments signed a Memorandum of Understanding (MOU) in which they agreed to collaborate in the development and production of military helicopters.

A series of further meetings now followed and these examined the current plans in both countries. In France the SA.330 Puma, a medium transport helicopter, had made its maiden flight in April 1965 and the design of the SA.340 Gazelle, a five-seat replacement for the Alouette 2 and 3, was well under way. In Britain

only the WG-13 showed real promise of being converted into hardware.

Eventually on 22 February 1967 a new and detailed Memorandum was signed. The two Governments agreed to collaborate on three basic types:
- an airportable tactical helicopter to be met by the Puma.
- a light observation helicopter to be based on the Gazelle.
- a utility/ASW/reconnaissance and anti-tank helicopter for which Westland would be responsible.

SA.330 Puma
A French helicopter, the Puma rates a very brief mention here because Westland was responsible for

the manufacture of about 30 per cent of the airframe, certain components and the assembly of the 48 aircraft ordered by the RAF and designated the Puma HC Mk 1. Rolls-Royce contributed about the same percentage to the 1,328shp Turmo IIIC4 engine. The first of these aircraft flew on 25 November 1970 and the RAF's 33 Squadron began taking delivery in late 1971.

This twin-engined helicopter has a crew of two and seats for sixteen, combat-equipped troops. To meet the RAF's needs some items of equipment, mainly avionics, are British and since delivery a number of important modifications have been embodied.

SA.341 Gazelle
While the 1967 MOU allocated responsibility for the development of the Gazelle and its engine to French Industry some reservations were expressed about its design, particularly its main and tail rotors. The original in-service date of a Skeeter replacement had been 1968,

Opposite page: An RAF Puma lifts an underslung load. (Author)

Below: A spectacular photograph of a 2 Flight AAC Gazelle diving over a ridge in Norway. (Rolls-Royce)

but this was clearly not possible now and the Memorandum stipulated a new date of 1970. Although the MOU did not mention numbers the British Army had in mind an order for 569 Gazelles, given that many units had their own light helicopter platoons and troops.

The first Gazelle prototype, the SA.340, flew in France on 7 April 1967 with the tail rotor and skids of the Alouette 2 and the engine and transmission of the Alouette 2 Astazou. The second prototype, which flew a year later, had a quite different tail rotor. Within a tall fin was enclosed a thirteen-bladed shrouded fan tail rotor known as a fenestron. A new engine, an Astazou IIN2, and a composite main rotor, developed with the German firm Bölkow, were also installed. Four pre-production aircraft, the SA.341, were now built by the French, the first flying on 2 August 1968. The third one, transported by sea to the UK, flew in April 1970. It was equipped to British Army standards for design studies and Service trials. At the same time the first Westland-built Gazelle prototype made its maiden flight on 28 April 1970. The first production SA.341, built again by the French, flew on 6 August 1971 and incorporated a number of improvements including a longer cabin and a more powerful Astazou III engine.

By this time Westland was able to go into production and the first Gazelle AH Mk 1 flew on 31 January 1972; the French designation was SA.341B. The Army, responsible also for procuring helicopters for the Royal Marines, was not the only Service to order the Gazelle. The Royal Navy ordered 36, designating them the HT Mk 2 (SA.341C), for training. These incorporated a stability augmentation system and rescue hoist. The first flew on 6 July 1972 and entered service at RNAS

Above: A Gazelle transits a Norwegian fjord. Royal Marines and Army Gazelles exercise in Norway every winter. (Rolls-Royce)

Opposite page, top: The streamlined shape of the Gazelle is shown to advantage here. (Museum of Army Flying)

Opposite page, bottom: A Royal Marines Gazelle armed with a 68mm rocket pod and equipped with flotation gear. (The Shephard Press Ltd)

Culdrose in December 1974. Six form the Royal Navy Display Team called the Sharks. The RAF have the HT Mk 3 (SA 341D) for training and a couple for communications flying, the first going to the Central Flying School in July 1973. Twelve civil SA.341 were sold by Westland. Of these two went to the Qatar Police and one to Point-to-Point for the movement of jockeys between race courses.

The British Army procured 212 Gazelles in five different batches with deliveries extending from August 1972 to January 1984. Nine are operated by the Royal Marines. The first 145 were built and tested at Yeovil and the remainder at Weston-super-Mare. The Gazelle first became operational in 660 Squadron AAC at Soest in BAOR on 24 June 1974. It has since served with distinction in Northern Ireland, Belize and the Falklands and for a short period in Rhodesia during the transition to independence. It will remain in service well into the 1990s.

The Gazelle has the air of a thoroughbred, an extremely good-looking streamlined five-seat helicopter. The cabin structure is composed of large transparent surfaces which provide excellent visibility for the crew but, on the other hand, simply visual detection by the enemy. The light alloy semi-monocoque fuselage consists of a cabin with two side-by-side seats for the pilot and observer and a bench seat for three in the rear. This rear seat can fold

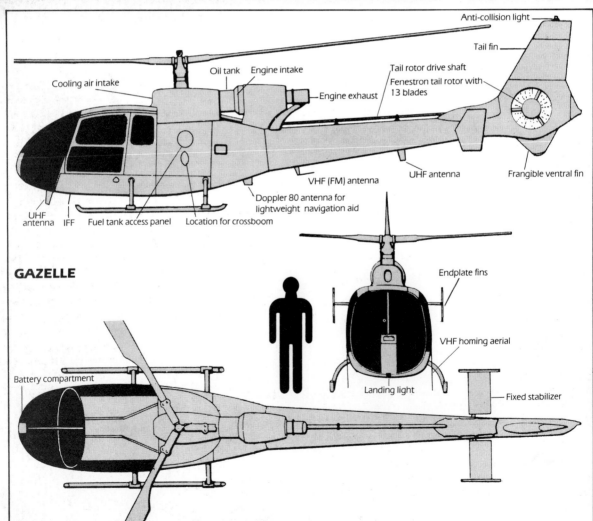

Anti-collision light

Tail fin

Oil tank   Engine intake

Cooling air intake

Tail rotor drive shaft

Engine exhaust

Fenestron tail rotor with
13 blades

VHF (FM) antenna

UHF antenna

Frangible ventral fin

Doppler 80 antenna for
lightweight navigation aid

UHF
antenna   IFF   Fuel tank access panel   Location for crossboom

GAZELLE

Endplate fins

VHF homing aerial

Battery compartment

Landing light

Fixed stabilizer

Opposite page: A Gazelle in an observation position. Note the size of the tail fin which encloses the fenestron tail rotor. (Museum of Army Flying)
Above: A 7 Regiment AAC Gazelle parked on the rocky pad at Cadenas in Belize, Central America. (Author)

into the space for the feet to form a cargo floor and a stretcher can be inserted into the cabin on the port side if the observer's seat is tipped forward and the rear back rest removed to give access to the baggage compartment. The 590shp Turboméca Astazou IIIA turboshaft engine is installed above the fuselage aft of the cabin. Just forward of the tail fin is a horizontal stabilizer with endplates and just below the fin is a small frangible ventral fin. The Gazelle has skids to which can be fitted ground handling wheels, flotation gear or skis.

In addition to being an operational helicopter, the Gazelle is used for basic and advanced flying training in the Army. Dual controls are fitted for both roles, the reason being that if in combat the pilot is incapacitated in any way the observer can take control and return to base. This is now the case with all operational and training helicopters. Observers are thus trained to handle the aircraft although they do not rate as co-pilots. One of their main tasks is to help the pilot in navigation and radio communications but their principal task is to observe and acquire targets by means of the Ferranti AF.532 gyro-stabilized sight mounted in the roof on the port side. The downtube is adjustable in height and when not required can be retracted sideways and locked close to the roof. The two magnifications are × 2.5 for search and × 10 for identification. The sight had been designed so that it can easily have a laser target marker or range-finder retrofitted.

The Gazelle has benefitted from a large number of modifications including an uprated engine, the 643shp

Astazou IIIN2, a more effective fenestron tail rotor to provide additional yaw control, the fitting of windscreen wipers to the curved canopy, originally thought to be unnecessary, various avionics improvements, including a Decca Doppler 80 light weight navigation aid, and a jet pipe deflector to reduce the infra-red signature. The effect of all these has been to raise the maximum take-off weight to 1,900kg (4,189lb), an increase of 200kg (441lb) from the first AH Mk 1.

To a boom protruding on both sides of the fuselage can be attached different items of equipment, but primarily the Nightsun searchlight or weapons. The Gazelle is not generally armed, but during the Falklands War a French Matra pod with six tubes for 68mm (2.7in) SNEB free-flight rockets was mounted on each side of the fuselage. The speed with which this installation was cleared is illuminating. The decision was taken on 7 April 1982 on the basis that a trial had been conducted on a Scout in 1970; no Gazelle, British or French, had been known to fire SNEB rockets although these were chosen since they form part of the Harrier's armaments. During Good Friday, 9 April, Westland worked on the aircraft modifications to permit trials and on Saturday the pods arrived from France. On Easter Sunday the flight trials were undertaken and on Easter Monday, 11 April, the firing trials were completed and the production contract was confirmed by telex to Matra. The next day the remaining pods to equip nine Gazelles arrived in the UK while Boscombe Down cleared the weapon system for shipboard operation. On Wednesday, 14 April, four aircraft sets of pods and modification kits arrived at RNAS Yeovilton for onward transmission to 3 Commando Brigade Air Squadron and an urgent operational requirement for a further buy was authorized in the Ministry of Defence.

Fifteen Gazelles were deployed to the Falklands; nine with the Royal Marine Commando Brigade Air Squadron and six with 656 Squadron AAC. Three were lost to enemy fire and others were damaged by bomb blast. On the day of the landings there would be no time for the infantry to clear those sites chosen for the Rapier batteries before daylight and so the planners were faced with a dilemma: should they wait for the two or three hours after daylight while the infantry got forward, and risk Argentinian air attacks during this time, or should they get Gazelles to clear the sites so that the Sea Kings could emplace the batteries shortly after dawn? In the event the latter course was chosen. The Gazelles had their SNEB rockets and the observers were positioned in the back of the cabin manning a general-purpose machine-gun. While they were engaged on this task it was suddenly noticed that a Sea King was heading towards 'uncleared' territory and a Gazelle went to head it off. As the Gazelle moved forward it was engaged by small arms fire from a platoon of withdrawing Argentinians. The pilot was badly wounded and the helicopter fell into San Carlos Water. Then began a heroic struggle by the observer, Sergeant Candlish, to save his conscious but helpless pilot. As Candlish towed him in the bitterly cold water towards the shoreline some 500m away both men came under fire again. As they reached the shore another Gazelle flew overhead and was engaged by the same group of Argentinians and crashed into a hillside, killing both crew. At that moment Candlish's pilot died. The squadron had got off to an unfortunate start but these tragic events seemed merely to stiffen the men's resolve. The pilot, Sergeant Evans, was awarded a posthumous Mention in Despatches for carrying out a successful ditching while mortally wounded, thus saving the life of his observer. A third Gazelle was also hit at this time but managed to limp back to its mother ship, the ill-fated *Sir Galahad*.

Above: More effective observation can be achieved with a sight fitted. The Ferranti AF 532 sight can be seen in the cockpit roof. (Ferranti)

Opposite page, top: Thirty-six Gazelle HT Mk 2 were built as training aircraft for the Royal Navy. (Westland Helicopters)

Opposite page, centre: A Mk 3 of the RAF flies over the Welsh mountains. (Westland Helicopters)

Opposite page, bottom: A civil SA 341 Gazelle above London during a demonstration flight in May 1972. (Westland Helicopters)

Because the Gazelle in 1982 did not have an observation sight and because there was no natural cover on the Islands it was not suited to the reconnaissance and observation role and after the first day was not often employed in this way. The SNEB rockets were only to be used for defensive purposes in a tight spot. They are not particularly accurate weapons and need a dive attack for delivery; it would thus have been uncomfortable, if not dangerous, to use them offensively close to enemy ground troops. For similar reasons of vulnerability and lack of a sight the Gazelle undertook no AOP nor the direction of Harrier attacks during the War. Instead, there was a heavy demand placed on it for the carriage of commanders and staff officers, for the re-supply of vital combat equipment given the very poor ground mobility, and for casualty evacuation.

During the battle for Darwin and Goose Green in support of the 2nd Battalion The Parachute Regiment, two Gazelles and two Scouts maintained an almost continuous shuttle service in bad weather and under frequent mortar and artillery fire. Mortar bombs, Blowpipe missiles, rations, water and bullets all went forward and casualties came back by day and night.

As the ground troops moved forwards towards Port Stanley the need to set up re-broadcast stations to maintain the link between them and San Carlos became evident. Inevitably some Argentinian troops had been bypassed and it became a potentially hazardous business flying in some apparently uncontested

areas. One Gazelle was brought down by a missile when it was carrying a repair team by night to one of these stations.

The Gazelle conclusively demonstrated its manoeuvrability and the fact that it was faster and had a better endurance than the Scout. However, it was much more difficult to load and unload quickly and it was susceptible to superficial damage, particularly to the cabin and doors. The need for constant IFF code and frequency changing, encoding/decoding transmissions, concentration on flying below 15m (50ft) often in bad weather and looking out for hostile aircraft all contributed to a high crew workload, relieved only by the installation of a stability augmentation system. Each crewman averaged six to eight flying hours day and night in each 24-hour period throughout hostilities.

The Gazelle has been a tremendous success as a joint Anglo-French project over the last ten years and has sold widely throughout the world in its various versions, although these have been French-built.

WG-13 Lynx

The Lynx was the last of the trio to fly and was the only one of which the British had design leadership. It has already been noted that in 1963 Westland were studying the WG-3 which was to have two 720shp Pratt & Whitney PT6A engines driving a modified Belvedere rotor through an improved Whirlwind gearbox. The aircraft was to be manoeuvrable and have a sustained speed of 298kph (185mph), require simple maintenance, be air-transportable and carry a crew of two and ten combat-equipped troops or 1,361kg (3,000lb) of freight underslung. After various ideas expressed by the Army had been studied, including an aircraft with a 1,814kg (4,000lb) lift, it was decided to stay with the aircraft weighing 3,630kg (8,000lb) and carrying 1,361kg (3,000lb); it was to be re-designated WG-13. By this time the Whirlwind gearbox had been abandoned in favour of a new gearbox with conformal gearing.

The major problem centred around the engine which was considered barely powerful enough; 800shp

Above: The first Lynx prototype. (Westland Helicopters)

chin turret, the Q being a utility helicopter and the R a two-seat tandem armed escort. The S sought to combine all roles in one. All configurations had the T-72 engine behind, rather than ahead of, the rotor shaft. In 1966 the possibility of developing naval and civil versions was examined and this suggestion resulted in the WG-13T, U, V and W for armed reconnaissance, utility, naval and civil use respectively, all with the T-72 engine and now a 13.4m (44ft) diameter rotor. In June 1966 a British Services requirement, superseding the 1964 Army requirement, was issued defining Army and Navy needs. Talks with the French by this time had also resulted in their desire for armed escort and ASW versions. Initial studies carried out in both countries had indicated that it should be possible to meet all roles with the same dynamic system although a streamlined fuselage would be needed for the French Army variant. Financial stringency soon put an end to the WG-13T armed reconnaissance version for the British Army but not for the French.

Two particular French requirements, a 13m (42ft 8in) diameter rotor and three seats for its armed helicopter, resulted in yet more project study. There appeared to be no way to boost the T-72 to the desired 825shp or build it under licence but at last, in December 1966, Bristol Siddeley's Small Engines Division took up the gauntlet and proposed a completely new 900shp engine, the BS-360. Technically it was just what was needed and its modular construction, whereby major assemblies could be removed individually, was particularly attractive. Doubts as to the advisability of combining a new airframe and a new engine and the delays in development likely to result were put to one side.

In February 1967 another MOU was signed and this stipulated five variants:

- Utility for the British Army with an in-service date of 1972.
- ASW and liaison for the French Navy; 1973.
- Reconnaissance and anti-tank for the French Army; 1973.
- Trainer for the RAF; 1974.
- ASW/ASV and reconnaissance for the Royal Navy; 1976.

Production was to be shared 70:30 between Westland and Aérospatiale.

Sixteen prototypes and twelve ground rigs were initially agreed with a maiden flight for mid 1970. In July 1967 the order to proceed was given but progress was delayed by problems with the engine. It did not begin bench runs until September 1969 and even then only developed about 700shp. A month later the French cancelled their requirement for an anti-tank version and subsequently three prototypes were also cancelled. To assist the rotor development programme a Scout was fitted with a representative, but smaller, semi-rigid rotor and flown for about 30 hours from

per engine was preferred and this would allow a reduction in weight by requiring a smaller rotor. No such engine was available. Various alternatives to the basic configuration were examined and identified by suffixes starting at WG-13D. The WG-13E, for example, featured the newly designed 770shp Continental T-72 engine and other designations through to WG-13P were submitted, all proposing ways of improving the engine and transmission so that the rotor diameter could be reduced from the proposed 15m (49ft 4in); the WG-13K investigated stub wings and a hinged tail rotor to give some 'pusher' thrust.

In October 1964 the Army issued a formal requirement for a utility helicopter, which could also be armed, to be in service in 1972. It was to be able to carry a crew of two and seven troops and have an economic cruise speed of 250kph (155mph). The WG-13Q, R and S were submitted in response. The Q and R both had a

August 1970. Eventually, in February 1971, the all-yellow first prototype was rolled out at Yeovil and made its maiden flight at the hands of Ron Gellatly on 21 March, some eight months later than planned.

While the Lynx has a conventional semi-monocoque pod and boom fuselage structure, it incorporates a number of interesting and innovative features. Perhaps the most important is the French-designed four-bladed semi-rigid rotor which offers better handling characteristics, greater reliability and less maintenance than a conventional rotor system. The flap and drag hinges have been replaced by flexible titanium elements. The control power of the rotor, roughly twice that of the Scout and four times that of the Wessex, allied to its stiffness, gives a rapid, crisp and well-damped response to control inputs – precisely what is required for

Above: XX153, the first development Lynx in Army utility configuration, almost inverted during a barrel roll. Roy Moxam demonstrated such a roll at the Farnborough Show in 1972. Positive G was maintained throughout. (Westland Helicopters)

tactical flying and shipboard operations. Indeed, the Lynx is quite capable of, and has demonstrated, aerobatic manoeuvres that very few helicopters can match. It has a roll rate of some 100° a second and can fly backwards at speeds up to 129kph (80mph). However, it must be said that the semi-rigid rotor also provides a higher level of vibration than is normal in a helicopter with an articulated rotor system. Another major feature of the Lynx is the conformal gearing of the main rotor gearbox which has achieved a two-stage reduction from an engine speed of 6,150rpm to a rotor shaft speed of 326rpm with only 40 per cent of the

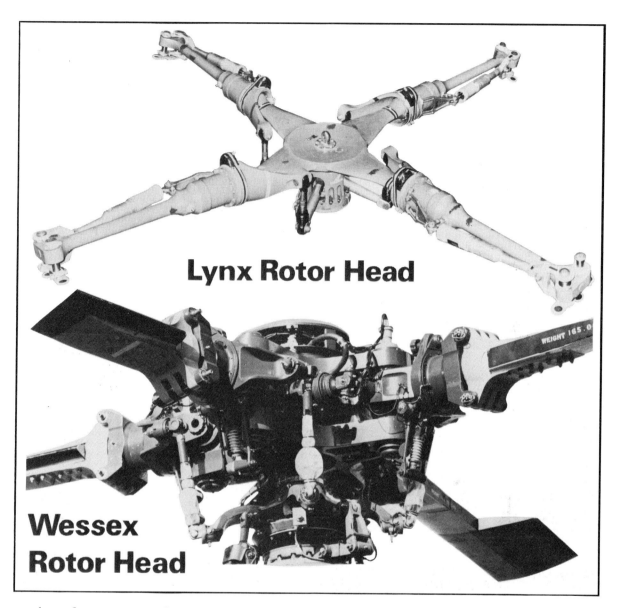

Lynx Rotor Head

Wessex Rotor Head

Above: The welcome trend towards simplicity! (Westland Helicopters)

number of gears compared to involute gearing in planetary arrangements. The gearbox is squat and together with two interchangeable side-by-side engines above the fuselage makes a compact package which helps to reduce the aircraft's height.

The third prototype, the second Lynx to fly, did not do so until September 1971 and then only with 700shp coming from each engine. By March 1972 800shp could be coaxed out of the engine and a monobloc rotor head had been fitted. Two months later the first naval aircraft, later to be equipped with the more bulbous nose to incorporate a radar antenna, joined the flight test programme. On 12 April 1972 the first development aircraft, in the Army utility configuration as opposed to the five basic prototypes, flew for the first time and on 20 June it set a new world speed record in

Above: The welcome trend towards simplicity! (Westland Helicopters)

the E.1.e class for speed over a 15–25km (9.32–15.5 miles) course of 321.74kph (199.92mph). Two days later, the same pilot, Roy Moxam, achieved 318.504kph (197.914mph) over a 100km (62.14 miles) closed circuit course. By this time the first Navy development aircraft had flown on 25 May 1972.

As October arrived it seemed that the engine problems were finally resolved when all aircraft in the flight test programme had been equipped with engines capable of 900shp. Despite the crash of the first naval development aircraft caused by loss of tail rotor control in November 1972, the flight trials were generally satisfactory although vibration and engine overheating were experienced.

In May 1974 an order was placed for the first 100 Lynx; for the AH Mk 1, the HAS Mk 2 and the Mk 2 for the French Navy. The latter, designated the Mk 2 (FN), differed only from the HAS Mk 2 by having French AS-12 missiles, dunking sonar, radar, radios and wheel brakes. Because the Aéronavale wanted the Alcatel dunking sonar the basic airframe had to be modified to have a hole in the cabin floor. The British Army AH Mk 1 and Royal Navy HAS Mk 2 differ in a number of respects. Whereas the Mk 1 has a skid undercarriage the HAS Mk 2 has a tricycle wheeled undercarriage with sprag brakes, each main leg carrying a single wheel splayed out at 27° (which can be manually rotated fore and aft) and the forward twin wheels steerable through 90°. Such an arrangement allows the aircraft to be rotated on to the optimum heading for take-off. To assist in maintaining a stationary position on touch-down on deck the rotor can provide negative thrust to the tune of 1,361kg (3,000lb). The Harpoon deck-securing system comes into play at the moment of

Above: The Army Lynx is robust and manoeuvrable, well suited to flying at very low level. (Westland Helicopters)

Right: The first Army development Lynx, its nose larger than the prototypes, set two world speed records in June 1972. (Westland Helicopters)

touchdown, enabling negative thrust to be reduced and the rotor to be stopped. A retractable deck-lock, mounted in the belly of the helicopter, is lowered to engage a honeycomb grid in the deck. Both the unarmed utility variant for the Army and the HAS Mk 2 on a SAR mission can carry up to nine troops or survivors seated in the cabin; alternatively, space is available for three stretchers and two seats. More usually the Mk 1 is equipped for anti-tank warfare and the Mk 2 for its ASW or ASV roles. Weapons systems and some avionics also naturally differ.

The first production aircraft to fly was an HAS Mk 2 on 10 February 1976 and it entered Royal Navy service in September when 700(L) Squadron was formed as a joint Royal Navy/Royal Netherlands Navy IFTU to

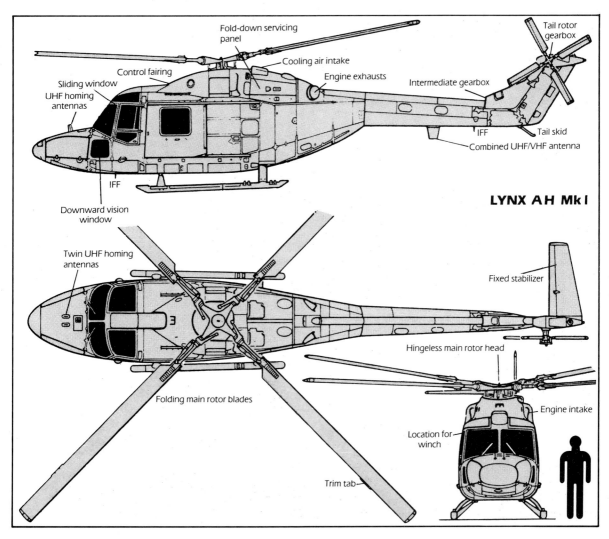

Fold-down servicing panel

Cooling air intake

Control fairing

Engine exhausts

Tail rotor gearbox

Sliding window

Intermediate gearbox

UHF homing antennas

IFF

Tail skid

Combined UHF/VHF antenna

IFF

LYNX AH Mk I

Downward vision window

Twin UHF homing antennas

Fixed stabilizer

Folding main rotor blades

Hingeless main rotor head

Engine intake

Location for winch

Trim tab

Opposite page, top: A Royal Navy Lynx Mk 2, armed with two Mk 46 torpedoes, demonstrates its ability to remain more stable on deck in a rough sea than its handling crew. (Westland Helicopters)

Opposite page, bottom: HMS *Birmingham's* Lynx hovers above the harpoon grid. (Westland Helicopters)

Above: A Royal Navy Lynx practises winching drills at dusk. (Rolls-Royce)

prove the aircraft operationally. The first HAS Mk 2 in operational service joined HMS *Sirius* towards the end of 1977 as part of 702 Squadron, formed as the operational and training squadron when the work of the IFTU was completed.

The BS-360 engine had by now acquired the name Gem, the first 900shp version being called the Gem 2. In January 1975 Rolls-Royce announced that it was to develop as a private venture an uprated engine of 1,050shp as the Gem 4. In production it became the 1,120shp Gem 41. This development proved timely to meet a Dutch requirement for a heavier aircraft at 4,763kg (10,500lb). To accommodate these more powerful engines the transmission had to be uprated and the so-called two-pinion gearbox was modified to become a three-pinion one.

The HAS Mk 2 has a crew of one pilot and one observer and a maximum take-off weight of 4,423kg (9,750lb). It is equipped with a Ferranti lightweight high-performance Seaspray Mk 1 search and tracking monopulse I-band radar. The scanner is located in the

nose and is for the detection of small, fast surface craft in a 180° forward-looking search pattern. Weapon loads can consist of two Mk 44 or 46 torpedoes, or two Mk 11 depth-charges, or four Sea Skua. The Sea Skua is a semi-active homing anti-ship missile weighing some 145kg (320lb) and with a range in excess of 15km (9.3 miles). It skims the sea under the height control of a radio altimeter and homes onto its target which is illuminated by the Seaspray radar. Unusually, the Sea Skua was used in anger in the South Atlantic, in 1982, before acceptance trials had been completed. This equipment and sophisticated avionics make the HAS Mk 2 adaptable to shipborne ASW, ASV search and attack, SAR, reconnaissance, troop transport and other general duties. This helicopter was designed to provide the submarine attack, surface reconnaissance and surface ship attack capability of the 51 frigates and destroyers on which it was to be deployed. Like the Wasp, it has no submarine detection equipment as a standard fit although MAD gear can be installed. The HAS Mk 2 offered better endurance and weapons load than the Wasp and, very importantly over water, two engines and a much improved adverse weather capability. Its ability to operate from a ship in terms of sea state and wind speed is believed to be better than any other naval helicopter world-wide.

Once the Gem 41 engine became available the Royal Navy decided to order a further twenty Lynx with this engine and three-pinion gearbox to supplement the 60 Mk 2. This new variant bears the designation HAS Mk 3 and has a maximum take-off weight of 4,876kg (10,750lb). A fairly new item of equipment that it carries is the Racal-Decca MIR-2 electronic support measure system known as Orange Crop, now also carried by the HAS Mk 2. This is essentially a radar warning receiver which permits the crew to locate and identify friendly and hostile radars. Externally, its presence is evident from six antennas giving 360° coverage in azimuth: two on the nose, one on each side of the rear fuselage and one at the rear of each sponson. Deliveries of the HAS Mk 3 began in March 1982 and as a result of the Falklands War when three Lynx were lost, one on board the *Atlantic Conveyor* and two as a result of bomb attacks on their mother ships, three more Mk 3 were ordered, with an order for a further seven following in mid-1985. In the meantime the HAS Mk 2 are now being upgraded to the Mk 3 standard. As part of a major avionics update package the Mk 3 is to be fitted with a new central tactical system (CTS) based on the Racal Avionics Management System 4000 (RAMS-4000). It is scheduled to fly in 1987 and will permit better handling of more data without an increase in crew workload. The CTS will collect, integrate and process sensor information and then present it as a tactical situation on a multi-function colour display. Navigation, communications and

Opposite page, left: A Mk 3 with two Sea Skua anti-ship missiles visible. The Orange Crop electronic support measure fairing is prominent on the nose. (Author)

Above centre: To the right of the roundel and at the rear of the sponson can be seen antennas for the Orange Crop. (Author)

Above: The Mk 3 has the more powerful Gem 41 engine and three-pinion gearbox which permitted the maximum take-off weight to increase to 4,876kg (10,750lb). (Westland Helicopters)

Left: To facilitate stowage aboard small ships the Lynx has folding main rotor blades and a folding tail. (Westland Helicopters)

Below: A Lynx with flotation bags deployed. Note how the wheels are splayed outwards. (Westland Helicopters)

Above: A Royal Navy Lynx with a Sea Skua missile waits on the after deck of the *Atlantic Conveyor*. Note the Wessex with folded blades to the left, making the area available for landing quite tight, and the visual signalling system in the foreground. (FAA)

Opposite page, top: A Lynx armed with eight TOW anti-tank missiles, four on each side of the fuselage. The gunner's sight in the roof is clearly visible. (Westland Helicopters)

Opposite page, bottom: G-LYNX, the Westland demonstrator, tests the TOW missile system installation in Norway. (Westland Helicopters)

weapons systems will be controlled by the CTS keyboard. In addition a Mil-Std 1553 databus, an improved 360° scan radar and possibly other sensors will be installed. Such major modifications will result in a new Mark number, the HAS Mk 8. Further improvements are possible: a bolted main rotor head, the new British rotor (page 211), more powerful engines and transmission which could take the maximum take-off weight to about 5,125kg (11,300lb).

Some 24 Royal Navy Lynx from 815 Squadron participated in the Falklands War, their first action coming on 25 April 1982 when two Mk 2 from HMS *Brilliant* attacked the *Santa Fe* with a Mk 46 torpedo and 7.62mm machine-gun fire. Because the Mk 46 is for use against submerged targets it missed, but at the time it was thought that the submarine was about to dive. The Sea Skua had been issued to Lynx units as the Task Force sailed South and on 3 May the Lynx from HMS *Coventry*, guided in by radar from a Sea King, picked up a patrol boat on its own radar, locked on and at 12.9km (8 miles) range ripple-fired two missiles. Both scored direct hits. While heading to pick up survivors, HMS *Glasgow's* Lynx detected what it thought to be the vessel on its Seaspray at a range of 24km (15 miles). The helicopter closed to 10km (6 miles), was unexpectedly fired upon and withdrew to 15km (9 miles), whereupon it launched two Sea Skuas. Despite being covered in ice, they launched correctly and removed most of

the superstructure of what was actually a different vessel, killing a large proportion of the crew. Four more missiles were fired in two separate missions against a coastal supply ship and a patrol boat, all being hits.

Besides having Sea Skua, fourteen 7.62mm kits were supplied for installation in the cabin door, nine MAD sets were issued for submarine detection and four Lynx carried electronic countermeasures for missile decoy. These four were sent to the two carriers to help in their protection.

The Lynx is now the Royal Navy's principal ASV helicopter. It has an excellent radar, potent weapons and good payload/endurance and it is expected to remain in service for at least another ten years.

Army Lynx

The first production Army Lynx flew on 11 February 1977. One hundred and sixty-two were originally authorized but this figure was reduced to 100 in the

1974 Defence Review; subsequently another 14 were ordered. The in-service date of 1972 was chosen since it was thought that by that time the early Scouts would be nearing the end of their fatigue lives and becoming increasingly difficult to keep operational.

The roles of the Lynx started off as the tactical movement of troops and supplies, airborne command post and casualty evacuation. The intention had been for the Lynx to be used as a utility helicopter and to fit in between the 340kg (750lb) lift of the Gazelle and the 2,500kg (5,511lb) lift of the Puma. But even before it entered service plans were afoot to arm it with anti-tank missiles. After lengthy deliberation over a number of possible contenders the Hughes TOW (Tube-launched, Optically-tracked, Wire-guided) missile with a range of 3,750m, which it can reach in 21 seconds, was chosen in 1976. For the first four years of its Army service the Lynx was used purely in the utility role until the retrofit programme began in 1981.

The Mk 1 mounts four TOW missiles on each side of its fuselage and can carry another eight reloads in the cabin. The gunner sits in the port seat and uses the M.65-gyro-stabilized sight which has been adapted from the US AH-1S Cobra sight so that it can be located in the roof. Magnifications are × 2.5 for search and × 12.5 for target tracking. Apart from a few Mk 1 used for conversion training, all Army and RM Lynx are equipped with TOW. During 1983 the warhead was exchanged for a more lethal one and the missile is now called Improved TOW (ITOW).

Many different weapons have been fired from the Mk 1 and it has proved itself to be an excellent weapons platform. Besides various rockets and guns and the French HOT anti-tank missile, two particularly interesting trials have concerned the American Hellfire and Stinger missiles. In September 1983 two Hellfire anti-tank missiles, homing onto a laser spot produced by a ground-based laser designator, hit targets on the Hjerkinn Test Range in Norway. This was the first ever firing of Hellfire from a non-US helicopter. Just two months before this three Stinger air defence missiles had been successfully fired from a Royal Navy Lynx in the UK. Both American and British manufacturers were keen to undertake these trials, for which they themselves paid, to demonstrate, first, that both missiles could be fired from non-US helicopters and, more positively, that they were compatible with the Lynx.

Army Lynx did not participate in the Falklands War, but they were temporarily deployed there shortly afterwards. Their tasks included providing an immediate reaction force to oppose any Argentinian landing,

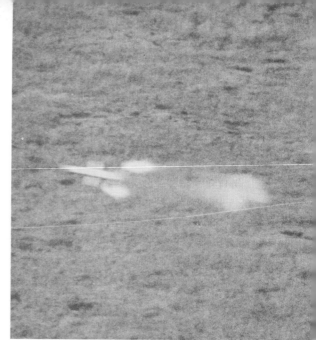

Top: The TOW has a maximum range of 3,750m and is wire-guided. (Westland Helicopters)

Right: Without its missiles but with all fixed fittings, the Lynx is well able to act in a tactical transport role. (Rolls-Royce)

Opposite page, top: A line-up of Army helicopters. From the bottom: Skeeter, Sioux, Gazelle, Scout and Lynx. (Museum of Army Flying)

Opposite page, bottom: A flight of four Lynx fire their missiles in BAOR. (Westland Helicopters)

Above: Dust, whipped up by the rotor downwash (note the tip vortices), about to envelope two Chieftains. (Rolls-Royce)

armed reconnaissance, the re-supply of remote radar and missile sites and liaison flying. In Northern Ireland they have been a striking success. Very often they work on the 'away day' principle, being on stand-by at a forward base and tasked as required. Bessbrook, in South Armagh, is perhaps the busiest heliport in Europe and the Mk 1 operate out of it by day and night on a variety of tasks, including the carriage of Eagle patrols which frequently mount snap vehicle check-points. Border patrols are conducted but helicopters are not allowed to cross the border even if, as sometimes happens, they are fired at by terrorists who then flee into the Irish Republic.

In 1983 the Army ordered another nine Lynx. These were to be Mk 5 with a more powerful engine and other modifications, but in 1984 it was decided to build only four Mk 5 for development purposes and have the remaining five aircraft as Mk 7. Westland undertook to build a sixth Mk 7 to replace the Mk 1 which had been converted into the pre-production Lynx 3. In conjunction with these orders, the decision was taken to retrofit all Mk 1 to Mk 7 standard. The first Mk 5 was delivered to RAE Bedford for trials in early 1985. In mid-year a further five Mk 7 were ordered for the Army

with deliveries to start in March 1987. The most important improvements for the Mk 7 follow the naval upgrading: the installation of the 1,120shp Gem 42-2 engine by uprating the Gem 2, the inclusion of the three-pinion gearbox and the fitting, additionally, of a cropped Westland 30 tail rotor turning in the opposite direction. This will be quieter as well as providing better yaw control which is required at the higher operating weights. The effect of these and other modifications will be to raise the maximum take-off weight to 4,876kg (10,750lb).

The AAC has been well pleased with the Mk 1 and looks forward to at least another fifteen years of service with it. The Royal Navy, Royal Marines and Army all operate the Lynx but the RAF does not. Required originally as the HT Mk 3 advanced trainer and SAR aircraft to replace the Whirlwind Mk 10 from 1974, it was cancelled well before the first Lynx prototype flew.

All Lynx for the French Navy have been built at Yeovil. Besides French role equipment the Mk 2 and Mk 4 mirror the HAS Mk 2 and HAS Mk 3 respectively.

Left: A Lynx fires a Hellfire anti-armour missile during a trial in Norway in September 1983. (Westland Helicopters)

Below: A Dutch Lynx Mk 27. (Westland Helicopters)

Lynx for Export

Naval variants of the Lynx have sold quite well, seven foreign navies including the French, ordering a total of 108 so far. The Brazilian Navy was the first off the mark, requesting nine Mk 21 for ASW; the Argentinians wanting two Mk 23 and the Royal Netherlands Navy ordering six Mk 25 for SAR in 1974. All these aircraft had the 900shp Gem 2 engine.

All remaining exports incorporated versions of the Gem 4, the three-pinion gearbox and higher take-off weights. The Dutch ordered another eighteen aircraft, ten Mk 27 with French dunking sonar and torpedoes, and eight Mk 81 with additional MAD gear. The Royal Danish Navy ordered eight Mk 80 for ASW and maritime patrol while the Argentinians wanted eight Mk 87 to supplement the two Mk 23 operated by their Naval Air Arm. The Falklands War intervened, however, and none was delivered before hostilities began. No Mk 23 were lost during the War because none entered the war zone. The West German Navy operates twelve Mk 88 in the ASW role; although for use on board frigates these do not have a folding tail but they do have a Bendix sonar. In late 1984 two more were ordered. The latest naval version to be ordered is the Mk 89 for coastal patrol and SAR with the Nigerian Navy which has three. This final mark has the Gem 43 engine which offers fifteen more shp but more importantly new components which reduce the cost of ownership; in particular a digital electronic fuel system in place of the previous hydro-mechanical system.

Nine other Lynx have been exported. The Royal Norwegian Air Force has six Mk 86 for SAR and it is only the Qatar Police who have bought the utility Lynx; in this instance, three Mk 28. An agreement was signed between Westland and the Arab Organization for Industrialization which envisaged building the Lynx in Egypt following an order for 50 for that country. However, this promising initiative unfortunately came to nothing, being suspended for political reasons.

Below: The Rolls-Royce Gem engine which powers a range of British and foreign-built helicopters. (Author)

Civil Lynx

In the early 1970s, after initial study on the WG-13W, Westland proposed a civil version of the Lynx as the 606. With the same rotor and transmission but a lengthened fuselage, a choice of either the Gem 2 or the Pratt & Whitney PT6B of similar power was offered. Maximum take-off weight was estimated at 4,309kg (9,500lb) and the 606 was designed to accommodate thirteen passengers. It generated little outside interest and it never entered production.

Army Lynx 3

At the Paris Air Show in 1977 Westland and VFW-Fokker announced that they were joining forces to produce a design for a combat helicopter to meet a Franco-German requirement designated the PAH-2 (PanzerAbwehrHubschrauber-2). Considerable work was carried out and a full-scale mock-up of the P.277, as the project was called, complete with a Lynx rotor system was built. For many reasons the Franco-German requirement nearly died and the P.277 was abandoned, but in the early 1980s President Mitterand and Chancellor Kohl breathed new life into the PAH-2 and Westland's interest was revived. It was thought this time that an improved version of the Lynx AH Mk 1 might be suitable for the Germans besides a number of other countries and a large market was predicted.

Above: The full-scale mock-up of the Army Lynx 3. Easily seen are the side-facing engine intakes, mast-mounted sight, wirecutter in the cockpit roof and pilot's night vision system in the nose. (Westland Helicopters)

Left: The Westland 606, a proposed civil version of the Lynx designed to accommodate thirteen passengers. It did not enter production. (Westland Helicopters)

After careful deliberation Westland announced on 21 June 1982 the start of a programme to upgrade the Lynx and call the new aircraft, confusingly, the Lynx 3; it should not be mixed up with the HAS Mk 3. Stepping-stones to the Lynx 3 were to be the successively improved Lynx 2, 2A and 2B, increasing in weight and sophistication. The Lynx 3, no longer a contender for the PAH-2 because the French and Germans are now proceeding with their own project having delayed the in-service date by some years, is a private venture by Westland to provide an assault helicopter for the possible battlefields of the late 1980s and 1990s. Although looking superficially like the Mk 1 and sharing many common and proven systems, it differs in many important respects. Obvious at a glance is the fixed wheeled undercarriage, the side-facing engine air intake filters, the longer nose and the thicker tail boom. By incorporating the rear fuselage and entire tail unit of the Westland 30, certain yaw control limitations in the Mk 1 have been overcome. Directional stability is particularly good, one result of reversing the direction of rotation of the tail rotor.

Less obvious are the 1,260shp Gem 60-3/1 engines and the degree of survivability and crashworthiness built in. The undercarriage, for example, can absorb heavy landings up to 6m/s (1,180ft/min). A more careful examination reveals the 300mm (1ft) extension of the front fuselage in the region of the cockpit doors to provide improved pilot vision and the naval heavy weapon hard points on the airframe. The main purpose of the Lynx 3 is as a weapons carrier and these hard points permit a very wide variety of weapons to be carried. Options are air-to-air and anti-armour missiles, cannon, free-flight rockets and a mine dispenser. A look inside reveals space for nine seated troops and a modern night vision goggle-compatible cockpit. Fuel capacity has been increased by 35 per cent.

To speed manufacture of the prototype, subsequently called preproduction, Lynx 3, the 310th Lynx airframe on the production line at Yeovil, destined for the Army, was taken and appropriately modified. On 14 June 1984, two weeks ahead of schedule, the 35 minutes' first flight took place and the aircraft, ZE 477, was then demonstrated at the AAC Centre and at the SBAC Show at Farnborough in September 1984. It proved to have less vibration than the earlier Lynx versions.

The production Lynx 3 will take advantage of advancing technology. ZE 477 has metal rotor blades, but in due course the composite blades developed

under the British Experimental Rotor Programme (BERP) will be retrofitted. These very advanced blades with their paddle tips and distributed aerofoils are expected to provide between 25 and 30 per cent more lift than the present blades besides offering many other advantages. Indeed, they represent as big an advance in technology as the step from wooden to metal blades. The Lynx 3 will employ the RAMS-3000 cockpit management system and the inclusion of a 1553B databus allows the later introduction of new sensors and weapons. These could include a weapon sight mounted above the mast, and incorporating a thermal imager for firing at night, and a separate nose-mounted forward-looking infra-red (FLIR) sight to aid the pilot in flying at night. ZE 477 has the standard rotor head, but the production model will have a hollow mast to permit the installation of the optional mast-mounted sight and a more modern bolted head.

Left: The first flight of the Lynx 3 took place on 14 June 1984. Here it is carrying dummy Hellfire missiles and a 20mm cannon. (Westland Helicopters)

Below: Unlike the Army Lynx Mk 1, the Lynx 3 has a fixed wheeled undercarriage and the tailboom and tail pylon of the Westland 30. (Westland Helicopters)

The Army Lynx 3 is not an attack helicopter, but by retaining a cabin and therefore the capability to carry troops or equipment, by being able to mount a wide selection of weapons and having a substantial degree of survivability, it is truly a day and night assault helicopter. Appropriately equipped it can assume any one of a number of roles: anti-armour, armed reconnaissance, tactical transport, logistic support, casualty evacuation with room for three stretchers fore and aft rather than diagonally as in the Mk 1, mine dispensing and SAR. No other helicopter in this weight class can match its armaments load of 1,542kg (3,400lb) with full fuel and this load is expected to increase. In a typical anti-armour mission the Lynx 3 will be able to carry eight TOW missiles and 250 rounds of 12.7mm machine-gun ammunition and remain on station for more than one and a half hours at a radius of action of 40km (25 miles) at sea level ISA.

It now remains to be seen how many customers Westland can interest in this multi-role helicopter. World-wide interest in it has been disappointing and no orders have yet been placed, although sales efforts continue. Some 70 hours of development flying have been completed.

Right: The Lynx 3 fires its cannon during trials in October 1984; outboard of it is a pod for unguided rockets. (Westland Helicopters)

Below: The pre-production Army Lynx 3 with metal rotor blades rather than the advanced rotor system ultimately planned for it. (Rolls-Royce)

Opposite page, bottom: The Army Lynx 3 is an assault helicopter able to carry a heavy and varied weapon load. (Westland Helicopters)

CHARACTERISTICS: GAZELLE AND LYNX TYPES

Designation	Gazelle AH Mk 1	Lynx AH Mk 1	Lynx HAS Mk 3	Lynx 3 (Pre-Prod)
Engine	Astazou IIIN2 643shp	2 × Rolls-Royce Gem 2 900shp	2 × Rolls-Royce Gem 41 1,120shp	2 × Rolls-Royce Gem 60-3/1 1,260shp
Rotor diameter	10.5m (34ft 5½in)	12.8m (42ft)	12.8m (42ft)	12.8m (42ft)
Fuselage length	9.53m (31ft 3¼in)	13.16m (43ft 2½in)	13.03m (42ft 9in)	13.8m (45ft 3in)
Height	2.72m (8ft 11¼in)	3.5m (11ft 6in)	3.48m (11ft 5in)	2.94m (9ft 8in)
Empty weight	850kg (1,874lb)	3,072kg (6,773lb)*	3,414kg (7,527lb)**	4,045kg (8,919lb)
Max gross weight	1,900kg (4,189lb)	4,355kg (9,600lb)	4,876kg (10,750lb)	5,897kg (13,000lb)
Max speed	264kph (164mph)	259kph (161mph)	232kph (144mph)	296kph (184mph)***
Range	670km (416 miles)	630km (391 miles)	593km (368 miles)	620km (385 miles)
Service ceiling	5,000m (16,400ft)	3,658m (12,000ft)	3,658m (12,000ft)	?

*Operating weight in anti-tank role. **Operating weight in ASV role. ***Estimated.

GAZELLE AND LYNX TYPES AND VARIANTS

GAZELLE: 294 built.
SA 341: Civil designation for 5-seat light passenger helicopter; 12 built. First flight (FF) 28 April 1970.
SA 341B/AH Mk 1: Military light reconnaissance helicopter; 203 built for Army, 9 for Royal Marines. FF 31 January 1972.
SA 341C/HT Mk 2: Trainer; 36 built for Royal Navy. FF 6 July 1972.
SA 341D/HT Mk 3: Trainer; 34 built, 33 for RAF and 1 for ETPS.
LYNX: 323 built and 20 on order.
WG-13 Basic prototype: Twin-engined utility helicopter for basic testing; 5 built. FF 21 March 1971.
WG-13 Development prototype: Development aircraft in Army utility and naval configurations; 8 built. FF 12 April 1972 (Army), 25 May 1972 (Royal Navy), 6 July 1973 (French Navy).
AH Mk 1: Utility helicopter with 9 seats but now principally armed with anti-tank missiles; 109 built for Army, 4 for Royal Marines. FF 11 February 1977.
HAS Mk 2: ASW/ASV helicopter armed with torpedoes or anti-ship missiles; 60 built for Royal Navy with majority being converted to Mk 3. FF 10 February 1976.
Mk 2: Similar to HAS Mk 2 but with wheel brakes instead of sprag units and French radar, sonar, radios and missiles; 26 built for French Navy. FF 4 May 1976.
HAS Mk 3: Similar to HAS Mk 2 but with 1,120shp engines and other improvements; 23 built for Royal Navy and 7 on order. FF 26 August 1980.
Mk 4: Similar to Mk 3 but with French role equipment; 14 built for French Navy.

AH Mk 5: Similar to Mk 1 but with 1,120shp engines; 4 built for Army. FF 20 November 1984.
AH Mk 7: Similar to Mk 5 but with cropped Westland 30 tail rotor and higher maximum take-off weight; 11 on order for Army.
HAS Mk 8: Improved version of Mk 3 with updated avionics.
Mk 21: Similar to HAS Mk 2; 9 built for Brazilian Navy.
Mk 23: Similar to HAS Mk 2; 2 built for Argentinian Navy.
Mk 25: Similar to HAS Mk 2 but for SAR; 6 built for Royal Netherlands Navy.
Mk 27: ASW variant with French dunking sonar and 1,120shp engines; 10 built for Royal Netherlands Navy.
Mk 28: Similar to Mk 1 but with 1,120shp engines and sand filters; 3 built for Qatar Police.
Mk 80: Similar to HAS Mk 2 but with 1,120shp engines; 8 built for Royal Danish Navy.
Mk 81: Similar to Mk 27 but with MAD gear; 8 built for Royal Netherlands Navy.
Mk 86: Similar to HAS Mk 2 but with 1,120shp engines and nonfolding tail for SAR; 6 built for Royal Norwegian Air Force.
Mk 87: Similar to Mk 23 but with 1,120shp engines; 8 ordered, 2 built but none delivered to Argentinian Navy.
Mk 88: Similar to Mk 86 but with American sonar; 12 built for West German Navy and 2 on order.
Mk 89: ASW/SAR version with 1,135shp engines; 3 built for Nigerian Navy.
Foreign Users: Argentina (2), Brazil (9), Denmark (8), France (40), Qatar (3), Netherlands (30), Nigeria (3), West Germany (14).
Lynx 3: Heavier and more powerful version of Lynx AH Mk 1 with 1,260shp engines and wheels. 1 built. FF 14 June 1984.

Navy Lynx 3

The Lynx 3 could attract sales in a naval version and Westland unveiled its plans for such an aircraft at the Royal Navy Equipment Exhibition in September 1983. A very realistic mock-up was on display at the 1984 SBAC Show. Similar to the Army Lynx 3 as regards airframe, engines and some systems, and to the HAS Mk 3 in some respects of naval equipment such as the Harpoon system, the Navy Lynx 3 will be able to offer more or less what the customer wants in terms of sensors and weapons although Sea Eagle and Exocet are too heavy. The RAMS-4000 and, mounted under the nose, the Seaspray Mk 3 radar with 360° coverage and a multiple target track-while-scan facility, are proposed.

Westland has no current plans to build a Navy Lynx 3 demonstrator, but will extrapolate experience gained from the development programme of the Army version which it will match in a maximum take-off weight of 5,897kg (13,000lb). Depending on the equipment fit

Opposite page, top: The full-scale mock-up of the Navy Lynx 3 displayed at the Farnborough Show in 1984. Below the nose is the fairing for the Seaspray Mk 3 radar antenna. The torpedo is a Stingray. (Author)
Opposite page, bottom left: The side-facing engine intake of the Lynx 3. (T. J. T. Everett-Heath)
Opposite page, bottom right: The Navy Lynx 3 mock-up with two Sea Skua missiles. (T. J. T. Everett-Heath)

the payload may be as much as 1,814kg (4,000lb). Endurance and range with twenty minutes' reserves will be three and a half hours and 650km (404 miles) respectively. In holding the weight to 5,897kg Westland hope to gain an advantage over heavier naval helicopters. The Navy Lynx 3 is big enough to carry sufficient fuel and armaments to match the endurance and killing power of larger helicopters yet remain below them in price and also be able to operate from frigates and other ships which cannot accept the bigger helicopters.

Like its Army counterpart the Navy Lynx 3 could be available from 1988/89 and will be adept at performing a wide choice of roles from ASW and ASV to SAR and electronic warfare.

Westland 30 and EH-101

Westland 30

With the advent of the Gem 41 engine and three-pinion gearbox Westland decided that it would be sensible to pursue, as a private venture, what appeared to be a natural progression from the Lynx to a bigger helicopter. The Company, aware of the potential of the commercial market, was keen to break into it, both to increase its business and to lessen its dependence on the British Government. World-wide offshore oil activities and the de-regulation of US airlines were contributory factors to this decision. Designated originally as the WG-30 but later changed to Westland 30 to reflect its primarily commercial orientation, design studies of the new helicopter began in early 1976. The target markets were the offshore oil industry where there was an established demand for short-range helicopters to undertake transport to rigs near the coast and shuttle duties between rigs, and the US commuter market where the demand for air links between hub airports and their surrounding satellites and city centres, following airline de-regulation, was growing.

The core of the design is the proven Lynx dynamic system about 85 per cent of which has been retained. However, to have a commercial transport helicopter, a completely new fuselage of greater volume and permitting a heavier payload is required; some seventeen passengers can be accommodated in a box-shaped cabin of airline standard proportions. This cabin is larger than that of any other helicopter in this weight class with a volume of 13cu.m (460cu.ft). Importantly for commercial operators it allows passengers to stand almost upright, having a height of 1.68m (5ft 6in). The engines, main rotor gearbox and shaft are located in an

Below: The first Westland 30 prototype during military trials on Salisbury Plain. (Westland Helicopters)

anti-vibration raft structure which is isolated from the cabin by elastomeric supports at the corners. Thus the semi-rigid rotor and all its attendant benefits can be retained without discomfiture to the passengers. The main rotor is similar to that of the Lynx but 51cm (20in) longer to provide for the extra lift demanded by the increased loading; the tail rotor and tail plane were initially the same. Before the Westland 30 prototype first flew Westland were aware that with the Gem 41 and associated dynamic system the aircraft would only be capable of carrying its passengers over the comparatively short ranges required by the target markets, but there was every intention of further development.

The one and only prototype made its maiden flight on 10 April 1979 and it was not long afterwards that it received a new tail rotor of 23cm (9in) larger diameter, slower tip speed and rotating in the opposite direction; external noise was thus reduced. At much the same time a new tail plane with endplate fins was installed in the lower half of the tail boom just forward of the fin to give improved yaw and pitch stability. As many proven components and assemblies as possible had been purchased off the shelf. Thus a Louis Newmark AFCS had been fitted to give a single pilot Instrument Flight Rules (IFR) capability; the undercarriage consisted of main and nose wheel oleos developed for the Islander/ Trislander aircraft, and Sea King main wheels were used. The prototype had a retractable undercarriage, but in the production version this is fixed in view of typical operator requirements for short but frequent flights; a retractable gear remains a customer option.

The first production version was the W.30-100 which flew for the first time on 27 September 1981. It is

Below: The prototype Westland 30 first flew in April 1979. (Westland Helicopters)

powered by two 1,135shp Gem 41-1 engines and has a maximum take-off weight of 5,602kg (12,350lb). It is this version that has been delivered to a number of operators: three to British Airways Helicopters (BAH), four to the Californian operator Airspur, one to Helicopter Hire at Southend and two to Omniflight Helicopter Services Incorporated in New Jersey for Pan American to operate in the New York City area. These aircraft can carry seventeen passengers in airline comfort, nineteen in a higher density seating arrangement or even 22 in cramped conditions over very short distances. BAH were the first to take the Westland 30, receiving the first aircraft on 6 January 1982. Based at Beccles in East Anglia, the BAH aircraft are used to carry gas rig workers and equipment out to rigs in the North Sea. Airspur began passenger operations on 9 May 1983 from Los Angeles International Airport. Given the traffic congestion in and around Los Angeles, Airspur, since taken over by Evergreen Helicopters, made the most of offering short duration, convenient and time-saving flights from outlying provincial airports into the International Airport to beat the traffic. Evergreen, however, ceased operations with the Westland 30 and some of these aircraft, which had been on lease, have now been returned to the UK.

No more Westland 30-100 were to be built because on 1 February 1983 the prototype of the Westland 30-100-60, or now the -160, flew. In this version the 1,260shp Gem 60-3 turboshaft replaced the Gem 41-1 and this had the beneficial effect of allowing the maximum take-off weight to rise to 5,806kg (12,800lb) with a consequent improvement in payload/range. The Indian Government expressed its intention to buy 27 of this version, 21 for the Oil and Natural Gas Commission (ONGC) and six for the Indian Air Force, and in 1984 trials with a -160 were undertaken in India. But in early 1985 it was reported that the deal, partially financed

Above left: British Airways operates three Westland 30-100. (Rolls-Royce)

Above centre: G-BIWY at work above the North Sea. (Westland Helicopters)

Above right: The third of British Airways' Westland 30. Used in support of British Gas it is powered by two Gem 41-1 engines and has a maximum take-off weight of 5,602kg (12,350lb). (Author)

with a loan from the British Government, had fallen through. This was not in fact the case, although progress towards clinching it slowed virtually to a standstill; in late summer the Indian Government rekindled Westland's hopes, although only for the ONGC; and at the time of writing, negotiations are still in progress. Earlier, however, having launched full production to fulfil the Indian requirement, Westland had found that they had twelve unsold Westland 30-100 and -160 on their hands and had begun to pursue other markets, particularly in Africa and Asia more vigorously. To meet the Indian specification the ONGC version has a lightweight electrical system and flotation gear.

On 3 September 1983 the first version of the Westland 30-200 flew. Again the major change was the engine, this time two 1,712shp General Electric CT-7 engines being installed. To handle the extra power a modified main rotor gearbox has been necessary. Visible differences are the shape of the upper fuselage decking which has been lengthened slightly to cater for the longer CT-7, and the sideways-facing engine air intakes. Maximum take-off weight is 5,806kg (12,800lb) but extra power is still available from the CT-7 to enhance both single engine and hot and high performance, features which are attractive to those who operate over built-up and confined areas, and in countries with high temperatures.

Whatever numbers of the Series 200 that may be sold it will serve a very useful function in easing the development and market entry of its more widely

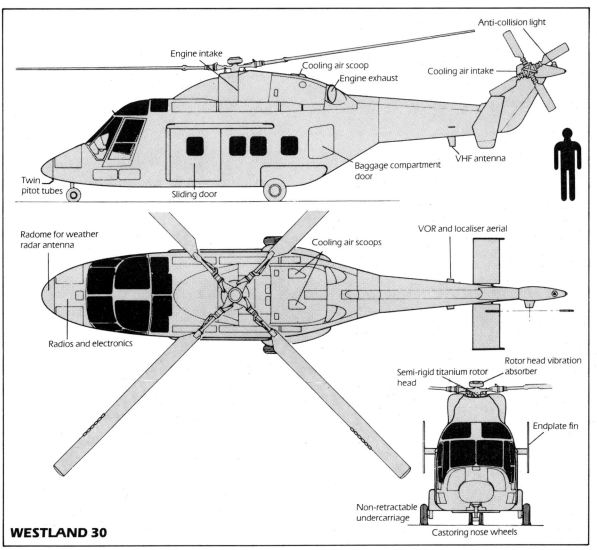

Anti-collision light

Engine intake

Cooling air scoop

Engine exhaust

Cooling air intake

VHF antenna

Twin
pitot tubes

Sliding door

Baggage compartment
door

Radome for weather
radar antenna

Cooling air scoops

VOR and localiser aerial

Radios and electronics

Rotor head vibration
absorber

Semi-rigid titanium rotor
head

Endplate fin

Non-retractable
undercarriage

Castoring nose wheels

WESTLAND 30

Above: The Californian operator, Airspur, was the first to take the Westland 30. Here, one is seen flying over Los Angeles. (Rolls-Royce)

applicable successor, the Series 300. On 5 September 1982 the British Government announced that it would provide £41M as a loan to launch development and production of both the Series 200 and 300; the long-term loan is to be repaid by a levy on sales.

The Westland 30-300 is a much bigger step forward. The available power from the CT-7 clearly permits higher operating weights in temperate climates. Thus it is intended to increase maximum take-off weight to 7,258kg (16,000lb) and to have an advanced composite main rotor system of five BERP blades and a five-bladed tail rotor. Besides the benefits of less noise and vibration the greater lift provided by the main rotor blades has precluded the need to enlarge the disc area which, had this been the case, would have necessitated re-design of the rotor hub and transmission. The main rotor gearbox will be uprated and the tail rotor transmission and airframe structure strengthened. Cabin dimensions will be the same, thus allowing seventeen passengers to be carried in some comfort with their baggage. The Series 300 will be both faster and have a better payload/range than all previous versions: the full passenger and baggage load can be transported over 398km (247 miles) at a cruise speed of 267kph (166mph). The Series 300 should fly in early 1986 but its future development thereafter remains uncertain.

Westland have not confined themselves to marketing the Westland 30 in only its civil versions. The -100 prototype carried out successful trials with the School of Infantry on Salisbury Plain in 1980 and demonstrated that it could transport fourteen battle-equipped troops, each weighing in total 127kg (280lb), or 22 troops with just personal weapons sitting on the floor. In the casualty evacuation role six stretchers and ten walking wounded could be accommodated.

The military version of the Series 300 is aimed at the RAF's Air Staff Requirement 404 for a Wessex and Puma replacement. Powered by two General Electric T700-701 turboshafts, military versions of the CT-7, and designated the Westland 30-300-404, or by the new Rolls-Royce/Turboméca RTM 322 (Westland 30-400-404), this proposed variant has a maximum take-off weight of 8,142kg (17,950lb) and a maximum cruising speed of 278kph (173mph) at the primary mission weight of 7,267kg (16,020lb). The ASR calls for thirteen combat-equipped troops, or an equivalent internal or external freight load, to be carried over a radius of action of at least 120km (75 miles) at speeds not less than 259kph (161mph). Whether or not the Westland 30-404, powered by either type of engine, meets the RAF's requirements in terms of performance has been under study for some time. It is in competition with Sikorsky's UH-60 Blackhawk and the Aérospatiale AS. 332 Super Puma. Where it is superior to its competitors is in its spacious cabin, which permits very rapid embarkation and disembarkation, a feature much prized by the military. Announcement of the winner has been long delayed, partly due to some doubts in Army circles that this size of helicopter is too small; one able to carry a platoon of over 30 men is perhaps more desirable. It is not inconceivable that the requirement might be met by the NH 90 (NATO Helicopter for the 1990s), a 7,258–8,165kg (16,000–18,000lb) naval and army support helicopter due in service in the mid 1990s. Aérospatiale, Agusta, Fokker, MBB and Westland have already launched feasibility studies, the first time that five European nations have launched a joint venture for the development of a new helicopter. If a review of operational capabilities indicates a proportion of larger helicopters, then the EH-101 and Chinook must come into consideration. If no requirement at all for a medium-sized tactical transport helicopter emerges, then Westland's hopes of sales abroad of the Westland 30 must inevitably fade. Whichever helicopter is eventually chosen for the RAF, it will have to be able to operate round the clock in all but the very worst weather. There are, however, no specific plans to make this transport helicopter capable of regularly flying within range of aimed enemy fire.

The newest version of the Westland 30 to be announced is the TT.30, the military Tactical Transport 30. It is derived from the Series 160 with a maximum take-off weight of 5,806kg (12,800lb) and aims to compete with such foreign-built helicopters as the Aérospatiale SA.365 Dauphin, Bell's 212/412/214ST and the Sikorsky S-76. It is heavier and has a greater payload/range than all of them apart from the much heavier 214ST, while claiming to be similar in price and considerably less than the 214ST. The first prototype has been converted as the TT.30 demonstrator.

EH-101

Royal Navy and Italian Navy studies into a replacement for their respective Sea King fleets began in the early 1970s, some of the options being merely modifications to the existing helicopters. By the end of 1977 it had become clear in the UK that a new airframe would be necessary to cater for the new naval requirements and in the second half of 1978 the three-engined Westland WG.34 was chosen for development. Before funds became scarce the fuselage of the first prototype had been built and considerable design work completed. Meanwhile, following a joint Declaration on European Helicopter Collaboration made by the French, German, Italian and UK Governments in 1978, a bilateral (UK/Italy) ministerial statement was signed the same year; this directed the naval staffs to explore collaborative possibilities for a new ASW helicopter. During 1979 the two naval staffs reached broadly similar conclusions about the desired characteristics of the helicopter and the time was fast approaching for a formal agreement to examine the feasibility of a common helicopter through collaboration. This resulted in the first Memorandum of Understanding (MOU 1) which was signed in November 1979.

Westland and Agusta formed a joint Company, EH Industries Ltd, in June 1980 and this was to be based in London. The common vehicle received the designation EH-101, although a story has circulated that this was the result of a printer's error; the original intention was EHI-01. A second MOU was signed on 12 June 1981. This started off a nine month period of work to assess the feasibility of meeting the joint military and a further civil requirement with the EH-101. In 1982 the UK and Italian MoDs accepted that the EH-101 would

meet the joint requirement despite the fact that the Royal Navy required the EH-101 to operate in the North Atlantic, while the Mediterranean posed completely different sonar problems for the Italian Navy; nevertheless approval to proceed to development was given. MOU 3, agreeing full development from 1 January 1984, was actually signed in retrospect – on 25 January 1984. A formal contract for the naval version followed a few weeks later, on 7 March.

. The costs are being shared 50:50 with each country's MoD, Industry Department and manufacturer contributing to the cost. Major design responsibilities are also shared, with Westland taking the cockpit, AFCS, cabin, undercarriage, engine installation and fuel system, and five main rotor blades while Agusta has the rotor head, rear fuselage, tail unit, main transmission system (sub-contracted to Fiat Aviazione), hydraulics and electrics. Systems integration will also be equally shared.

The EH-101 is to have three engines, the well-tried General Electric 1,725shp T700-401. Of modular construction, this engine has an excellent specific fuel consumption and a reputation for reliability. It could subsequently be replaced by the RTM 322 if this Anglo-French engine proves to be competitive. Three engines give the EH-101 unrivalled capability, whereby with one inoperable engine it can still fly away from the hover at maximum weight.

Ships' ASW sensors are now becoming more and more adept at detecting submarines at ranges outside the envelope of the weapons carried by the ship. The naval EH-101, which will have a crew of four and carry weapons and sensors, is designed for completely autonomous adverse weather day and night operations and to act as an integral part of the ship's weapons system and an extension of it out to the limit of the helicopter's endurance.

The Royal Navy's EH-101 will have a maximum take-off weight of 13,000kg (28,660lb). Although designed primarily for ASW, it will also be able to undertake ASV, troop-carrying, SAR, logistic and EW roles when required. Later versions may be dedicated to airborne early warning. Although 0.75m (2ft 5½in) longer with rotors turning than the Sea King, the EH-101 will be able to launch from, and recover to, a Type 23 frigate in high sea states in wind speeds up to 93kph (58mph) from any direction and without restriction to the ship's manoeuvring. It can then fit into the frigate's hangar. This will be possible by means of an automatic powered folding main rotor and a tail boom which folds forwards and downwards. Such an ability to fly from small ships not only imposes dimensional constraints but also demands a high degree of flying agility. The EH-101 will also operate from *Invincible*-class carriers, Royal Fleet Auxiliaries and other ships. The nature of the EH-101's roles calls for the ability to carry a heavy weapon and sensor load to its operating area and then remain on station for a substantial period. It will, therefore, have a disposable load of 6,083kg (13,413lb) and be able to remain on station for sonobuoy monitoring purposes, depending on how far away it is from its ship, for up to five hours with a full mission payload – longer than any current type. Maximum cruise speed will be 274kph (170mph).

To carry out its naval roles effectively the EH-101 will be equipped with appropriate sensors and weapons. A chin radome will house the antenna for a search radar with a 360° sweep, possibly the Ferranti Blue Kestrel; sonobuoys and a more powerful GEC Avionics AQS-903 acoustic processor will also be carried. While the Royal Navy plans to dispense with a sonar, at least for the time being, such equipment is preferred by the Marina Militare Italiana which considers it to be the primary detection service in the difficult sonar conditions in the Mediterranean; Royal Navy EH-101, on the other hand, will respond to submarine detections by long-range towed arrays. It will be possible to install up to four homing torpedoes, probably Stingray, or other weapons. The avionics system will have three main parts and will be based on two dual redundant Mil-Std 1553B multiplex databuses which link the basic aircraft management and mission systems and each of which can assume the functions of both if necessary. The aircraft management system uses a dual redundant management computer which takes care of all computation connected with navigation, communications, IFF, control and display, performance, and health and usage monitoring as well as providing storage facilities for mission planning, checklists and so on. The navigation system in the naval aircraft will include Doppler, an inertial reference system using a new ring-laser gyro, an attitude and heading reference system and the Navstar Global Positioning System. The EH-101 is the first helicopter programme to adopt a ring-laser gyro navigation system as standard equipment. The AFCS will be an advanced duplex digital single pilot IFR system. The mission system in the naval EH-101 also has a dual redundant mission computer which will undertake tracking, sensor management and control and display. Extensive use of colour cathode-ray tubes (CRT) will be made in place of conventional instruments, the basic systems display philosophy being not to display information unless it is required. Engine information will be presented on vertical strips.

Three versions of the EH-101 are planned: naval, commercial transport with Westland leading and a civil/military utility with a cargo hold and rear-loading ramp on which Agusta has the lead. These versions will of course enjoy a great deal of commonality with the major differences being confined to the avionics and rear fuselage. The military utility version will be able to lift up to 28 combat-equipped troops. The Royal Navy requires some 50 aircraft initially with the Italian Navy quoted as wanting 38. The majority of these aircraft are earmarked for ASW. It is quite likely that the Royal Navy will make a further purchase, particularly of the utility version, to replace the Commando. It is not inconceivable that the EH-101 will be procured as a Wessex/Puma replacement as already mentioned. A market survey was conducted in 1980/81 to determine the world-wide demand for a 13,610kg (30,000lb) helicopter as a possible replacement for the Sikorsky S-61. A requirement for some 4,000 military and commercial aircraft was identified, with a share for EHI of perhaps 1,000.

The commercial transport variant is a larger aircraft with a maximum take-off weight of 14,290kg (31,510lb)

Below: A rear view of the EH-101 mock-up taken at the 1985 Paris Air Show. (Westland Helicopters)
Opposite page, bottom: Mock-up of the advanced cockpit design for the EH-101. (Westland)

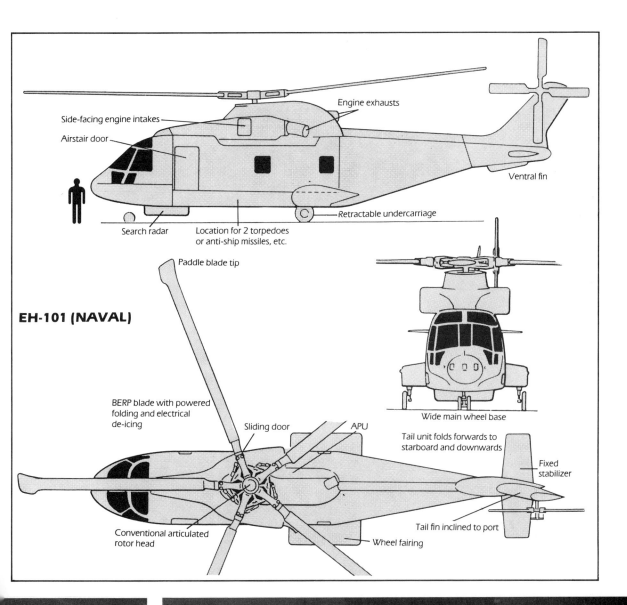

Engine exhausts

Side-facing engine intakes

Airstair door

Ventral fin

Search radar

Location for 2 torpedoes
or anti-ship missiles, etc.

Retractable undercarriage

EH-101 (NAVAL)

Paddle blade tip

Wide main wheel base

BERP blade with powered
folding and electrical
de-icing

Sliding door

APU

Tail unit folds forwards to
starboard and downwards

Fixed
stabilizer

Conventional articulated
rotor head

Wheel fairing

Tail fin inclined to port

and designed to carry up to 30 passengers over a distance of 1,020km (634 miles) at a typical cruise speed of 274kph (170mph). The attractive cabin offers more than 1.8m (6ft) of headroom, four abreast seating, overhead lockers, galley and toilet. The disposable load in this variant will be 6,699kg (14,769lb) and 6,548kg (14,436lb) in the utility variant, most useful for offshore oil support or the movement of light vehicles and other heavy equipment.

Naval ASW and commercial offshore helicopters operate in much the same harsh environment and thus their requirements are broadly similar. It has been the requirements of potential commercial operators which have to some major degree influenced the design philosophy of the EH-101, requirements with which the naval staffs agree: safety, reliability and low operating costs. Furthermore, the civil requirement for long range at medium altitude dovetails well with the military demand for the ability to take-off with only two engines working. In the commercial variant, General Electric 1,920shp CT7-6 will be installed.

The design of the EH-101 involves no major advanced high-risk technology but rather current state-of-the-art practices. Substantial use of composites will, nevertheless, be made. The five-bladed main rotor system will, perhaps surprisingly, have a conventional articulated rotor head rather than a semi-rigid one, but, with the use of elastomeric bearings and multiple-path loading, will be much simpler and safer than that of the Sea King. The main blades will incorporate BERP

technology and, in the naval version, will have electrical de-icing, the importance of which was confirmed once again during the Falklands campaign. The semi-rigid tail rotor will also be of composite materials and use elastomeric bearings. Primary flight controls will be conventional and have mechanical transmission; fly-by-wire or fibre-optic links are not presently contemplated.

The complex financial arrangements have taken some sorting out, but the 25 January 1984 MOU confirmed joint funding from development through to production and the programme was formally launched. This followed three years of development funded on a short-term basis.

The first of nine pre-production aircraft is planned to fly by the end of 1986 and one ground test vehicle will be built. Of these ten, Westland will build five that fly while Agusta build the remaining four and the ground test vehicle. The commercial transport version will be available for delivery from late 1989 in advance of the naval variant which will require extra systems development and will not enter service before about 1992. EH Industries contemplate sales of some 700 helicopters in this class by the year 2000. While there will be a single source of manufacture for components, assembly lines will run in both countries, at Yeovil and Cascina Costa. It is also conceivable that other countries will join the programme.

The EH-101 is a large and complicated project which depends on six different sources of funding. Managing such an international programme consisting of three versions, reconciling conflicting operational requirements, smoothing the ruffled feathers of national pride and diffusing potentially explosive situations is going to demand diplomacy, tact and immense patience. But motivation is not lacking and it must be hoped that the way forward is tranquil since the programme is vital to the health of both the British and Italian helicopter industries and of extreme importance to a large number of systems and components manufacturers.

WESTLAND 30 AND EH-101 TYPES AND VARIANTS

WESTLAND 30: 14 built and 21 on order (not confirmed).

SERIES 100: Initial production version of transport helicopter for 17 passengers and two 1,120shp engines. 11 built, including one prototype. First flight (FF) 10 April 1979.
Foreign User: USA (6).

SERIES 160: Similar to Series 100 but heavier and with 1,260shp engines. 1 converted from Series 100, 2 built and 21 on order (not confirmed). FF 1 February 1983.

SERIES 200: Similar to Series 160 but heavier and with 1,712shp engines. 1 built. FF 3 September 1983.

SERIES 300: Similar to Series 200 but with 5-bladed main and tail rotors, and heavier. FF due early 1986.

TT.30: Military version of Series 160. One converted from series 100. FF 16 May 1985.

EH-101: Multi-role naval, civil passenger and medium utility helicopter. FF due by end of 1986.

Opposite page, top: A model of the EH-101 displayed in the static exhibition at the 1984 Farnborough Show. (Author)

Opposite page, bottom: The mock-up of the EH-101 without rotor blades. (Westland Helicopters)

CHARACTERISTICS: WESTLAND 30 AND EH-101

Designation	Westland 30-160	EH-101 (Royal Navy)	EH-101 (Commercial)
Engine	2 × Rolls-Royce Gem 60-3 1,260shp	3 × General Electric T700-401 1,725shp	3 × General Electric CT7-6 1,920shp
Rotor system	13.31m (43ft 8in)	18.6m (61ft)	18.6m (61ft)
Fuselage length	14.23m (46ft 8in)	19.5m (64ft)	19.5m (64ft)
Empty weight	3,167kg (6,983lb)	6,917kg (15,255lb)	7,591kg (16,734lb)
Max gross weight	5,806kg (12,800lb)	13,000kg (28,660lb)	14,290kg (31,505lb)
Max speed*	219kph (136mph)	274kph (170mph)	274kph (170mph)
Range	425km (264 miles)	1,297km (806 miles)	1,668km (1,036 miles)

*Max cruise speed.

The Future

Like most other systems the helicopter has enjoyed the many benefits brought about by the ever-quickening technological revolution. That it appeared to lag behind fixed-wing aircraft in the 1950s and 1960s was perhaps because of the lack of payload/range and space available. Even so, the quest for enhanced flight performance tended to transcend all other characteristics desired in a helicopter and roles were largely dictated by performance capabilities. Now, however, the techniques of miniaturization and other technical advances have brought the helicopter to the brink of a new era of dynamic growth which will embrace the whole spectrum of helicopter technology. Comprehensive use of composite materials, fuel-efficient engines, advanced management and mission systems, optical flight controls, new weapon systems and many other features will have a role. Two particular aspects will continue to receive critical attention: the reduction of vibration and an increase in reliability. Vibration has always been a fundamental problem which succeeding

generations of aircrew have learned to accept. With the great need now to improve crew and weapons-system performance, increase reliability and reduce maintenance and life-cycle costs, it is vitally important to minimize vibration. Perhaps the best way is to tackle it at source – at the rotor.

A discussion on the many facets of this new technology is outside the scope of this book, and indeed deserves to be treated fully in its own right. Thus nothing more than a cursory reference to just a few examples of the new technology that is likely to find its way into the next generation of helicopters is given in this chapter.

Composite Materials
The initial use of composite materials to replace the more conventional aluminium alloy was confined to the manufacture of secondary structural parts made of very fine glass fibres impregnated with epoxy resin. These fibres give a structure great strength and stiffness

along the fibres, the resin only being present to hold the fibres together and to stabilize them when subject to compressive loads. Any structure needing strength across the fibres in different directions must have layers of fibres in these directions. The benefit offered by this form of construction is that it is comparatively simple for a designer to 'tailor' his structure to meet the predicted design loads.

When newer fibres, particularly carbon, which are lighter but have better stiffness characteristics than glass fibres, arrived, the use of composite materials in aircraft construction spread.

The BERP, funded by both Westland and the MoD, has been in progress since the late 1970s. It was split into three phases. The first addressed the design and manufacture of advanced section rotor blades while the second was concerned with advanced rotor blade tips. The third phase, now in progress, involves the design, manufacture and flight test of a rotor which incorporates the experience gained from the first two phases. It is Westland's intention to install the new rotor system on the Lynx 3, the Westland 30 and the EH-101. The composite rotor blades have an aerofoil section which changes along the span and ends with wide-chord paddle-shaped tips. These tips are both swept and tapered and by having a wider chord their thickness can be reduced compared to the rest of the blade. The consequent advantages are reduced compressibility and drag on the advancing blade. To decrease the possibility of tip stall on the retreating blade the point at which the paddle tip meets the constant-chord section of the blade generates a vortex which helps to stabilize the airflow over the tip region. A whole host of practical benefits arise, among which are an increase in payload of approximately 25 per cent as a result of the increased rotor thrust, or a decreased rotor size (blade chord or diameter) for the original payload, higher flight speeds, better manoeuvrability and lower noise; the blades are easier to manufacture, have unlimited fatigue life and they will have lower life-cycle costs.

On 9 August 1985, the first flight test of the BERP blades took place at Yeovil, installed on an Army utility Lynx. Initial impressions were favourable. Compared with the Army Lynx flying the standard rotor system, higher level speeds with noticeably less vibration have been achieved. Composite blades have already been developed for the Sea King (without the paddle tip) and successfully flown. They are now entering production and all Royal Navy and RAF Sea Kings will have the new blades retrofitted. In due course the blades are likely to be given a life of about 10,000 hours, some four times longer than the average life of a conventional metal blade. Certainly the Mk 42B and 42C Sea Kings for the Indian Navy will have them. The composite tail rotor blade for the Sea King first flew in 1979 and produced a 25 per cent increase in thrust. A version of this blade, shorter by 15cm (6in), is on the Westland 30.

Because composite blades have proved that they possess a rare combination of strength and durability, fail-safety and damage tolerance, aerodynamic efficiency, unlimited fatigue life and low weight, they have already started to supersede metal rotor blades. The strength of a modern composite blade was demonstrated when a section of a Bell 214 blade with a chord of 25.4cm (10in) cut through a 9.5cm (3.75in) diameter oak branch with no more than damage to the paint.

The Lynx has a semi-rigid titanium rotor hub, but the time is fast approaching when composite hubs offering even greater strength and flexibility start to replace them. The EH-101 will have a combined metal and composite rotor hub.

Engines

The demand for turboshaft engines in the 1,500–3,000shp class over the next decade and beyond is expected to be enormous: at least 10,000 to the year 2000. Rolls-Royce and the French company Turboméca are thus collaborating to produce a new family of engines known as the RTM 322. These engines will be built round a common engine core which can be used as a basis for turboshaft, turboprop and turbofan derivatives over a comparatively wide power range: as far as the turboshaft is concerned, 1,800 to 2,800shp. The aim is to produce simpler and more reliable engines which are lighter, cheaper and more fuel-efficient. Cost may be the most important and keeping the purchase price as low as possible has been traditionally achieved at the expense of fuel consumption and weight. In practical terms Rolls-Royce are

Left: The paddle-shaped rotor blade tip offers many aerodynamic advantages as well as lower noise and easier manufacture. (Author)

trying now to achieve a 15 per cent reduction in specific fuel consumption and a 30 per cent reduction in weight and first cost per shp. The recent trend towards more complicated and expensive engines should therefore be reversed, or at least slowed.

The launch engine, the RTM 322-01, was bench run for the first time on 15 December 1984 as a gas generator; in other words, without the power turbine which is being built by Turboméca. The first complete engine run took place in January 1985. Flight testing is planned to begin in early 1986 with certification in 1987. This is a turboshaft engine with the core sized to provide a rating of 2,100shp. It consists of five basic modules to facilitate maintenance and has a three-stage axial compressor and a single-stage centrifugal compressor to produce a compression ratio of 15:1. By adding another axial compressor stage this could become 17.7:1. Remarkable advances in compressor technology have allowed an increase in compression ratios with, simultaneously, fewer axial compressor stages. For example, the Nimbus has a compression ratio of 5.5:1 with two axial stages, the Gnome achieves 8:1 with ten and the Gem 60 14:1 with four axial stages. Two turbine stages, with only the first cooled, are used in the RTM 322 and this should simplify future growth. Uncooled single crystal blades are used for the second stage and these permit higher turbine entry temperatures.

Engine control is by means of a full authority digital electronic control (FADEC) system which is much more sensitive and accurate than the traditional hydraulic-mechanical metering of fuel; it also permits engines to be run much more closely to their operating limits and provides automatic engine starting and matching of torque between two or more engines. Two of the axial stages have variable guide vanes tied to the FADEC.

Military helicopters operate in a wide range of militarily and climatically hostile environments. The RTM 322-01 offers as optional modules an infra-red suppressor and an inlet particle separator. The aim of the suppressor is to reduce exhaust gas and metal temperatures down to a level at which they cannot be detected by enemy sensors or used for missiles to home on to. The particle separator ensures that dust, sand and water are removed from the airflow before it enters the engine. This separator is designed as an integral module but it can be removed and the engine run without it.

Rolls-Royce and Turboméca signed a licensing agreement in the first half of 1985 whereby Pratt & Whitney is permitted to build and sell the engine for helicopters operating in North America. The testbed helicopter for the engine trials will be a Sikorsky UH-60 Black Hawk, now in service in large numbers in the US Armed Forces. Retro-fitting this helicopter with the RTM 322

would be a major coup for Rolls-Royce and Turboméca who, of course, also have their sights on NH-90, EH-101 and the new attack helicopter for the British Army.

Avionics

'Avionics' is aviation-speak for aviation electronics and as a discipline its importance and capabilities have grown immensely in recent years. Any system is limited by the information it can gather, process and display, but significant strides have been made in the last few years in the development of sensors and displays, and processing power has increased dramatically. Some believe that the pendulum is swinging towards the philosophy that the next generation of combat helicopters will be avionics and weapons systems simply encased in, and propelled by, whatever it is that is necessary to get them, and keep them, airborne. Such a view is supported by the fact that the American IBM Corporation is putting itself forward as a primary contractor for the next generation of US Army combat helicopter, the airframe manufacturer being a secondary member of the team. Flight performance, once considered the most important feature of any aircraft, is now becoming of comparatively less importance than firepower, reliability, survivability and avionics systems performance.

The importance of the cockpit(s) as a well-protected and easy-to-work-in operations centre cannot be over-emphasized. Westland, in conjunction with the avionics industry, has for some years now been involved in extensive research into advanced cockpits for the next generation of helicopters. The principal aims are to reduce manufacturing and ownership costs and improve significantly the man-machine interface. While there is a crew it will always be the focus of attention and the source of complex human engineering problems. These and the attendant electronic and mechanical problems demand substantial research and development to resolve. Westland stand to benefit from experimental work being carried out at RAE Bedford on the development of cockpit display systems. Currently such work is centered on aids to very low level tactical flying (known as nap of the earth, abbreviated to NOE) and flight tests have been under way with a Wessex for many months. It is not Bedford's intention, however, to develop displays suitable for production, but rather to demonstrate hardware and techniques by means of flight testing and make available the fruits of their labours to industry.

Enormous demands are placed on a military combat helicopter crew in terms of flying and navigating the aircraft, communicating with a variety of ground and air agencies, IFF code changing, surviving in the combat zone and actually engaging the enemy; these demands grow when the crew is wearing NBC protective

Above: The Rolls-Royce/Turboméca RTM 322 advanced technology engine for the 1990s. (Author)

clothing or flying in poor weather, day or night, or all simultaneously. If the crew cannot cope with all that is required of them the effectiveness of the mission suffers. Very strenuous efforts are thus being made to reduce crew workload. By means of selected automation 'cockpit-keeping' duties can be diminished and the crew freed to a large extent to concentrate on what is happening on the battlefield.

The development of computer technology has been gaining speed and has led to lighter, smaller and more powerful computers as a consequence of the advance in the development of very high power integrated circuits. The first steps have been taken towards the ultimate goal, a digital integrated avionics system which can include a selection of subsystems: mission and cockpit management, survivability sensors, flight controls, health monitoring of components, etc. In simple terms the building block comprises a storage unit, a computer which processes the data gathered by the sensors and a cockpit control and display unit.

Avionics technology is a vast subject and cannot be treated here. Suffice it to say that research is proceeding into such exciting and challenging topics as artificial intelligence, voice input and output, active control technology (ACT), night vision and many others. Today's battlefield is significantly more complicated than hitherto and events on it are more compressed. The crew of a helicopter, for example, threatens to be overwhelmed by the amount of complex information available to it and the speed at which ground is won and lost.

Artificial intelligence is the manipulation of knowledge through reason and probability with the use of a computer. Such knowledge is a combination of facts and experience and the latter can be programmed to provide logical 'rules of thumb'. This discipline is intended to assist the crew in making decisions from a mass of confused information by increasing the speed at which they are made and by improving their accuracy: for example, in the selection of the order of targets to be engaged given the weapons available, the terrain, the weather, the range and so on; or giving warning of impending failure in an aircraft system and advising what is the best action to take. The recognition of speech is already well advanced, but one of the major challenges is now to integrate voice control into a helicopter cockpit. Such control, if it is completely effective, will permit the crew to manage many cockpit systems without ever taking their hands from the flying controls or their eyes off the outside world.

Pilot workload will be lightened with the incorporation of ACT which, besides the application of avionics technology, involves fundamental changes to the helicopter's characteristics. The system includes the replacement of today's mechanical control rods by fibre-optic links between the pilot's controls and the rotor actuators. Such a system offers automatic optimum interlinking of the controls as a function of the state of flight so that responses to the pilot's inputs are essentially 'pure'; in other words, rolling, pitching and yawing motions are decoupled, unlike present systems. A further extension of the concept could utilize a novel form of manoeuvre demand control system whereby the pilot directly commands a change to the helicopter's attitude. Stability could be varied in order to

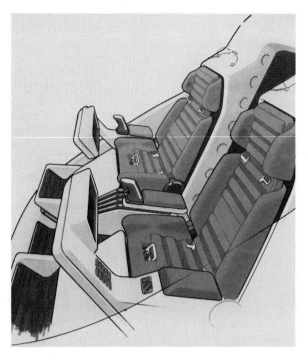

Above: An artist's impression of a possible helicopter cockpit of the future. Note the CRT displays, side-arm controllers and absence of rudder pedals. (Westland Helicopters)

the processor interface unit which provides Mil-Std 1553B databus management and control besides interfacing to non bus-compatible sensors and systems. The control and display unit (CDU) incorporates a CRT monochrome display, line keys and a data entry keyboard. The final element of the basic system is a mission data cartridge, known as the data transfer device (DTD). This is a solid state memory pack which allows operations staffs to prepare navigational, communications and tactical information on the ground in a flight command post and then transfer it to the aircraft systems in about five seconds by pushing the cartridge into a ready-made slot in the cockpit. Similarly, information can be inserted into the DTD during flight for post-flight analysis. While the CDU is the main means to display information, up to six functions, such as flight information, weapons status, navigation and communications data, and video from sights, can be presented on a monochrome multi-function display (MFD). This and the CDU are both night goggle-compatible. The RAMS is also able to monitor the mechanical and airframe health of the helicopter by automatic checking of temperatures, pressures, torque and so on. Integrated control and display systems of this type reduce workload, provide more information to the crew and save weight and space.

Survivability

The tactical aspects of surviving on the battlefield are discussed briefly on page 211. But much can be done at the design stage of a combat helicopter to improve the prospects of survival, and this characteristic is now high on the list of design priorities. The designer must bear in mind the need to save the men first, then the machine and finally the mission. To achieve these three aims, in simple terms, the helicopter must be made difficult to detect, difficult to hit if detected, able to continue the mission if hit and, if all else fails, the crew must be able to survive the crash if the helicopter is shot down.

A great deal of work is now going into all these aspects but, whereas the first three elements are of concern only to the military, all helicopter operators are vitally interested in crashworthiness. The designer has a set of progressive objectives and these are to:
1. Maintain a protective shell around the occupants.
2. Keep this shell injury-free.
3. Limit G forces to tolerable levels for the occupants.
4. Prevent a post-crash fire.
5. Permit immediate escape.
The airframe structure must provide protection in the event of the helicopter rolling over, and mass items, such as rotors, engines and transmissions, must be prevented from penetrating the shell. They must therefore be able to withstand high vertical, longitudinal and lateral deceleration forces. One way to

optimize agility on the one hand and weapons platform stability on the other. Survivability will be enhanced, not only through greater manoeuvrability, but also because fibre-optic links are much less likely to be hit than normal control rods. Furthermore, there is a much smaller penalty in terms of weight and volume in providing a back-up fibre-optic system compared to a mechanical one.

Conventional flight controls, cyclic stick, collective lever and rudder pedals, may well be superseded by a single-handed controller, thus leaving the pilot's other hand and both feet free – for what remains to be seen. A controller for either hand would be preferable in case the pilot is incapacitated in one arm. A four-axis controller for roll, pitch, yaw and collective is one option but there are others; for example, a three-axis one with normal rudder pedals to control yaw. This might be the best for the most complicated manoeuvres such as a descending, decelerating turn or a climbing, accelerating turn. The incorporation of a sidearm controller would permit a more ergonomically-designed cockpit whereby more comfortable sitting positions for the crew can be provided and instruments, displays and switches located in more logical places.

A taste of things to come as far as management systems are concerned is the RAMS-3000/4000, the former already flying in the Army Lynx 3 and the American Hughes 530MG. The heart of the system is absorb vertical impacts is to have energy-absorbing landing gear, and this is why skids are giving way to wheels. The Army Lynx Mk 7 skid undercarriage can only cope with a vertical descent of 1.37m/s (4.5ft/sec) whereas the Navy Lynx Mk 3 with its wheels can accept at least 3.35m/s (11ft/sec). For the Lynx 3 the undercarriage was designed to tolerate a vertical impact at 6m/s (20ft/sec). More than double this figure can be accepted by the most modern American combat helicopters.

By having a tough shell the occupants are protected from external forces; they must not then succumb to injury as a result of the inward buckling of the shell, of head strikes, of being cut on sharp edges or hit by flying debris. Interior equipment must be restrained or padded, or break off cleanly in a safe direction. Crash-attenuating seats limit the load on the occupants. There are a number of ways of building such seats, but the aim is for the crewman to descend vertically in his seat on impact. In modern combat helicopters, crew seats have a stroke of about 30cm (12in). Five-belt safety harnesses minimize any risk of slipping free.

Post-crash fires have claimed many lives. The only practical way to prevent them is to contain the fuel. Considerable research is going into the development of virtually instantaneous fire detection and suppression systems and fireproof and crashworthy fuel tanks. These must also cope with internal fuel tank explosions when incandescent fragments or incendiary bullets penetrate the empty space above the fuel level and ignite the air/fuel mixture. Fuel and vent lines must also be crash-resistant with self-sealing breakaway valves. Fuel spillage is a problem, and suction pumps, anti-spill vents and float valves all help to minimize the possibility of spills. Rapid exit from a crashed helicopter is facilitated by jettisonable doors and windows, but as yet no practical way has been found to effect safe ejection prior to an inevitable crash. The main problem, of course, is the rotor system and the jettisoning of the blades to allow upwards ejection of the crew; the alternative perhaps – fraught with difficulties – is sideways ejection. For the moment, research is going into survival after the crash.

Measures to enhance survivability inevitably add to the weight and cost of a helicopter, take up space and consume electrical power. These penalties must then be weighed against the degree of survivability achieved to reach the most cost-effective solution – a judgement that will never be easy.

Night Vision

The Falklands War proved without question the value of night vision devices. Many of the helicopter crews of all three Services used image-intensification devices. But image intensification only enhances the amount of visible light reaching the eye. Mist, smoke or simple camouflage will degrade, if not defeat, image intensification. The answer is thermal imaging which converts the radiation emitted by every object in the infra-red region of the electro-magnetic spectrum into a visual image. The image depends on the temperature of the object, hence 'thermal image', but whether a vehicle of any kind or a man, it stands out from its background which is normally cooler. The infra-red detector is the key element and a sensitive one can distinguish between temperatures of less than 1° K difference. It follows, therefore, that thermal imagery is unaffected by mist, normal smoke and camouflage.

It was the discovery of the detecting properties of cadmium-mercury-telluride by Messrs Lawson, Nielson and Young at the Royal Signals and Radar Establishment at Malvern in the mid 1970s that proved to be the technical breakthrough and which unleashed the recent research and development effort.

Because thermal imaging sights are comparatively heavy, bulky and expensive, most nations will probably only be able to afford thermal imaging in the gunner's sight for night and poor visibility target engagement, the pilot having to make do with the latest goggles to help him fly. Such a combination, of course, does not allow the pilot to see as well as his gunner and in certain circumstances this could be a distinct disadvantage and a flight safety hazard. The more affluent countries that can afford thermal imaging – or forward-looking infra-red (FLIR) as it is often known – for the pilot will probably retain the 40° field of view, considered the best compromise: above this figure resolution is degraded, while a smaller field involves more head turning to gauge height, speed and rate of descent. The loss of peripheral vision is a serious handicap when flying NOE, when the pilot needs to be able to see forwards, sideways and downwards, and thus the sensor will be slaved to his line of sight. The thermal picture will be presented in front of his eyes so that, in whatever direction he is looking, he can see his 40° view. Normal flight information, by means of symbols and figures, can be superimposed on the thermal picture so that the pilot can devote his attention, almost exclusively, to outside the cockpit. A great deal more research into detector sensitivity and cooling, and system reliability and robustness amongst other characteristics can be expected. Weights must be reduced and detection ranges increased within the confines of the laws of physics.

The major threat to the application of all new technology is cost. Not only is it important to minimize growth in costs, or even reverse the recent upward trend, but it is at least as important to get value for money. Funds are limited and any piece of equipment that cannot be produced and operated economically, is not both efficient and reliable, and is not essential, is unlikely to find many buyers.

British Helicopters in the European Land Battle

It was probably the appearance of the Sycamore Mk 11 on the annual field exercises in the British Army of the Rhine (BAOR) from 1951 that was to lead ultimately to the Army getting its own armed helicopters and to have the fleet that it has today. Their potential as a battlefield vehicle, comparatively easily concealed and able to land more or less anywhere, was quite evident; these exercises merely served to reinforce the experience being gained in Malaya where RAF Dragonflies and Royal Navy and RAF Whirlwinds were proving their worth in support of Army operations in the jungle.

Nevertheless, to the RAF, as it entered the jet age, the helicopter was no more than a sideshow. To divert more than token funds and manpower to something so obscure was considered simply wasteful. To the Army, on the other hand, it was becoming essential to increase the level of light aviation support and to have a utility helicopter that could carry a reasonable load of troops or supplies.

JEHU

After some exhortation from the War Office, the Air Ministry, despite its misgivings about the cost-effectiveness of the helicopter, particularly its payload/range, vulnerability and mechanical complication, agreed to the formation of a joint Army/RAF helicopter unit on an experimental basis; it was to be named the Joint Experimental Helicopter Unit (JEHU). JEHU was formed on 1 April 1955 at RAF Middle Wallop with a view to conducting trials on the use of utility helicopters in the field. For the first year the unit was equipped with six Sycamore Mk 14, but in March 1956 six Whirlwind Mk 2 were taken on strength to form a second flight. All these aircraft were paid for by the Army and were thus the first powered aircraft to be owned by that Service since 1918. The Sycamores were far from ideal for logistic tasks but they were suitable for organizational trials, as well as testing various navigation, instrument and night-flying aids. Ground/air communications, evasive tactics, camouflage and refuelling in the field were all closely examined. When the Whirlwinds arrived the logistic trials could start and these tackled loading and unloading techniques and the carriage of troops, internal cargo and underslung loads.

The plans for 1956 included moving to BAOR to take part in the autumn exercises so that the helicopter's value as a logistic vehicle under field conditions could be assessed. But the looming crisis over the Suez Canal in July prevented this, the War Office and Air Ministry deciding to give JEHU operational status. The success of the helicopters in Operation 'Musketeer' confirmed the belief that they could provide a highly desirable additional element of mobility. Thus JEHU continued in existence for another three years after it returned to the UK. It busied itself trialling more items of equipment, techniques and procedures in the UK, BAOR and with the Royal Marines at sea. Indeed, the links established with the Royal Navy and Royal Marines during the Suez Operation and strengthened thereafter ultimately led to the Commando Carrier concept.

JEHU was disbanded on 31 December 1959, all the aircraft going to the RAF because of the 1,814kg (4,000lb) weight limit for Army aircraft set in 1957. The result was that the responsibility for operating battlefield helicopters was split between the Army and the RAF. The same arrangement still pertains today whereby the Army operates the light reconnaissance (Gazelle) and armed/utility (Lynx and Scout) helicopters while the RAF has the light transport (Wessex and Puma) and medium-lift (Chinook) helicopters.

JEHU had been instrumental in developing many tactical and technical aspects involved in the operation of a support helicopter squadron in the field. The results of the trials were adopted and further refined in subsequent years by the Royal Navy Commando and RAF Support Helicopter Squadrons.

JEHU had not been alone in formulating tactical doctrine and procedures. 1906 AOP Flight, later 1906 Helicopter Flight, was also busy examining and testing various ideas which were better suited to smaller reconnaissance and utility helicopters. In a few short years AAC squadrons were to put those that were appropriate to tropical climates into practice in Aden and Borneo.

Roles for Army Helicopters

The attraction of the helicopter for the Army is that it is not constrained by terrain, minefields and routes blocked by chemical or nuclear action, refugees or saboteurs. Furthermore, it can move at about five times the speed of the fastest cross-country ground vehicle. To the Army the light helicopter is a piece of equipment of the ground forces and is used in a ground environment in conjunction with infantry, tanks and artillery. To a unique extent it can combine the two basic elements of combat: fire and movement. Army helicopters are under the command of the ground formation commander, but this is not true of the RAF's helicopters which remain under Air Force command and are only in support of the Army. Although BAOR can expect to have the use of them on most occasions, there is no guarantee that they will always be available. Such an arrangement complicates planning.

As the mid 1960s approached, the number of Army and RAF helicopters earmarked for the European battlefield began to grow. With the Sioux and Scout entering service in significant numbers it was possible to expand the roles assigned to Army helicopters from the rather narrow spectrum of reconnaissance and observation, direction of fire, liaison and casualty evacuation. These and the additional roles adopted in the 1960s still hold good today. Reconnaissance and observation is considered to be one of the most important. The three-dimensional ability of the helicopter enables the crew to 'see over the hill' and into 'dead ground' – areas which ground observers cannot see because of the undulation of the terrain. The light reconnaissance helicopter is invaluable for the visual and photographic observation and surveillance of topographical features such as rivers and artificial obstacles, and for the tracking of enemy movement. It is of inestimable value also for carrying commanders about the battlefield so that they can view possible enemy lines of approach, check the 'going' and choose appropriate defensive positions.

A traditional role for Army aircraft has always been the direction of artillery fire. With their increased height aircrew can see targets which ground observers cannot and it is also easier for them to see the fall of shot and so correct it more quickly. Mortar and other kinds of fire can be controlled equally easily. Acting as forward air controllers, Army crews are well able to direct close-support aircraft on to their targets by means of their enhanced view of the battlefield, their familiarity with the air environment, and their ability to get to the right place more quickly than ground personnel.

Already touched upon is the value of the helicopter in assisting the functions of command, control and communications, known as C^3. Commanders can use

helicopters to get a much better picture of their sector of the battlefield and they can do it at speed. Helicopters can act as airborne relay stations when communications are poor and their crews can act as traffic police to help unblock congestion on the roads or re-route units on the move. Commanders can even fight the battle from a helicopter if they so wish. Indeed, in Borneo one brigade commander was quoted as saying: 'I command my brigade with a Scout helicopter. I cannot do it any other way. There is no other way.' Although the European environment is completely different from that of Borneo, the advantages offered by having an airborne command post have already been recognized.

The Army's helicopters are too small and too few to contribute much in the way of lifting personnel or equipment. Nevertheless, they are able to carry small parties of men and light stores considered to be vital for the forward troops, for example, radio batteries and urgently needed ammunition. Stores can be carried internally or as an underslung load. As they return from the forward areas these helicopters can bring back casualties.

The final and perhaps most significant role for the Army's helicopters, armed action, was seen to have great potential although in the mid 1960s it was still in its infancy. It has come a long way in the last twenty years. By 1965 the first trials of heliborne anti-tank missiles had taken place and machine-guns, rapid-firing miniguns, cannon and free-flight rockets had all been tested and all found to have their shortcomings. It was decided to pursue the topic of missiles and a four-phase trial called Helltank was arranged for 1966/67.

Roles for RAF Helicopters

While the AAC was developing its roles and organizations the RAF was similarly engaged with its Whirlwinds, Wessex and Belvederes, although the latter were soon to be retired. These helicopters were called short-range transports, but they and the Puma are now referred to as light transport or support helicopters to distinguish them from the medium-life helicopter, the Boeing-Vertol Chinook. Only the Soviet Union possesses heavy lift helicopters. From an Army point of view, light transport helicopters can carry a section of combat-equipped infantry while the Chinook can move a complete platoon; indeed, on one occasion in the Falklands 81 paratroops were moved in a single lift over a short distance. The purpose of the RAF's larger helicopters is to increase the tactical mobility of the Army by the rapid movement of troops, their equipment and combat supplies. Such moves are planned as almost always being out of contact with the enemy. Logistic support of the Harrier Force also absorbs some of the RAF helicopter effort.

In the support of 1st British Corps (1 (BR) Corps) in BAOR the greater lift capability of these aircraft enables larger numbers of men to be moved than can be managed by Army helicopters, although in the 1960s there were not enought support helicopters available to lift even one infantry battalion in a single lift. In 1966 it was agreed that the Army would require, world-wide in the 1970s, sufficient support helicopter lift for six infantry companies but with only one of these company lifts being in BAOR. The aim in BAOR was to have the ability to re-deploy quickly a few men to meet a sudden threat anywhere within the Corps area. In practical terms this meant transporting some 120 combat-equipped troops over a radius of action of about 120km (75 miles). Today, for example, when no other means are readily available, light transport helicopters can be employed to take infantry teams equipped with anti-tank missiles to blocking positions to stem an armoured breakthrough. Rather than move a company of men, however, these helicopters can be allocated to the rapid re-supply of vital combat supplies to those units in desperate need.

Underslung by these helicopters can be field guns, ammunition pallets, missiles, fuel drums, certain items of bridging equipment and defence stores. The ammunition demands of modern weapons were well illustrated during the advance on Port Stanley during the Falklands War. In the final twelve hours five artillery batteries fired the equivalent of four years' training ammunition for one regiment. Helicopters flew forward 21,000 rounds of 105mm ammunition in an express shuttle service.

On their return from the front line the evacuation of casualties in significant numbers will do much to maintain morale among the fighting troops. In either nuclear/chemical or conventional warfare the intensity of any conflict in Europe is likely to be very high, with many wounded.

With only a limited number of transport helicopters and no medium-lift helicopters in BAOR, 1 (BR) Corps could not be said to have had in the 1960s any kind of airmobile capability apart from moving a few groups of 10–12 men to positions where they could observe the flanks, prevent surreptitious infiltration or block an avenue of approach. Thus, in the 1960s, RAF support helicopters were seen more as battlefield logistic vehicles than as tactical transport helicopters; at least, the very word transport in their title seemed to rule out any ideas of assault within contact of the enemy. Nothing has changed since and British infantry still have no assault helicopter to carry them into battle. Besides participating in Army operations once a European war has begun, the RAF's helicopters would be extremely busy during any period when alert measures are taken, moving mines, missiles, ammunition, stores and key personnel to their battle positions.

Although the earlier transport helicopters could be armed, the prevailing view was that to arm them would detract from their payload/range, would inevitably cost money and was not strictly necessary since they would not knowingly fly within range of aimed enemy fire. These helicopters were bulky, not very agile, and vulnerable. The RAF's arming philosophy has not changed even with the introduction of the Puma.

The Anti-Tank Role

The aim of the Helltank trial, which took place in the UK in 1966 and BAOR in 1967, was in general terms to evaluate the effectiveness of the helicopter in the tactical reconnaissance and anti-tank roles, and the tank, using its main armament, in opposition to the helicopters so employed. Despite some inevitable constraints imposed by the absence of actual helicopter weapon systems and simulators and the helicopter tactics used, it was soon discovered that when helicopters opposed stationary tanks the exchange rate of helicopters shot down to tanks destroyed only just favoured the helicopter. When the tanks started to advance, the exchange rate rose sharply in favour of the helicopter. The Helltank trial thus confirmed the value of the anti-tank helicopter and the decision was taken in 1969 to equip 24 Scouts in BAOR with the SS-11 missile and AF-120 sight. It was a decision that received its share of criticism on the grounds that the number of armed helicopters was pathetically insignificant in view of the Warsaw Pact threat and that, furthermore, the Scout was itself hardly likely to survive in the lethal environment anticipated. Despite these early misgivings the armed action role of the AAC has developed into its most important and exciting one for very good reasons; the Scout/SS-11 combination has now been replaced by a much greater number of Lynx/TOW. It should be remembered at this juncture that there is no conflict between the anti-tank helicopter and the Harrier in the engagement of tanks. With its high speed and greater and more varied armaments load the Harrier is well suited to attacking tank concentrations in depth beyond the range of the Army's anti-tank missiles; there is no overlap unless a deliberate decision is made in a crisis for the Harriers and other close-support aircraft to engage tanks in the contact battle area.

There is no evidence to suppose that the importance of the tank is waning. In any attempt to overwhelm

NATO defences as quickly as possible, there is little doubt that the Warsaw Pact would employ a combination of surprise, speed and concentration of forces. The striking power of these forces lies in vast quantities of modern tanks, supported by mechanized infantry, self-propelled artillery and attack helicopters. Fixed-wing ground attack aircraft on both sides will have a major role, but as far as tank killing is concerned much will depend on the crew's ability to navigate to, acquire and identify the target, possibly in poor visibility and under a low cloud base, all in the face of surface-to-air weapons of all kinds. Forced to fly higher because of their speed and weapon delivery dive angles, fixed-wing aircraft more easily attract attention and are exposed to ground fire for relatively long periods.

Armed helicopters, on the contrary, can move slowly among ground obstacles, using them and the terrain for cover; they can operate in worse weather and there will be times when only they can get airborne to fight at low level. During the Falklands War, for example, there were occasions, particularly during the early stages of the battle for Darwin and Goose Green, when the weather was just good enough for helicopters, but not good enough for the ground-attack Harriers to get airborne. The critics of the combat helicopter have always pointed to its alleged vulnerability and until a war in Europe puts it to the test doubts as to whether it can survive to carry out its roles effectively on a modern battlefield will remain – a situation no less true, of course, of any other battlefield weapon system. Nevertheless, in lower-intensity conflicts elsewhere in the world (for example, Afghanistan and Lebanon) there has been no reluctance to risk helicopters, and the loss rates have been considered acceptable.

Survivability

In recent years much serious thought has been given to reducing the vulnerability of the helicopter. The keys to survival are: preventing detection by the enemy visually, aurally, on radar, by infra-red devices and electronically, and the crew's ability to discover anything that may be a threat to them including wires and other obstacles that are hard to see. As is already quite obvious the single most important element in preventing detection is good use of the terrain, thereby resulting in minimum exposure of the helicopter to the enemy. This includes keeping clear of known or suspected enemy positions and not operating beyond the forward lines of friendly troops except for a specific reason. The mounting of sights above the rotor mast to allow practically the entire helicopter to remain hidden while hovering behind cover, yet still able to observe is now being tested by the US Army and, if successful, this step towards even greater survivability is very likely to be followed in due course. It should be noted that helicopters with such sights will also have greater

tactical flexibility because of the larger number of positions from which they can observe and indeed launch missiles. For missile-armed helicopters what is required is a missile with the longest possible range and short time of flight, or a hyper-velocity missile, or one that is 'fire and forget'; one with an indirect fire mode whereby it does not lock on to its target until after it has been launched would be particularly welcome. In this instance the helicopter may not expose itself at all. While the threat from the ground may be paramount, helicopter crews do not ignore the threat from enemy helicopters and fixed-wing aircraft.

Various methods are now being adopted to reduce the different signatures of a battlefield helicopter and they are further complemented by warning devices to alert the crew to danger; for example, when the helicopter has been acquired on radar. If detected it is obviously a good thing to avoid being hit. The use of good tactics, the first firing of weapons and making the most of the helicopter's agility and manoeuvrability can all contribute in this respect. However, many helicopters have been hit by small arms and machine-gun fire and have been able to continue with their missions. Indeed, the battlefield helicopter has proved itself much more capable of absorbing fire than theory would tend to suggest. Used properly there is no reason why the helicopter should be any more vulnerable than the tank to the respective weapons ranged against it. Nevertheless, a modern combat helicopter employs a mixture of ballistically tolerant materials, systems redundancy, armour plating and so on to minimize the likelihood of being shot down. Hand in hand with its more aggressive roles a dedicated attack helicopter possesses a greater degree of survivability than a multi-role helicopter. For the battlefield of the late 1980s and 1990s this is one major reason to support the development of attack helicopters and it is one reason why more and more countries are buying, or are planning to buy, them.

To survive is clearly not enough. By dint of its unparalleled mobility and flexibility, its excellent communications and the fact that it provides a stable platform for a variety of weapons, the combat helicopter can make a very positive contribution to the armoured battle. Particularly important is its ability to achieve surprise by moving troops and firepower very quickly and unexpectedly about the battlefield area. The Lynx is admirably suited to providing a rapid reaction anti-armour force to counter enemy penetrations while ground forces re-deploy. It is a tenet of faith that combat helicopters are most effective when operating in close conjunction with the ground forces.

Reconnaissance and Target Acquisition

The primary task for the Gazelle reconnaissance helicopter is to discover the main axes of the enemy advance. Reconnaissance and observation in the face of the enemy are notoriously difficult, but the installation of the observation sight into the roof of the Gazelle will not only result in better quality information but also improve that helicopter's prospects of survival by allowing it to stand off from the enemy at greater ranges.

The Gazelle, with its ability to select quickly a variety of vantage-points and to climb to height if necessary, can acquire and identify targets at longer distances than ground observers and then hand them over to the Lynx/TOW or close-support aircraft. This ability to see farther than someone on the ground is crucial. Such a person is not normally able to find targets much beyond 2,500m and sometimes much less. If enemy tanks advance to contact at an average speed of 20kph (12.5mph) – 333m a minute – the defence has 7½ minutes in which to halt or destroy them, all the while under heavy fire itself, before those tanks arrive at the defensive positions. Helicopters, on the other hand, can acquire, identify and engage these targets at significantly longer ranges and therefore attrition can begin much earlier.

Target Engagement

The impact of artillery and helicopter long-range anti-tank fire, besides taking a toll of enemy armour at the earliest moment, will cause tank crews to close their hatches and may force them to deploy earlier than they had planned, thus slowing down the rate of advance. This will buy time for the ground commander. Closed down, a tank crew has greater difficulty in negotiating obstacles and firing at targets while on the move. The chances of seeing a helicopter when it is lurking in ambush behind cover 4,000m away are slim. Besides, the tank crews are probably more concerned with enemy tanks and other ground targets. Nevertheless, the Lynx must unmask from cover to fire and because the TOW missile is wire-guided the line of sight from helicopter to target must be maintained until missile impact. During the missile's time of flight the helicopter is vulnerable to other weapons within range. It is normal practice to move rapidly out of sight after each engagement and re-appear elsewhere. While the Lynx is firing, the Gazelles act as 'sheepdogs', guiding other Lynx into new firing positions, keeping track of the overall battle situation and watching out for any immediate danger from enemy combat helicopters, SAMs and other air-defence weapons. All these systems are a greater threat than enemy tanks and therefore must be destroyed or suppressed before tank-killing is started or resumed. The maximum use of all countermeasures, such as electronic, chaff or smoke, must be used to degrade acquisition and tracking by the enemy. The usual British tactics of employing anti-tank helicopters in small groups to nibble away at the opposing tanks is probably less effective than concentrating a much larger number in a single action to deliver a much heavier blow. This doctrine has come about because of the lack of numbers, but the option of concentrating these groups is always available to the Corps commander.

New Roles

Mainly for financial reasons the British Army has never yet chosen to indulge in specialist helicopters because of their lack of versatility and flexibility. They have no place in Northern Ireland and, given the limited numbers available, would have been of less value than multi-role helicopters in the campaigns in Aden, Borneo, Cyprus and elsewhere. In the eyes of the UK defence hierarchy the helicopter has always been seen as a general-purpose machine adaptable to different roles; the Lynx is a particularly good example of this philosophy. But this does not mean that Service helicopter operators have not been aware of the value of a limited diversity of types. The trend towards specialist attack helicopters is gaining pace and the British Army will almost certainly follow the lead taken by the Americans, Russians, French, Germans and Italians. Indeed, at the 1985 Paris Air Show it was announced that Westland and Agusta were to join forces in a feasibility and pre-definition study of a developed version of the Italian A.129 Mangusta light attack helicopter. Such a helicopter could be used by both British and Italian armies for anti-tank and anti-helicopter missions.

With the increased potency of modern attack helicopters like the American AH-64 Apache and the Soviet Mi-28 Havoc, the likelihood of close combat between helicopters looms ever larger. Much has been written about this topic of late, but suffice it to say that combat helicopters must now include an air-to-air role alongside their other ones. For the time being it may only be defensive but the time will assuredly come when air-to-air becomes the primary role for a proportion of helicopters. These helicopters will certainly require a good flight performance in terms of speed, manoeuvrability and rate of climb besides having the appropriate weaponry. Current anti-tank helicopters can assume this role, defensively, by being equipped with the requisite weapons and sights, even though some anti-tank missiles will probably have to be removed to provide the necessary weight and space.

Another area where there have been spectacular strides in recent years is electronic warfare (EW). Indeed, there are some who claim that the initiative in battle will lie with the side that commands the electro-magnetic spectrum. EW embraces defensive electronic countermeasures (ECM) which every combat helicopter needs to a greater or lesser degree, and electronic support measures (ESM). ESM includes the interception, location and jamming of enemy transmitters and the collection of Intelligence. Helicopters can make ideal platforms for electronic devices and a few of the RAF's Pumas or their replacement would be suitable for this task, given their available space and payload. Allied to this is the C^3 role. While the division of command responsibility between the Army and RAF remains, senior Army commanders will probably want to use their own Army aircraft for this purpose. Without its TOW missiles the Lynx would be satisfactory and it would not be very difficult to modify a number as airborne command posts; in so doing, these would be lost to the anti-armour role as such role changes are not simple.

The task of a battlefield helicopter can be stated simply as to look, to fight or to carry. Despite the trend towards specialization – the eye in the sky, the airborne weapon system and the flying truck – the multi-role helicopter will remain in service as the helicopter mainstay for many years yet, and will be able to make its presence felt in ways the specialist attack helicopter, for example, cannot.

Despite the few support helicopters in BAOR they are vital to the well-being of 1 (BR) Corps. Their role is not a glamorous or spectacular one, but it must be remembered that they are not assault helicopters and will not fly deliberately in view of the enemy unless the risk is considered worthwhile. The laying of mines at short notice by helicopter in the path of an enemy thrust or on a weakly guarded flank has great attractions and such a role could be undertaken by these helicopters in the future. The introduction of the Chinook, albeit in small numbers, has made a huge difference to the RAF capability to lift heavy and bulky items of equipment or more than twice as many troops as the Puma.

The US Army has an Air Assault Division and the Russians have a number of air assault brigades. The former has helicopters dedicated to it, the latter as yet has not. But the establishment of these formations goes some way to redressing the balance between mobility and firepower. Since the Second World War, firepower has increased enormously while mobility has advanced from walking pace to the speed of armoured personnel carriers moving across country at about 20kph (12.5mph). In facing a numerically superior opponent who uses massive firepower with speed and surprise to bludgeon his way forward, the defence must be able to manoeuvre its limited firepower with even greater speed. A wide range of weapons for area devastation or precision targets could be mounted on different helicopters of the British fleet or on future specialist helicopters. This would be a step beyond conventional airportability and helicopter anti-tank warfare and is what a previous Commander-in-Chief Allied Forces Central Europe, General Dr von Senger und Etterlin,

has called 'air-mechanization'. An air-mechanized force consisting of reconnaissance, air defence, attack and transport helicopters, the latter to carry infantry reconnaissance and anti-tank teams and combat supplies, would be able to attack from positions of great depth in the rear or, in defence, dominate an area by ground-based and airborne fire. Such a force would be ideal for the delaying battle and as a very versatile reserve for counter-attack. The point about air mechanization, or airmobility, as it is more familiarly known, is that it is much more than mere airportability. The helicopters are part of the normal equipment of the unit, just like ground vehicles, and the troops themselves are trained to use the different types of helicopters in all combat situations.

Attractive as such a proposition is, to establish such a force would necessitate fundamental changes to the present system of command and control and would require the diversion of considerable resources from other land systems to helicopters. Until such a concept has been proved by other nations there is little or no likelihood that the British Services will form and equip such a force.

For the moment, however, it is the helicopter-tank battle which generates the most interest although this may soon be superseded by combat between helicopters. The forward march of technology will undoubtedly impinge upon helicopter doctrine and tactics. As the tank's protection, day and night cross-country mobility and firepower are enhanced, so will these characteristics be matched by improved helicopter performance and survivability, an ability to operate at night and in adverse weather, and new weapons and sighting systems. A new long-range anti-armour missile to replace the TOW and known as TRIGAT is now under development. Its impact effect on the most modern tanks will be destructive and it will be what every helicopter crew wants, 'fire and forget'. This will increase the crew's prospects of survival and offer a reduced time between missile launches. Thus the exchange ratio between tanks and helicopters destroyed will alter even more in favour of the latter. But neither helicopters nor tanks operate in isolation on the battlefield and the helicopter's present effectiveness against the threat spectrum can only be maintained by means of advancing technology and the evolution of doctrine and tactics.

Appendices

BRITISH ROTARY-WING AIRCRAFT

First Flight	Manufacturer	Type	Name	Original Engine	Number Built	Remarks
1914	Denny Bros	SO.60		41hp V-4	1	First tethered flight in 1909.
1924	RAE	Brennan		230hp Bentley BR-2	1	First tethered flight in a shed in 1922.
1926	Avro	C-6		130hp Clerget 9Bb	2	A; 6C and 6D built.
1927	Avro	C-8		180hp Armstrong Siddeley (AS) Lynx	6	A; 8L-I, -II, -III, 8R, 8V and 8W built.
1927	Avro	C-9		70hp AS Genet 1	1	A.
	Parnall	C-10		70hp AS Genet 1	1	A; crashed on first take-off in 1927.
	Parnall	C-11		120hp A.D.C. Airdisco	1	A; crashed on first take-off in 1928. Believed later re-built and flown.
1928	Avro	C-17		85hp A.D.C. Cirrus 3	2	A; 2 versions.
1929	Avro	C-12		100hp Avro Alpha	1	Hydrogiro.
1929	Avro	C-19		80hp AS Genet 2	29	A; 5 versions.
	Saunders	Isacco 3		32hp Bristol Cherub (4) & 100hp AS Genet	1	Tethered hops only in 1929.
1931	de Havilland	C-24		120hp de Havilland Gipsy 3	1	A; only rotary-wing aircraft ever built by de Havilland.
1932	Comper	C-25		85hp Pobjoy R	1	A.
	?	Kay 32/1		?	1	A; flight uncertain.
1933	Avro	C-30	Rota 1	140hp AS Genet Major 1A	100?	A; only 12 Royal Navy/RAF aircraft called Rota.
1933	Weir	W-1		40hp Douglas Dryad	1	A; also known as C-28.
1934	Weir	W-2		45hp Weir flat twin	1	A.
1935	Westland	CL-20		90hp Pobjoy Niagara S	1	A.
	Westland	C-29		600hp AS Panther 2	1	A; did not fly.
1935	A.R.III (Hafner Gyroplane) Company	A.R.III		84hp Pobjoy Niagara 3	2	A; Mk 2 built from remains of Mk 1.
1935	Oddie, Bradbury & Cull	Kay 33/1		75hp Pobjoy R	1	A.
1936	Weir	W-3		50hp Weir Pixie	1	A.
1937	Weir	W-4		68hp Weir Pixie	1	A.
1938	British Aircraft Manufacturing Co.	C-40	Rota 2	175hp Salmson 9NG	7	A; prototype was a converted C-30A which flew in 1936. 5 for Royal Navy.
1938	Weir	W-5		50hp Weir	1	Twin rotors on outriggers.
1939	Weir	W-6		205hp de Havilland Gipsy 6	1	Twin rotors on outriggers.
1942	Hills & Sons		Rotachute	—	20?	RWG; 3 prototype versions.
1943	M.L. Aviation		Rotabuggy	—	1	RWG; towed flights only.
1944	Cierva	W-9		205hp de Havilland Gipsy 6	1	Torque counteracted by jet thrust; no tail rotor.
1947	Bristol	Type 171	Sycamore	450hp Pratt & Whitney (P&W)	178	13 versions.
1947	Fairey	FB-1	Gyrodyne	525hp Alvis Leonides (AL)	2	CH.
1948	Cierva	W-14	Skeeter	106hp Jameson	88	Development taken over by Saunders-Roe in 1951; 11 versions.
1948	Cierva	W-11	Air Horse	1,620hp Rolls-Royce (RR) Merlin 24	2	Three rotors, two side-by-side.
1949	Westland	WS-51	Dragonfly	520hp AL 50	139	Sikorsky-designed helicopter built under licence with British engine; 7 versions.
	Firth	FHO 1/4		145hp de Havilland Gipsy Major 10	1	Twin side-by-side rotors; built in 1951/2; flight uncertain.
	Murray	M.1		36hp Jap 99	1	Did not fly.
1952	Bristol	Type 173		520hp AL 173 (2)	5	3 versions.
1952	Westland	WS-55	Whirlwind	600hp P & W R-1340-40	436	13 versions of which 4 had turboshaft engine.
1954	Fairey		Jet Gyrodyne	525hp AL	1	CH; converted from Gyrodyne with rotor blade tip jets.
1955	Fairey		Ultra-Light Helicopter	250shp Turboméca Palouste BnPe 2	6	Rotor blade tip jets.

First Flight	Manufacturer	Type	Name	Original Engine	Number Built	Remarks
1955	Westland		Widgeon	520hp AL 521/2	15	3 converted from Dragonflies.
1955	Hunting Percival	P.74		750hp Oryx N.Or 1 (2)	1	Rotor tip jet drive; did not fly; engine runs 1956.
1957	Fairey		Rotodyne	2,800shp Napier Eland (NE) N.El 3 (2)	1	CH; rotor blade tip jets.
	Bristol	Type 191		850hp AL Major (2)	3	Did not fly.
1958	Westland		Westminster	3,150shp NE 229A (2)	2	
1958	Westland	WS-58	Wessex	1,450shp Napier Gazelle (NG) 161	369	12 versions, all except Mks 1 and 3 having twin turboshaft engines.
1958	Bristol	Type 192	Belvedere	1,650shp NG Series 2 (2)	26	Production taken over by Westland.
1958	Saunders-Roe	P.531		325shp Turmo 603	15	4 prototype/pre-production versions built; subsequently taken over by Westland.
1961	Westland	(P.531)	Scout	635shp RR Nimbus 101	148	
1962	Westland	(P.531)	Wasp	710shp RR Nimbus 103	134	
1962	Rotorcraft		Grasshopper	65hp Walter Mikron (2)	2	Original design and construction by Servotec Ltd; 2 coaxial, contra-rotating rotor systems. 2 versions.
1965	Westland	47G-3B-1	Sioux	270hp Lycoming TVO-435-B1A	253	Unsupercharged version also built.
1969	Westland	WS-61	Sea King	1,500shp RR Gnome H.1400 (2)	269	27 different versions; 37 aircraft on order.
1969	Cierva Rotorcraft	CR.LTH-1	CR Twin	145hp RR Continental 0-300-C (2)	3	2 coaxial, contra-rotating rotor systems.
1970	Westland	SA-341	Gazelle	590shp Astazou IIIN	294	Anglo-French joint venture; 4 British versions.
1971	Westland	WG-13	Lynx	900shp RR Gem 2 (2)	323	Anglo-French joint venture; 19 British production versions; 20 on order.
1979	Westland	WG-30	Westland 30	1,120shp RR Gem 41-1 (2)	21	5 versions; 21 on order (not confirmed).
1984	Westland		Lynx 3	1,260shp RR Gem 60-3/1 (2)	1	Pre-production.
	Westland	EH-101		1,725shp General Electric T700-401 (3)		Anglo-Italian joint venture; first flight due end 1986.

Notes:

1. Besides the EH-101 only rotary-wing aircraft actually built up to the end of 1984 are included in this Appendix. The entry refers to the first prototype as regards first flight and engine details.

2. All entries refer to helicopters except where annotated. Abbreviations are as follows: A: autogiro; CH: compound helicopter; RWG: rotary-wing glider.

3. The numbers column includes prototypes, pre-production and production aircraft. Occasionally an aircraft is later modified to such an extent that it is given a different designation, e.g. the Jet Gyrodyne was a substantially modified Gyrodyne, and it is therefore counted separately.

4. In 1959/60 Saunders-Roe built ten XROE-1 one-man collapsible rotor-cycles for the US Marine Corps. Design and development had been undertaken by the American firm, Hiller Helicopters, and therefore these aircraft cannot be included as British.

HELICOPTER PROJECTS AND DESIGNS

Year	Type	Engine	Take-off Weight (kg)	Rotor Diameter (M)	Seats	Remarks
1935	Asboth AH.5	213hp Le Rhône (2)		2 × 9.98	2	Coaxial, contra-rotating rotors. Agreement between Hungarian Asboth and Air Ministry for drawings to be used for construction by Blackburn Aeroplane Co.
1939	Hafner/Short Bros PD.6	Pobjoy Niagara 5	454	11.9	1	To meet Spec. A.10/39. Construction begun but abandoned because of the war.
1942	Weir W.7	205hp de Havilland Gipsy 6		2 × ?	Pilot + 2	To meet Spec. S.22/38 for Royal Navy observation aircraft at sea. Possibly 600hp Rolls-Royce Kestrel engine. Side-by-side rotors.

Year	Type	Engine	Take-off Weight (kg)	Rotor Diameter (M)	Seats	Remarks
1942	Weir W.8	205hp de Havilland Gipsy 6		12.2	1	Experimental machine to investigate reactive propulsion. Engine exhaust through rotor blade tips; no tail rotor.
1946	Weir W.10	510hp Armstrong Siddeley Cheetah	2,222	14.0	1 + 5	Similar layout to W.8/9.
1948	Cierva W.11T	1,620hp RR Merlin 502 (2)	11,350	3 × 16.46	2 + 36	Larger version of W.11.
1948	Cierva W.12	500hp Alvis Leonides (2)		3 × 14.32	2 + 12	Smaller version of W.11.
1950	Hunting Percival (HP) P.72		1,905	12.8	1 + 3	General-purpose helicopter.
1951	Westland W.80	Bristol Hercules (2)	11,113	28.6	2 + 36	
1951	Westland W.81	3,190shp AS Double Mamba	8,845	22.86	2 + 30	First design to place engines above cabin roof.
1951	Westland W.85	1,050shp AS Adder (6)	24,040	31.7	102 pax	Two engines at end of each of 3 rotor blades; nose-loading ramp.
1951	Westland W.90	8,000shp AS Sapphire (3)	93,440	59.74	450 troops	One tip-mounted engine on each blade.
1952	HP P.86/1	Napier Oryx (4)	13,155	2 × 33.5	40-60 pax	Compound helicopter.
1952	Bristol Type 181	3,940shp Bristol Proteus (2)	21,772	2 × 21.94	80 pax	Tandem rotor; helicopter bus for BEA.
1953	Bristol Type 190	83thp Bristol ramjets (2)	544	7.92	1 + 1	To meet Spec. H.144T (met by Fairey Ultra-Light Helicopter).
1954	HP P.91	Saro pulse jets (2)	544	9.75	1 + 1	To meet Spec. H.144T.
1954	HP P.96	Napier Oryx		19.2		To meet Spec. HR.146 (met by Bristol 191 which was then cancelled).
1954	Short Bros. SB.8	de Havilland Gipsy Major		9.3	1 + 1	To meet Spec. H.144T.
1954	HP P.98/1			21.4		To meet Spec. HR.149 for Royal Canadian Navy.
1954	Auster B.9	Ramjet			1 + 1	
1954	Bristol Type 193	1,500shp Lycoming T.55 (2)	8,164	2 × 14.9	2 + 16	Tandem rotor to meet Spec. HR.149.
1954	HP P.105	825hp Oryx N.Or.4 (2)	4,535		2 + 10	
1955	Bristol Type 199	4,000shp RR Tyne (4)	27,215	2 × 14.6	3 + 50	High-speed convertible rotor aircraft.
1957	Bristol Type 203	1,025shp de Havilland Gnome	2,994	14.8	2 + 9	Projected Sycamore replacement.
1958	Bristol Type 194	1,175shp de Havilland Gnome (4)	15,332	2 × 16.76	3 + 52	Six-bladed tandem rotor with stub wings. In competition with Rotodyne and Westminster.
1959	Bristol Type 214	1,175shp de Havilland Gnome (2)	5,126	22.2	2 + 16	Support helicopter.
1959	Fairey Rotodyne Z	5,250shp RR Tyne (2)	27,215	31.7	3 + 54	Also known as FA-1.
1959	Westland WS-61	1,450shp Napier Gazelle (2)		18.9	2 + 23	Civil version of the Sea King, to be known as the Wiltshire.
1960	Bristol Type 192C	1,465shp Napier Gazelle (2)	9,072	2 × 14.9	3 + 23	Tandem rotor; civil variant of Belvedere.
1960	Bristol Type 192D	1,465shp Napier Gazelle (2)	8,618	2 × 14.9	3 + 30	Projected larger version of the Belvedere.
1962	Westland WG.1	Bristol Siddeley Gnome H.1600 (4)	16,216	2 × 17.37	33 troops	Tandem rotor for ASW and heavy lift.
1962	Westland WG.3	720shp Pratt & Whitney PT6A (2)	4,990	13.72	15 troops	WG.3C with 2 × 1,200shp Gnomes.
1962	Westland WG.4	Turboshaft engines (2)	7,710	18.55	24 troops	Medium lift and ASW.
1964	Westland WG.5	Turboshaft engine	1,090	9.75	1 + 2	Unit light helicopter.
1964	Westland WG.7	(2)	5,670			Superseded WG.4.
1965	Westland WG.11	(4)			60 troops	Compound helicopter; superseded WG.1.
1965	Westland WG.12		1,135		1 + 3	Superseded WG.5.
1968	Westland WE.01	370shp Allison T.63 (4)	3,402	2 × 5.94	1 + 5	Tilt rotor. Two crew and 10 visualized for 6,345kg (13,990lb) version.
1969	Westland WE.02A	GE T.64-16 (4)	30,390	2 × 18.28	70 pax	Tilt rotor; each system to have 6 blades and be driven by 2 engines.
1969	Westland WE.02B	GE T.64-S5B (4)	34,700	2 × 18.28	84 pax	Heavier version of WE.02A.
1972	Westland Lynx 606	900shp RR Gem 2 (2) or P&W PT6B-34 (2)	4,309	12.8	2 + 12	Civil version of Lynx.
1977	Westland W.34	Turboshaft engines (3)	10,886	16.92	3/4 crew	ASW.
1977	Westland/VFW-Fokker P.277	1,050shp RR Gem 4 (2)	4,763	12.8	2	Tandem-seat attack helicopter to meet German PAH-2 requirement.
1982	Westland Lynx AH Mk 6	900shp RR Gem 2(2)	4,536	12.8	2 + 9	Wheeled version of the Lynx Mk 1

Notes:
1. This appendix is only a representative list of projects and designs and does not claim in any way to be complete.
2. The year given in the left-hand column should only be taken as an indication of when work was in progress.

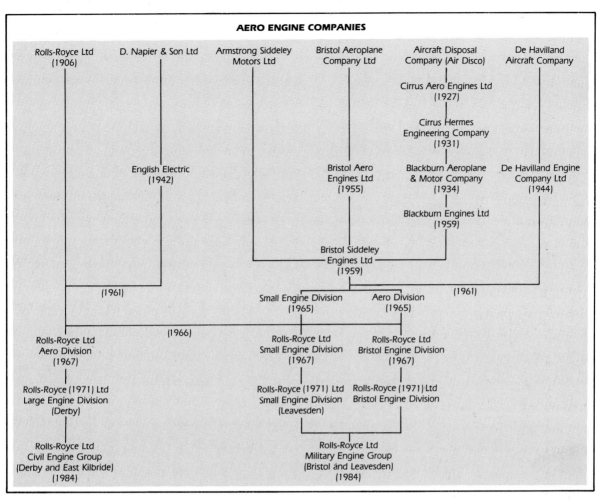

AERO ENGINE COMPANIES

Rolls-Royce Ltd (1906)

D. Napier & Son Ltd

Armstrong Siddeley Motors Ltd

Bristol Aeroplane Company Ltd

Aircraft Disposal Company (Air Disco)

De Havilland Aircraft Company

Cirrus Aero Engines Ltd (1927)

Cirrus Hermes Engineering Company (1931)

English Electric (1942)

Bristol Aero Engines Ltd (1955)

Blackburn Aeroplane & Motor Company (1934)

De Havilland Engine Company Ltd (1944)

Blackburn Engines Ltd (1959)

Bristol Siddeley Engines Ltd (1959)

(1961)

(1961)

Small Engine Division (1965)

Aero Division (1965)

(1966)

Rolls-Royce Ltd Aero Division (1967)

Rolls-Royce Ltd Small Engine Division (1967)

Rolls-Royce Ltd Bristol Engine Division (1967)

Rolls-Royce (1971) Ltd Large Engine Division (Derby)

Rolls-Royce (1971) Ltd Small Engine Division (Leavesden)

Rolls-Royce (1971) Ltd Bristol Engine Division

Rolls-Royce Ltd Civil Engine Group (Derby and East Kilbride) (1984)

Rolls-Royce Ltd Military Engine Group (Bristol and Leavesden) (1984)

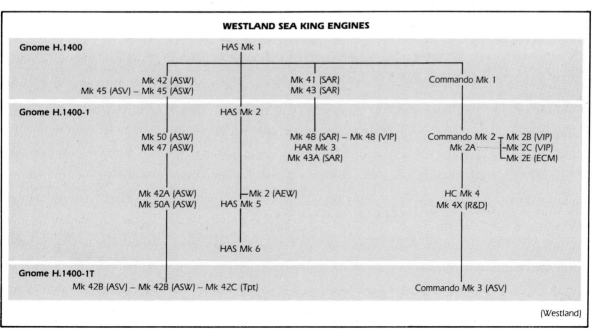

WESTLAND SEA KING ENGINES

Gnome H.1400

HAS Mk 1

Mk 42 (ASW)
Mk 45 (ASV) – Mk 45 (ASW)

Mk 41 (SAR)
Mk 43 (SAR)

Commando Mk 1

Gnome H.1400-1

HAS Mk 2

Mk 50 (ASW)
Mk 47 (ASW)

Mk 48 (SAR) – Mk 48 (VIP)
HAR Mk 3
Mk 43A (SAR)

Commando Mk 2 ⊤ Mk 2B (VIP)
Mk 2A ├ Mk 2C (VIP)
└ Mk 2E (ECM)

Mk 42A (ASW)
Mk 50A (ASW)

Mk 2 (AEW)
HAS Mk 5

HC Mk 4
Mk 4X (R&D)

HAS Mk 6

Gnome H.1400-1T

Mk 42B (ASV) – Mk 42B (ASW) – Mk 42C (Tpt)

Commando Mk 3 (ASV)

(Westland)

List of Abbreviations

AAC   Army Air Corps
AACC   Army Air Corps Centre
ACT   Active Control Technology
AEW   Airborne early warning
AFC   Air Force Cross
AFCS   Automatic Flight Control System
AFEE   Airborne Forces Experimental Establishment
AFM   Air Force Medal
AGL   Above ground level
AH   Army Helicopter
AOP   Air Observation Post
APU   Auxiliary power unit
ASR   Air Staff Requirement
ASV   Anti-surface vessel
ASW   Anti-submarine warfare
BAH   British Airways Helicopters
BAOR   British Army of the Rhine
BEA   British European Airways
BERP   British Experimental Rotor Programme
C^3 Command, Control and Communications
CAOR   Civil Aviation Operational Requirement
CDU   Control and Display Unit
CRT   Cathode-Ray Tube
CTS   Central Tactical System
DFC   Distinguished Flying Cross
DSC   Distinguished Service Cross
DSO   Distinguished Service Order
DTD   Data Transfer Device
ECM   Electronic Counter Measures
ESM   Electronic Support Measures
ETPS   Empire Test Pilots' School
EW   Electronic Warfare
FAA   Fleet Air Arm
FADEC   Full Authority Digital Electronic Control
FLIR   Forward-Looking Infra-Red
HAR   Helicopter Air Rescue
HAS   Helicopter Anti-Submarine
HC   Helicopter Cargo
HCC   Helicopter Cargo and Communications
HF   High Frequency
HOT   Haut Subsonique Optiquement Téléguidé (Tiré d'un Tube)
hp   Horse power
HR   Helicopter Rescue

HT   Helicopter Trainer
HU   Helicopter Utility
IFF   Identification friend or foe
IFR   Instrument Flight Rules
IFTU   Intensive Flying Training Unit
ISA   International standard atmosphere. This is defined as a temperature of 15°C (59°F) at mean sea level, a pressure of 1013.25 millibars and a density of 1,225 grams/cu.m. The rate of decrease of temperature with height is taken as 6.5°C (11.7°F) per 1,000m (3,280ft)
ITOW   Improved Tube-launched, Optically-tracked, Wire-guided
JEHU   Joint Experimental Helicopter Unit
km   Kilometres
kph   Kilometres per hour
LAPADS Lightweight Acoustic Processing and Display System
LS   Landing Site
MAD   Magnetic anomaly detection. The package is towed on a cable and the equipment is able to detect very small disturbances in the Earth's magnetic field caused by the magnetic material of a submerged submarine
MATCH   Medium Range Anti-Submarine Torpedo Carrying Helicopter
MBB   Messerschmitt–Bölkow–Blohm
MFD   Multi-Function Display
Mil Std Military standard
m   Metres
mm   Millimetres
MoD   Ministry of Defence
MOU   Memorandum of Understanding
mph   Miles per hour
NBC   Nuclear, Biological, Chemical
NOE   Nap of the Earth. Very low-level tactical flying using natural terrain cover and contours
NVG   Night vision goggles
RAE   Royal Aircraft Establishment

RAF   Royal Air Force
RAMS   Racal Avionics Management System
REME   Royal Electrical and Mechanical Engineers
RFA   Royal Fleet Auxiliary
RM   Royal Marines
RN   Royal Navy
RNAS   Royal Naval Air Station
rpm   Revolutions per minute
SAM   Surface-to-air missile
SAR   Search and Rescue
SAS   Special Air Service (Regiment)
SBAC   Society of British Aerospace Companies
shp   Shaft horse power
SNEB   Société Nouvelle des Etablissements Brandt
TANS   Tactical Air Navigation System
TOW   Tube-launched, Optically-tracked, Wire-guided
UHF   Ultra high frequency
ULH   Ultra-Light Helicopter
Vertrep Vertical replenishment
VHF   Very High Frequency
VIP   Very important person
VOR   VHF Omni-range; a navigation aid
VTOL   Vertical take-off and landing

Glossary

Advancing blade. The rotor blade that is moving forward into the relative airflow; the retreating blade is the one moving in the direction of the airflow

Angle of attack. The acute angle between the chord line of a rotor blade and the relative airflow

Angle of incidence. The acute angle between the chord line and the horizontal or longitudinal axis of the helicopter

Anhedral. The slope downwards, relative to the horizontal, of the surface from root to tip

Articulated rotor system. A rotor system in which individual blades are free to flap

Autogiro. A rotorcraft driven by a propeller and lifted by a rotor which turns freely in flight under the single influence of the air flowing through the blades

Autorotation. When autorotating a helicopter descends under control but without power from the engine. The rotor blades continue to rotate at the same speed because of the upward flow of air through the disc

Blade loading. The ratio of the aircraft's maximum take-off weight to the total blade area

Bus. Busbar, the main terminal in an electrical system

Chord. The distance between the leading edge and trailing edge of an aerofoil section, or rotor blade

Coaxial, contra-rotating rotor system. Two sets of main rotor blades, mounted on a common axis, but turning in opposite directions. The torques cancel each other out and therefore no tail rotor is required

Collective (lever). On the pilot's left-hand side, this lever has the effect of changing pitch on all the main rotor blades simultaneously. It is used to make the helicopter climb or descend

Compound helicopter. A helicopter that also has wings and/or propellers to assist the main rotor system to provide lift and/or propulsion

Convertiplane. A rotorcraft that in flight can change from getting lift from its rotor blades to getting it from wings, and vice versa

Coning. Rotor blades are said to cone when, instead of rotating in the horizontal plane passing through the rotor hub, they sweep out the shape of a shallow cone and thus produce an angle between the blades and the horizontal plane

Cyclic (stick). The pilot's 'control column' by means of which he can make the helicopter go forwards, backwards and to each side. His movements are transmitted to the rotor blades

Dampers. Found in the rotor head where lead/lag movement is provided, dampers act in a similar fashion to shock absorbers

Derated. Engine restricted to power less than the theoretical maximum available

Dihedral. The slope upwards, relative to the horizontal, of the wings from root to tip

Disc loading. The ratio of gross weight of the helicopter to the rotor disc area

Disposable load. The total mass that can be loaded on to the helicopter; it includes the crew, fuel, payload, etc.

Dutch roll. A combined yawing and rolling oscillatory motion which, if not damped, may ultimately lead to structural failure

Fire and forget missile. A missile which does not require either the target to be tracked, or itself to be guided, by any operator

Free turbine. A turbine that is mechanically independent of the engine apart from being connected by bearings and the gas stream. It can thus run at its own speed

Ground effect. Also ground cushion. It is caused by the downwash of air from the rotor being reflected back upwards from the ground to produce a 'cushion' of air beneath the helicopter. It follows that less power is required to hover in ground effect, known as HIGE, than to hover out of ground

effect (HOGE). The depth of the cushion is approximately equivalent to the length of the helicopter's main rotor blade

Ground resonance. A forced or self-induced large amplitude vibration which produces a sympathetic resonance between the main rotor system and the undercarriage when the aircraft is on the ground

Hinges. An articulated rotor has hinges to allow the blades to flap, drag and feather. Feathering may be achieved by pitch change bearings

Hot and high. The adverse combination of high altitude and high ambient temperatures

Pitch. The acute angle between the chord line of a rotor blade and the plane of rotation of the main rotor, normal to the rotor shaft

Range (maximum). The distance a helicopter can fly with all standard fuel tanks full; the fuel reserve required for emergencies is included in the calculation. With maximum fuel on board the full useful load cannot always be carried. Conversely, if the full load is required this can only be achieved at the expense of carrying less fuel and therefore range is decreased

Rotor decay. A substantial decrease in rotor rpm

Rotor head (or hub). The top part of the rotor system, incorporating the hinges, to which the rotor blades are attached

Rotor solidity. The total area of the rotor blades expressed as a percentage of the disc area

Semi-active (homing). Homing on to radiation reflected from a target which is illuminated by radar or laser energy from another source

Semi-monocoque. A type of construction where the skin, i.e. of the fuselage, is relieved of the full load by longitudinal girder-members and transverse frames to which the skin is riveted

Semi-rigid rotor system. An integral rotor system, without flapping or drag hinges, which permits limited flexing in the flapping and dragging planes

Service ceiling. The maximum height at which the helicopter is ever likely to be used. It is defined as that height at which the rate of climb has become reduced to 30.5m (100ft) per minute

Speed (maximum). The maximum straight and level speed at mean sea level

Swashplate. The device on the rotor shaft which permits pitch changes to be made to the rotor blades

Systems redundancy. Two or more identical systems in case one is damaged

Tandem rotor. A twin rotor system, fore and aft, in which the torques cancel each other out

Torque. A 'twisting moment', the turning effect of force. When under power the fuselage of a helicopter tends to turn in the opposite direction to the rotation of the single main rotor. A tail rotor is therefore installed to counter this torque reaction and help provide directional control

Translational flight. Usually used to describe the phase of horizontal accelerating flight between leaving the hover and losing the supplementary lift provided by the ground cushion

Turboshaft engine. A 'conventional' gas turbine engine, having a common shaft which drives the compressors and transmission

Yaw. The motion around the normal axis. The normal axis passes through the centre of gravity and is vertical when the aircraft is flying straight and level

Bibliography

Boulet, Jean, *L'Histoire de l'Hélicoptère*. Editions France-Empire, 1982.

Brie, Reginald (compiler); *A History of British Rotorcraft 1866–1965*. Westland Helicopters Ltd, 1968.

Courtney, Frank, *Flight Path: My Fifty Years of Aviation*. Kimber, 1971.

Ethell, Jeffrey and Price, Alfred, *Air War South Atlantic*. Sidgwick & Jackson, 1983.

Gablehouse, Charles, *Helicopters and Autogiros*. Muller, 1967.

Gibbs-Smith, Charles, *Aviation*. HMSO, 1970.

Hobbs, Jack, *Bristol Helicopters: A Tribute to Raoul Hafner*. Frenchay Publications, 1984.

Jackson, Aubrey Joseph, *Avro Aircraft Since 1908*. Putnam & Co., 1965.

Jackson, Aubrey Joseph, *British Civil Aircraft 1919–1959*, vols 1 and 2. Putnam & Co., 1959.

Jackson, Robert, *The Dragonflies*. Arthur Barker Ltd, 1971.

Lambermont, Paul and Price, Anthony, *Helicopters and Autogiros of the World*. Cassell, 1970.

Lee, Sir David, *Eastward: History of the Royal Air Force in the Far East, 1945–72*. HMSO, 1984.

Lee, Sir David, *Flight from the Middle East: A History of the Royal Air Force in the Arabian Peninsula and Adjacent Territories, 1945–72*. HMSO, 1978.

Mead, Peter, *Soldiers in the Air: The Development of Army Flying*. Ian Allan, 1967.

Milne, J. M., *Flashing Blades Over the Sea: History and Development of Helicopters in the Royal Navy*. Maritime Books, 1980.

Shapiro, Jacob, *The Helicopter*. Muller, 1957.

Taylor, John W. R. and Allward, Maurice, *Westland 50*. Ian Allan, 1965.

Thetford, Owen, *British Naval Aircraft*. Putnam & Co., 1978.

Wragg, David, *Helicopters at War*. Robert Hale, 1983.

Official publications:

The Military Balance 1985–86. International Institute for Strategic Studies, 1984.

Statement on the Defence Estimates 1985. Cmnd 9430. HMSO, 1985.

Index

Very closely resembling the Mk 42B, the Advanced Sea King, seen here
armed with a Sea Eagle missile, is now being marketed by Westland.
(Westland helicopters)